CALCULUS, COMPLEX NUMBERS AND POLAR CO-ORDINATES

ELLIOTT
FRYER
GARDNER
HILL

Holt, Rinehart and Winston of Canada, Limited
Toronto   Montreal

H. A. Elliott
Associate Director
Service for Admission to College and University
Ottawa, Ontario

K. D. Fryer
Associate Dean, Faculty of Mathematics
University of Waterloo
Waterloo, Ontario

J. C. Gardner
Superintendent of Schools
The Carleton Board of Education
Ottawa, Ontario

Norman J. Hill
Head of Mathematics Department
St. Mary's Collegiate and Vocational Institute
St. Mary's, Ontario

Copyright © 1972   by

Holt, Rinehart and Winston of Canada, Limited
Toronto   Montreal
All Rights Reserved

ISBN 0-03-921052-9

Printed in Canada
6 7 8 9   79 78 77 76

CONTENTS

SLOPES AND TANGENTS

1.1. The Slope of a Line

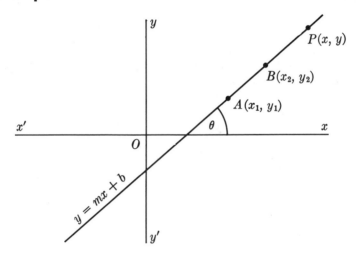

Figure 1.1

The equation

$$y = mx + b$$

represents a line, and the slope of this line with respect to the x-axis is given by $\tan \theta = m$ (see Figure 1.1). This is the *slope-intercept* form of the equation of a line.

If the line passes through a point $A(x_1, y_1)$, then

$$y_1 = mx_1 + b,$$

and by subtraction we obtain

$$y - y_1 = m(x - x_1).$$

This is the *slope-point* form of the equation of a line.

1

The slope of a line can also be expressed in terms of the co-ordinates of points on the line. Thus, if $A(x_1, y_1)$ and $B(x_2, y_2)$ are on the line $y = mx + b$,

$$m = \tan \theta = \frac{y_2 - y_1}{x_2 - x_1}.$$

Therefore,

$$y - y_1 = \frac{y_2 - y_1}{x_2 - x_1}(x - x_1)$$

is another form for the equation of the line AB. This is the *two-point* form of the equation of a line.

If $\triangle x = x_2 - x_1$, the difference between the abscissae of A and B, and $\triangle y = y_2 - y_1$, the difference in the ordinates of A and B, then we can rewrite this equation as

$$y - y_1 = \frac{\triangle y}{\triangle x}(x - x_1).$$

We note that an elementary conclusion from the above is the fact that all segments of a line have the same slope.

Example. Given the points $P(2, 1)$ and $Q(4, 6)$, find the slope of the line segment PQ and the equation of the line PQ.

Solution:

$$\text{Slope} = \frac{\triangle y}{\triangle x} = \frac{6 - 1}{4 - 2} = \frac{5}{2}.$$

Therefore, the equation of the line PQ is

$$y - 1 = \frac{5}{2}(x - 2),$$

$$y - 1 = \frac{5}{2}x - 5,$$

$$y = \frac{5}{2}x - 4.$$

EXERCISE 1.1

1. Find the equations of the lines with slope 2 through the points
   (a) $(0, 1)$, (b) $(3, 4)$, (c) $(-2, 1)$, (d) $(3, -1)$, (e) $(-1, -1)$.

2. Find the equations of the lines through the point $(2, 3)$ with the following slopes.
   (a) 2 (b) -3 (c) $-\frac{1}{2}$ (d) $\frac{7}{3}$ (e) $.6$ (f) $\frac{1}{2}$
   (g) $\frac{1}{3}$ (h) -2 (i) $-\frac{1}{3}$ (j) $-\frac{5}{3}$ (k) $-\pi$ (l) $\sqrt{2}$

3. Which pairs of lines in question (2) are perpendicular?

4. Find the slope of the line that passes through each of the following pairs of points.

   (a) (3, 6), (1, 2)   (b) (−1, 2), (3, 2)   (c) (3, 4), (−1, 4)

   (d) (2, −2), (3, 5)   (e) (0, 4), (−2, −1)   (f) (2, 3), (2, −4)

5. Which lines in question (4), if any, are parallel to (a) the x-axis? (b) the y-axis?

1.2. The Slope of a Secant

DEFINITION.   A *secant* is a line that cuts a curve in two or more distinct points.

If we draw the graph of the quadratic function, we obtain a curve. For example, Figure 1.2 shows a sketch graph of

$$y = x^2 \quad \text{for} \quad -5 \le x \le 5, \quad x \in Re.$$

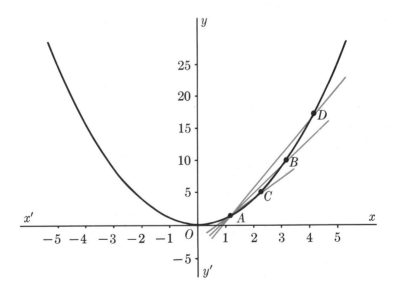

Figure 1.2

For such a curve we can calculate the slope of the secant through two points, say A and B, on the curve. If we keep A fixed and choose some other point C on the curve, the slope of AC is not in general the same as the slope of AB. In Figure 1.2, the slope of AC is less than the slope of AB, and the slope of AD is greater than the slope of AB. These statements merely re-emphasize the fact that a line is the only curve of constant slope.

Example 1. Points $A(1, 5)$ and $B(2, 19)$ are on the graph of

$$y = 2x^3 + 3.$$

Find the slope of the secant AB.

Solution:

$$\text{Slope of the line } AB = \frac{19 - 5}{2 - 1}$$

$$= 14.$$

Example 2. Find the slope of the secant of the graph of

$$y = 4x^2$$

through the two distinct points where $x = x_1$ and $x = x_2$.

Solution:

When $x = x_1$,

$$y = 4x_1^2,$$

and when $x = x_2$,

$$y = 4x_2^2.$$

Therefore, the two points are $P(x_1, 4x_1^2)$ and $Q(x_2, 4x_2^2)$, and

$$\text{the slope of } PQ = \frac{4x_2^2 - 4x_1^2}{x_2 - x_1}$$

$$= \frac{4(x_2^2 - x_1^2)}{x_2 - x_1}$$

$$= \frac{4(x_2 + x_1)(x_2 - x_1)}{x_2 - x_1}$$

$$= 4(x_2 + x_1).$$

EXERCISE 1.2

1. Find the slope of the secant of the curve

$$y = x^2$$

through each of the following pairs of points.

(a) $(2, 4)$, $(3, 9)$ (b) $(1, 1)$, $(2, 4)$ (c) $(0, 0)$, $(4, 16)$

(d) $(2, 4)$, $(-2, 4)$ (e) $(-1, 1)$, $(-3, 9)$ (f) $(3, 9)$, $(-2, 4)$

2. Find the slope of the secant of

$$y = 2x^4$$

through each pair of points at which x has the following values.

(a) 1, 2   (b) -1, 3   (c) 2, -1

3. Find the slope of the secant of each of the following curves through the points at which $x = 1$ and $x = 3$.

(a) $y = 2x + 6$

(b) $y = x^2 - 4$

(c) $y = x - 3x^3$

(d) $y = \dfrac{4}{x} - 1$

(e) $y = \dfrac{2}{x^2 - 4}$

(f) $y = \dfrac{1}{x - 1} + 3$

1.3. The Tangent to a Curve ✓

Two distinct lines in a plane intersect in o .e point if they are not parallel, but a line and a curve frequently intersect in mo.e than one point, if they intersect at all.

DEFINITION. A tangent to a curve at a point A on the curve is the limiting position of a sequence of secants AB_n where $\{B_n\}$ is any set of points on the curve such that the length of the chord AB_n approaches zero.

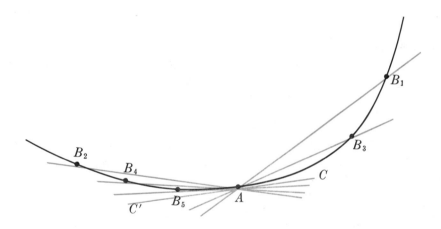

Figure 1.3

Note that, in the above definition, $\{B_n\}$ must be *any* set of points such that the length of the chord AB_n approaches zero. In particular, all $\{B_n\}$ may be on one side of A or on the other side of A, or in fact some B_n may be on one side of A and some on the other. The only requirement is that the length of AB_n approaches zero eventually as the sequence of points B_n is continued. Obviously, we choose a sequence of points

$$B_1, B_2, \cdots, B_n, B_{n+1}, B_{n+2}, \cdots$$

such that

$$AB_{n+1} < AB_n$$

for large values of n.

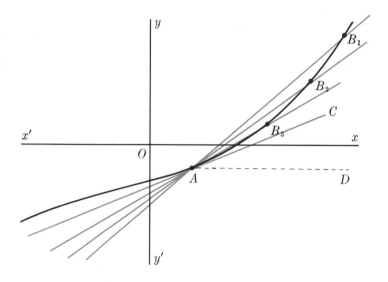

Figure 1.4

Now each pair of points A and B_n determines a line, and so we can find the slope, m_n, of the line AB_n for each value of n. From Figure 1.4, it appears that, as B_n approaches A, the slope of the line AB_n approaches the value of slope of AC, the tangent at A; that is, the value of $\tan \angle DAB_n$ approaches the value of $\tan \angle DAC$. This is the case in general, and we call the slope of the tangent to the curve at A the slope of the curve at A. We shall discuss this more fully in algebraic terms in a later chapter. For the present, we shall assume that, if the values of the slopes of the lines AB_1, AB_2, $\cdots$, AB_n, $\cdots$ approach a unique value, this value is the slope of the tangent.

Example. The following table gives the co-ordinates for a sequence of points B_n on a curve and also the co-ordinates of A. Find the slopes of the lines AB_n. What is probably the slope of the tangent at A? What assumption is made in this conclusion?

	A	B_1	B_2	B_3	B_4	B_5	B_6
x	1.0	1.5	.8	1.1	.9	1.05	.95
y	2.0	4.5	1.28	2.42	1.62	2.205	1.805

Solution:

Slope of $AB_1 = \dfrac{4.5 - 2.0}{1.5 - 1.0} = \dfrac{2.5}{.5} = 5$.

Slope of $AB_2 = \dfrac{1.28 - 2.0}{.8 - 1.0} = \dfrac{-.72}{-.2} = 3.6$.

$$\text{Slope of } AB_3 = \frac{2.42 - 2.0}{1.1 - 1.0} = \frac{.42}{.1} = 4.2 \, .$$

$$\text{Slope of } AB_4 = \frac{1.62 - 2.0}{.9 - 1.0} = \frac{-.38}{-.1} = 3.8 \, .$$

$$\text{Slope of } AB_5 = \frac{2.205 - 2.0}{1.05 - 1.0} = \frac{.205}{.05} = 4.1 \, .$$

$$\text{Slope of } AB_6 = \frac{1.805 - 2.0}{.95 - 1.0} = \frac{-.195}{-.05} = 3.9 \, .$$

The slope of the tangent at A is probably 4. It is assumed that the curve does not change suddenly near A.

EXERCISE 1.3

1. For each of the following curves, calculate the ordered pairs corresponding to the values 1, 1.5, 1.2, 1.1., 1.01, 1.001 for x.

   (a) $y = x^2$ (b) $y = x^3$ (c) $y = \dfrac{1}{x}$ (d) $y = x^2 + 2x$

   Calculate the slopes of the secants joining the point corresponding to $x = 1$ to each of the other points. Estimate the slope of the tangent at the point where $x = 1$ in each case.

2. For each of the following curves, calculate the ordered pairs corresponding to the values 3, 2.5, 2.9, 2.95, 2.99 for x.

   (a) $y = 4x^2$ (b) $y = 2x^3$ (c) $y = \dfrac{10}{x}$ (d) $y = x + \dfrac{1}{x}$

   In each case, calculate the slopes of the secants joining the point corresponding to $x = 3$ to each of the other points. Estimate the slope of the tangent at the point where $x = 3$ in each case.

3. For each of the following curves, calculate the slopes of the secants joining the point where $x = 5$ to the sequence of points where x has the values 5.5, 4.5, 5.1, 4.9, 5.01, 4.99.

   (a) $y = \dfrac{x^2}{5}$ (b) $y = \dfrac{x^3}{10}$ (c) $y = \dfrac{25}{x}$ (d) $y = 5x - 10$

   Estimate the slope of the tangent at the point where $x = 5$ in each case.

4. Repeat question (3) for the point where $x = -2$ and the sequence of points where x has the values $-2.5, -1.5, -2.1, -1.9, -2.01, -1.99$.

5. By choosing a suitable sequence of points near A on the curve

$$y = x^2$$

   where

   (a) $x = 3$,   (b) $x = -1$,   (c) $x = -4$,   (d) $x = 2$,

   estimate the slopes of the tangents at these points.

1.4. The Slopes of Tangents to the Curve $y = x^2$

Let us consider the curve whose equation is $y = x^2$ near the point $A(3, 9)$. We can form a table of values for $3 \leq x \leq 3.1$.

	x	y
B_1	3.1	9.61
B_2	3.01	9.0601
B_3	3.001	9.006001
B_4	3.0001	9.00060001
B_5	3.00001	9.0000600001
.	.	.
.	.	.
.	.	.
A	3	9

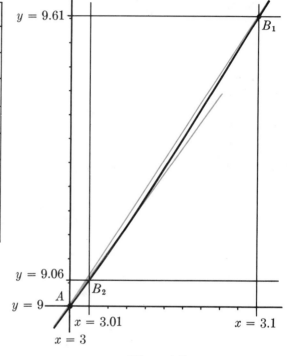

Figure 1.5

We easily see that

$$\text{the slope of } AB_1 = \frac{9.61 - 9}{3.1 - 3} = 6.1,$$

$$\text{the slope of } AB_2 = \frac{9.0601 - 9}{3.01 - 3} = 6.01,$$

$$\text{the slope of } AB_3 = \frac{9.006001 - 9}{3.001 - 3} = 6.001,$$

$$\text{the slope of } AB_4 = \frac{9.00060001 - 9}{3.0001 - 3} = 6.0001,$$

$$\text{the slope of } AB_5 = \frac{9.0000600001 - 9}{3.00001 - 3} = 6.00001,$$

. . . .

It seems probable therefore that the slope of the tangent at $A(3, 9)$ is 6. We can verify this value for the slope by drawing an approximate tangent to the curve at A with a straightedge, and we see that the slope of the line is approximately 6.

If we perform the same calculations with $x = 2.9, \ 2.99, \ 2.999, \ 2.9999, \ \cdots,$ 3, we find the sequence of values for the slopes of the corresponding secants to be 5.9, 5.99, 5.999, 5.9999, $\cdots$. Again these values would indicate that the slope of the tangent at $(3, 9)$ is 6. In fact, we definitely say that the slope of the tangent at $A(3, \ 9)$ is greater than 5.99999 and less than 6.00001. If we continue the sequences, we can find values even closer to 6.

Notice we have assumed that the curve does not change suddenly near the point A, and in fact the equation for the function shows that this must be the case. The values of x^2 do not change suddenly near $x = 3$ for $x \in Re$.

If we consider some other point on the curve $C(-2, 4)$ and perform similar calculations for a sequence $-1.9, \ -1.99, \ -1.999, \ \cdots$ of values of x near $x = -2$, we obtain the values $-3.9, \ -3.99, \ -3.999, \ \cdots$ for the slopes. We may conclude that the slope of the tangent at $C(-2, 4)$ is -4.

We note that the slopes of the tangents at points to the right of the origin are positive and that those to the left are negative.

We can consider the situation near the point A in another way. For what values of $x > 3$ can we find points B_n such that the slope of AB_n differs from 6 by less than .001? From our calculations above, we see that any points B_n for which $3 < x < 3.001$ satisfy this requirement.

If we look closely at our results, we can see that, if we wish the slope of AB_n to differ from 6 by less than .0000001, the value of x at B_n must differ from 3 by less than .0000001.

EXERCISE 1.4

1. Use a sequence of eight points on $y = x^2$ corresponding to $x = 2.1, \ 1.9,$ 2.01, 1.99, $\cdots$ to show that the slope of the tangent at $(2, 4)$ must be greater than 3.999999 and less than 4.000001.

2. Select a sequence of points near $(-1, 1)$ on the curve $y = x^2$ to show that the slope of the tangent at $(-1, 1)$ is less than -1.99999 and greater than -2.00001.

3. By considering the three points where $x = 2.499999999, \ 2.5,$ and 2.500000001 on the curve $y = x^2$, find two values between which the slope of the tangent at $(2.5, 6.25)$ must lie.

4. The slope of the tangent at the point $A(3.\dot{3}, 11.\dot{1})$ on the curve $y = x^2$ is to be calculated to five significant figures. Find two points sufficiently close to A from which the slope can be calculated to this accuracy.

5. The slope of the tangent at $P(\pi, \pi^2)$ on the curve $y = x^2$ is to be calculated to three significant figures. Find two points sufficiently close to P from which the slope can be calculated to this accuracy. $(\pi \simeq 3.14159265.)$

1.5. The Slope of the Curve y = x² at a Point

We wish to calculate the slope of the tangent to the curve whose equation is $y = x^2$ at a point $P(x_1, y_1)$ in the same way that we have calculated the values at particular points in the previous sections.   To do this, we consider a sequence of points Q_n near P and see if the slope of PQ_n approaches a unique value as Q_n approaches P.   Let us consider a point Q to be any representative point of the sequence of Q_n.   The co-ordinates of Q may be taken as $(x_1 + h,\ y_1 + k)$ where h and k are small.   Note that, as P and Q are on the curve $y = x^2$, we have

$$y_1 = x_1^2$$

and

$$(y_1 + k) = (x_1 + h)^2.$$

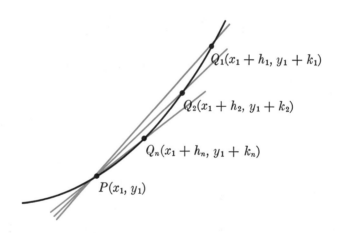

$$Q_1(x_1 + h_1, y_1 + k_1)$$

$$Q_2(x_1 + h_2, y_1 + k_2)$$

$$Q_n(x_1 + h_n, y_1 + k_n)$$

$$P(x_1, y_1)$$

Figure 1.6

$$
\begin{aligned}
\text{Slope of } PQ &= \frac{y_1 + k - y_1}{x_1 + h - x_1} \\
&= \frac{(x_1 + h)^2 - x_1^2}{x_1 + h - x_1} \\
&= \frac{x_1^2 + 2x_1h + h^2 - x_1^2}{h} \\
&= \frac{2x_1h + h^2}{h} \\
&= 2x_1 + h, \quad h \neq 0.
\end{aligned}
$$

Now as Q approaches P, that is, $PQ \to 0$, the secant PQ approaches the tangent at P, h approaches zero, and k approaches zero. The last expression for the slope of PQ shows that, under these circumstances, the slope approaches $2x_1$; that is,

$$Q \text{ approaches } P,$$
$$PQ \text{ approaches } 0,$$
$$h \text{ approaches } 0,$$

and

$$\text{the slope of } PQ \text{ approaches } 2x_1.$$

Thus we say that the slope of the tangent to $y = x^2$ at $P(x_1, y_1)$ is $2x_1$.

Notice, however, that we do not and cannot make h equal to zero anywhere in the above work; we only allow h to become smaller and smaller as PQ approaches zero in length.

In the same sense, Q never coincides with P; it only approaches nearer and nearer to P. In this case, the slope of PQ differs from $2x_1$ (the slope of the tangent at P) by h, that is, by the difference between the abscissa of Q and x_1 (the abscissa of P). This is not true for all curves, but for any curve the difference is always less than some finite multiple of h.

Although we have used a particular point $P(x_1, y_1)$ in the above calculation, we could perform the calculation for any point (x, y) on the curve; the slope of the tangent at *any* point (x, y) on the curve $y = x^2$ is given by $2x$.

EXERCISE 1.5

1. By the method of this section, calculate the slope of the curve $y = x^2$ at the point (a) $(2, 4)$, (b) $(3, 9)$.

2. If $B(x_1 - h, y_1 - k)$ is chosen as the representative of the sequence of points near $A(x_1, y_1)$ on the curve $y = x^2$, calculate the slope of the tangent at A.

3. Find the slope of the graph of $y = x^2$ at each of the following points, using the result that the slope at (x_1, y_1) is $2x_1$.
   (a) $(10, 100)$ (b) $(.5, .25)$ (c) $(-5, 25)$
   (d) (n, n^2) (e) $(\frac{1}{4}, \frac{1}{16})$ (f) $(-1.4, 1.96)$

4. Find the point on the graph of $y = x^2$ at which the slope is
   (a) 8,   (b) -5,   (c) $\frac{1}{5}$,   (d) $4n$ (e) $-.\dot{3}$,   (f) -10^8.

5. If, on the graph of $y = x^2$, the point A is (x_1, y_1) and B is $(x_1 + h, y_1 + k)$, and $0 < h < 10^{-10}$, calculate corresponding inequalities for k. If the slope of AB is given by the symbol $(2x_1 + l)$ find corresponding inequalities for l.

6. $A(x_1, y_1)$ and $B(x_1 + h, y_1 + k)$ are two neighbouring points on the curve $y = x^2$. Find inequalities for h such that, if h satisfies the inequalities, the difference between the slope of AB and $2x_1$ is required to be less than 10^{-24}.

1.6. The Derivative of the Quadratic Function

The general real quadratic function determines the set of ordered pairs

$$f = \{(x,\, y) \mid y = ax^2 + bx + c,\ \ a \neq 0,\ \ a,b,c \in Re,\ \ x \in Re\}$$

where a, b, c are fixed real numbers.

From our previous study of the linear function, we know that the slope of the line $y = x$ is 1, that the slope of the line $y = bx$ is b, and that the slope of $y = c$ is 0. We also know that the slope of $y = bx + c$ is equal to b, which is the same as the slope of $y = bx$.

The following table gives the values of the slopes at x of the curves $y = f(x)$.

$y = f(x)$	Slope at x
c	0
x	1
bx	b
$bx + c$	b
x^2	$2x$

This table might suggest the following result, though on rather weak evidence:

if $y = ax^2 + bx + c$, then the slope at x is $2ax + b$.

Let us first consider a particular case, $y = 3x^2$. Consider a point A on the curve $y = 3x^2$, which is given by the ordered pair

$$(x_1,\, y_1) = (x_1,\, 3x_1^2)$$

and a neighbouring point B given by the ordered pair

$$(x_1 + h,\, y_1 + k) = (x_1 + h,\, 3(x_1 + h)^2).$$

$$
\begin{aligned}
\text{Slope of } AB &= \frac{(y_1 + k) - y_1}{(x_1 + h) - x_1} \\[1mm]
&= \frac{3(x_1 + h)^2 - 3x_1^2}{x_1 + h - x_1} \\[1mm]
&= \frac{3x_1^2 + 6x_1 h + 3h^2 - 3x_1^2}{h} \\[1mm]
&= \frac{6x_1 h + 3h^2}{h} \\[1mm]
&= 6x_1 + 3h, \qquad h \neq 0.
\end{aligned}
$$

We see that,

as B approaches A,

h approaches 0,

and, hence, that

the slope of AB approaches $6x_1$.

Therefore, we may state that, if $y = 3x^2$, the slope at x is $6x = 3(2x)$.

The more general result,

$$\text{if } y = ax^2, \text{ then the slope at } x \text{ is } 2ax,$$

is obtained in the same way.

For the general quadratic, we may proceed in the same way. Let $A(x, y)$ be any point, and $B(x + h, y + k)$ the representative of a sequence of neighbouring points, on the curve

$$y = ax^2 + bx + c.$$

Then

$$y + k = a(x + h)^2 + b(x + h) + c$$

and

$$\text{the slope of } AB = \frac{(y + k) - y}{(x + h) - x}$$

$$= \frac{a(x + h)^2 + b(x + h) + c - (ax^2 + bx + c)}{x + h - x}$$

$$= \frac{a(x^2 + 2xh + h^2 - x^2) + b(x + h - x) + (c - c)}{h}$$

$$= \frac{2axh + ah^2 + bh}{h}$$

$$= 2ax + b + ah, \quad h \neq 0.$$

Thus,

as B approaches A

and h approaches 0,

the slope of AB approaches $2ax + b$.

We note that

$$\frac{(y + k) - y}{(x + h) - x} = \frac{k}{h}$$

and so, as h approaches zero and k also approaches zero, $\frac{k}{h}$ at x approaches the limiting value $2ax + b$. We may write this result in the following form: if

$$y = ax^2 + bx + c,$$

then

$$\lim_{h \to 0} \frac{k}{h} = 2ax + b.$$

The value of this limit at x is called the value of the derivative at x. The symbol $D_x y$ is used for this value; thus, if

$$y = ax^2 + bx + c,$$

then

$$D_x y = 2ax + b.$$

DEFINITION.   If $f = \{(x, y) \mid y = f(x),\ x \in Re\}$ and $(x + h,\ y + k)$ is also an ordered pair of f, then $\lim\limits_{h \to 0} \dfrac{k}{h} = D_x y$, if the limit exists.

In this notation, our previous results for the slopes of graphs can be rewritten as follows:

$$\begin{aligned} &\text{if } y = x, & D_x y &= 1, \\ &\text{if } y = ax, & D_x y &= a; \\ &\text{if } y = ax + b, & D_x y &= a; \\ &\text{if } y = ax^2, & D_x y &= 2ax. \end{aligned}$$

We note that, in all these cases, $D_x y$ has a unique value for each value of x, and so $D_x y$ is the value of a function. This is true in general, and this function is called the derivative; the symbol f' is frequently used for the derivative. Thus, if

$$f : x \longrightarrow f(x) \quad \text{and} \quad y = f(x),$$

then

$$f' : x \longrightarrow f'(x) \quad \text{and} \quad D_x y = f'(x).$$

EXERCISE 1.6

1. Prepare a table for the values of $D_x y$ for the functions that we have considered in this section.

2. Calculate from first principles the slope of the graph of
$$y = 2x - x^2$$
at the point where $x = a$.

3. Calculate from first principles the slope of the graph of
$$y = ax^2$$
at the point $(x_1,\ y_1)$ on the graph.

4. Use the results in the table prepared in question (1) to calculate $D_x y$ for each of the following.
    (a) $y = x^2 + 2x + 1$ (b) $y = 6x^2 - 5x + 1$
    (c) $y = x^2 - 4x - 1$ (d) $y = 4 + 6x - x^2$
    (e) $y = (x - 3)(x - 4)$ (f) $y = (x - 2)(x + 5)$
    (g) $y = 8x - 3x^2 + 2$ (h) $y = 4 - x - 12x^2$
    (i) $y = 3(x^2 + 2x + 4)$ (j) $y = 4(x - x^2)$
    (k) $y = 5(x + 1)^2$ (l) $y = 3(2 - x)^2$
    (m) $y = \pi x^2 + \sqrt{2}x$ (n) $y = \frac{1}{3}x^2 - \frac{2}{3}x + \frac{5}{6}$

5. Calculate the slopes of the graphs of the equations in question (4) at the points where $x = 2$ and $x = -3$.

1.7. The Derivative of a Cubic Function

The function $f : x \rightarrow x^3$, which determines the ordered pairs

$$f = \{(x, y) \mid y = x^3, \ x \in Re\},$$

is called a cubic function, and its partial graph is shown in Figure 1.7 for $-2 < x < +4$. If we draw an approximate tangent at the point $(2, 8)$, we find that the slope is approximately 12.

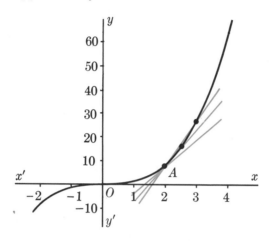

Figure 1.7

If we establish a table of values for a set of points B_n with values of x near 2, we obtain

	B_1	B_2	B_3	B_4	$\cdots$	A
x	2.1	2.01	2.001	2.0001	$\cdots$	2
y	9.261	8.120601	8.012006001	8.001200060001	$\cdots$	8

The slope of $AB_1 = \dfrac{9.261 - 8}{2.1 - 2} = \dfrac{1.261}{.1} = 12.61;$

the slope of $AB_2 = \dfrac{8.120601 - 8}{2.01 - 2} = \dfrac{.120601}{.01} = 12.0601;$

the slope of $AB_3 = \dfrac{8.012006001 - 8}{2.001 - 2} = \dfrac{.012006001}{.001} = 12.006001;$

the slope of $AB_4 = \dfrac{8.001200060001 - 8}{2.0001 - 2} = 12.00060001.$

Again the slope of AB_n is approaching a unique value as B_n approaches A. In this case, the value appears to be 12.

Note that, when the abscissa of B_n differs from that of $A(2)$ by .0001, the slope differs from 12 by .0006 approximately. If we want the slope of AB_n to differ from 12 by less than .0000001, we can do so by choosing the abscissa of B_n to differ from 2 by less than .00000001. In fact, we can make the slope as close to 12 as we like by choosing B_n close enough to A.

If we wish to find the slope at any point $P(x, y)$ on the curve $y = x^3$, we consider the slope of the chord PQ, where Q is the point $(x + h, y + k)$, as Q approaches P. As P and Q are on the curve, we have

$$y = x^3$$

and

$$y + k = (x + h)^3.$$

$$\text{Slope of } PQ = \frac{(y + k) - y}{(x + h) - x}$$

$$= \frac{(x + h)^3 - x^3}{h}$$

$$= \frac{x^3 + 3x^2h + 3xh^2 + h^3 - x^3}{h}$$

$$= \frac{3x^2h + 3xh^2 + h^3}{h}$$

$$= 3x^2 + 3xh + h^2.$$

We see that,

as Q approaches P,

h approaches 0,

and, hence, that

the slope of PQ approaches $3x^2$.

Therefore, the slope of the tangent to the curve $y = x^3$ at $P(x, y)$ is $3x^2$. In derivative notation, if

then

$$y = x^3,$$

$$D_x y = 3x^2.$$

For the general cubic function

the derivative is

$$f : x \rightarrow ax^3 + bx^2 + cx + d,$$

$$f' : x \rightarrow 3ax^2 + 2bx + c.$$

In this general case, we find the value of the derivative of the function at x by adding the values of the derivatives at x of the individual terms in the function:

$$D_x(ax^3 + bx^2 + cx + d) = D_x(ax^3) + D_x(bx^2) + D_x(cx) + D_x(d)$$

$$= 3ax^2 + 2bx + c.$$

EXERCISE 1.7

1. From first principles, calculate $D_x y$ for
$$y = ax^3.$$

2. From first principles, calculate $D_x y$ for
$$y = ax^3 + bx^2 + cx + d.$$

3. Use the values of known derivatives to calculate $D_x y$ for each of the functions determined by the following equations.

(a) $y = 5x^3$ (b) $y = x^3 - 2x^2$

(c) $y = \dfrac{x^3}{12}$ (d) $y = \dfrac{x^2}{2} - \dfrac{x^3}{6}$

(e) $y = 27 - 3x^3$ (f) $y = 3x - 2x^3$

(g) $y = (x^2 + 1)(x - 2)$ (h) $y = 2x(x + 1)(x + 3)$

(i) $y = (x^2 + 2x - 3)(x + 2)$ (j) $y = (x - 1)(x^2 + x + 1)$

4. Find the slope of the tangents to the graphs of each of the following equations at the points indicated.

(a) $y = 2x^3 + 8x$,   at $x = 2$

(b) $y = 3x^2 + 2x^3$,   at $x = -1$

(c) $y = x^3 - 3x^2 + 6$,   at $x = 3$

(d) $y = 2x^2 - 4x + x^3$,   at $x = 1$

(e) $y = 2x^2 - 8x^3 + 6$,   at $x = 2$

(f) $y = x^3 - 27x$,   at $x = -3$

1.8. The Derivative of the Reciprocal Function

The reciprocal function
$$f : x \to \frac{1}{x}$$

determines the graph whose equation is
$$y = \frac{1}{x}.$$

Consider any point $P(x, y)$ and a neighbouring point $Q(x + h, y + k)$ on the curve whose equation is $y = 1/x$, $x \neq 0$ (see Figure 1.8); then
$$y = \frac{1}{x}$$

and
$$y + k = \frac{1}{x + h}.$$

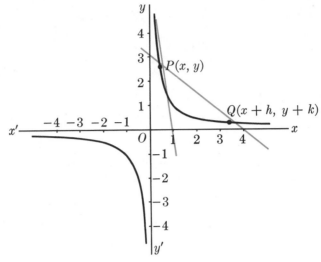

Figure 1.8

$$\text{Slope of } PQ = \frac{(y + k) - y}{(x + h) - x}$$

$$= \frac{\dfrac{1}{x + h} - \dfrac{1}{x}}{x + h - x}$$

$$= \frac{\dfrac{x - (x + h)}{(x + h)x}}{h}$$

$$= \frac{x - x - h}{(x + h)xh}$$

$$= \frac{-h}{(x + h)xh}$$

$$= \frac{-1}{(x + h)x}, \quad h \neq 0.$$

We see that,

as Q approaches P,

h approaches 0,

and hence, that

the slope of PQ approaches $-\dfrac{1}{x^2}$;

that is, if

$$y = \frac{1}{x},$$

then

$$D_x y = -\frac{1}{x^2}.$$

In the same way, if

$$f : x \rightarrow \frac{e}{x},$$

we can show that

$$f' : x \rightarrow -\frac{e}{x^2}.$$

Note that $x = 0$ is excluded from the domain of the function, and so $D_x y$ cannot exist at $x = 0$.

Again, by adding the derivatives, we can form the derivative of the sum of $f : x \rightarrow \frac{e}{x}$ with any of the functions that we have discussed previously. For example, if

$$f : x \rightarrow bx^2 + \frac{e}{x},$$

then

$$f' : x \rightarrow 2bx - \frac{e}{x^2}.$$

EXERCISE 1.8

1. The function

$$f : x \rightarrow \frac{1}{x}$$

and its derivative are not defined when $x = 0$, but they are defined for small values of x, both positive and negative. What is the behaviour of the slope of the tangent to the graph (a) when x is numerically small and positive? (b) when x is numerically small and negative?

2. Find $D_x y$ for each of the following.

(a) $y = x - \dfrac{1}{x}$

(b) $y = x^2 + \dfrac{2}{x}$

(c) $y = \dfrac{x + 1}{x}$

(d) $y = \dfrac{x^2 + 2x + 1}{x}$

3. Find the slope of the tangent to the graph of each equation in question (2) at the point where

(a) $x = 1$,   (b) $x = 3$,   (c) $x = -1$,   (d) $x = 100$.

4. Sketch the graph of $y = x + \dfrac{1}{x}$. What happens at $x = 1$ and $x = -1$?

5. Show that the derivative, f', of

$$f : x \rightarrow \frac{1}{x^2}$$

is

$$f' : x \rightarrow -\frac{2}{x^3}.$$

1.9. The Equation of the Tangent to a Curve

In all the cases discussed in the earlier sections, we have established that the slope of the tangent to a curve at $P(x_1, y_1)$ is given by the value of the derivative with respect to x when $x = x_1$. For example,

for the curve $y = x^2$, the slope of the tangent at (x_1, y_1) is $2x_1$;

for the curve $y = 2x^3$, the slope of the tangent at $(2, 16)$ is $6(2)^2 = 24$;

for the curve $y = \dfrac{3}{x}$, the slope of the tangent at $\left(2, \dfrac{3}{2}\right)$ is $-\dfrac{3}{2^2} = -\dfrac{3}{4}$.

Therefore, we can find the equation of the tangent at a point on a curve by using the slope-point form of the equation of a line.

Example.   Find the equation of the tangent to the curve

$$y = 5x^2 - 2x - 12$$

at the point where $x = 2$.

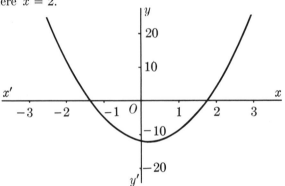

Figure 1.9

Solution: When $x = 2$,

$$y = 5(2)^2 - 2(2) - 12$$
$$= 20 - 4 - 12$$
$$= 4.$$

The value of the derivative with respect to x is

$$D_x y = 5(2x) - 2(1) - 12(0)$$
$$= 10x - 2,$$

and when $x = 2$,

$$D_x y = 10(2) - 2$$
$$= 18.$$

The slope of the tangent at $(2, 4)$ is 18, and therefore the equation of the tangent to the curve at $(2, 4)$ is

$$y - 4 = 18(x - 2),$$
$$y = 18x - 36 + 4,$$
$$y = 18x - 32.$$

EXERCISE 1.9

Find the equations of the tangents to the graphs of the following functions at the points where x has the value given.

1. $y = x^2$ at   (a) $x = 2$,   (b) $x = -3$.

2. $y = (x + 1)^2$ at   (a) $x = 1$,   (b) $x = -2$.

3. $y = x^3$ at   (a) $x = 3$,   (b) $x = -3$.

4. $y = \dfrac{1}{x} - x^2$ at   (a) $x = 2$,   (b) $x = -2$.

5. $y = 2x^3 - 3x^2$ at   (a) $x = 1$,   (b) $x = 3$.

6. $y = \dfrac{x^2}{2} - x + \dfrac{1}{4}$ at   (a) $x = 3$,   (b) $x = \dfrac{1}{2}$.

7. $y = x^2 + 4x - 5$ at   (a) $x = 2$,   (b) $x = 1$.

8. $y = x^3 + x - \dfrac{2}{x}$ at   (a) $x = -1$,   (b) $x = \dfrac{1}{4}$.

9. $y = \dfrac{1}{3}x^2 + 2x - \dfrac{3}{x}$ at   (a) $x = 3$,   (b) $x = -\dfrac{1}{3}$.

10. Find the equation of a tangent to the graph of
$$y = x^2 + 3x - 4$$
that is parallel to
$$2y = 3x.$$

11. Find the equation of the tangents to the graph of
$$y = x + \frac{1}{x}$$
that are parallel to
$$y + 2x = 0.$$

12. Find the equation of the tangents to the graph of
$$y = x^3 + 2x^2 - 2x$$
that are perpendicular to
$$2y + x + 5 = 0.$$

13. Find the equation of the tangent to the graph of

$$y = 2x^2$$

at $(\frac{1}{2}, \frac{1}{2})$.   Find the equation of a tangent that is perpendicular to the tangent at $(\frac{1}{2}, \frac{1}{2})$.

14. The graphs of the two functions defined by

$$y = x^2 - 1 \quad \text{and} \quad y = 1 - x^2$$

intersect in two points. Show that the tangents to the two curves at these points of intersection form a parallelogram.

15. Two curves are said to be tangential to each other when they have a common tangent at a point of intersection. Show that the graphs of

$$y = \frac{1}{x} \quad \text{and} \quad y = 3x - 2x^2$$

are tangential at a point where they intersect.

Chapter Summary

The equation of a line:

slope-intercept form, $y = mx + b$

slope-point form, $y - y_1 = m(x - x_1)$

two-point form, $y - y_1 = \dfrac{y_2 - y_1}{x_2 - x_1}(x - x_1)$

The slope of a secant and a tangent to a curve

$y = f(x)$	$D_x y = f'(x)$
c	0
x	1
x^2	$2x$
x^3	$3x^2$
$\dfrac{1}{x}$	$-\dfrac{1}{x^2}$

If $$f(x) = ax^3 + bx^2 + cx + d + \frac{e}{x}$$

then

$$D_x\left(ax^3 + bx^2 + cx + d + \frac{e}{x}\right) = aD_x(x^3) + bD_x(x^2) + cD_x(x) + 0 + eD_x\left(\frac{1}{x}\right)$$

$$= 3ax^2 + 2bx + c - \frac{e}{x^2}.$$

The equation of a tangent to a curve at a point

REVIEW EXERCISE 1

1. Calculate the slope of the secant of the graph of each of the following between the points whose abscissae are given.

   (a) $y = 5x^2$, $\qquad\qquad x = 1 \qquad$ and $\quad x = 3$

   (b) $y = 2x^2 + 3x - 5$, $\qquad x = -1 \quad$ and $\quad x = 1$

   (c) $y = 4x - 2x^3$, $\qquad\quad x = 0 \qquad$ and $\quad x = 2$

   (d) $y = x - \dfrac{4}{x}$, $\qquad\qquad x = 1 \qquad$ and $\quad x = 4$

   (e) $y = 4 - x^2$, $\qquad\qquad x = -2 \quad$ and $\quad x = +2$

   (f) $y = 2x^3 - \dfrac{6}{x}$, $\qquad\qquad x = 3 \qquad$ and $\quad x = -1$

2. Find the equations of the secants in question (1).

3. Find from first principles the value of the derivative at x of
$$f : x \to 2(x^2 - x)$$

4. Using the values of the derivatives calculated in this chapter, find the value of the derivative at x of each of the following.

   (a) $4x^2 + 6$ $\qquad\qquad\qquad$ (b) $5x^3$

   (c) $3x - 2x^3$ $\qquad\qquad\qquad$ (d) $2x - \dfrac{4}{x}$

   (e) $(3x - 1)(x - 3)$ $\qquad\qquad$ (f) $(x^2 + 1)(2 + x)$

   (g) $\dfrac{x^2 + 4x + 5}{x}$ $\qquad\qquad$ (h) $\dfrac{x^3 - 2x}{5x^2}$

   (i) $(x + 1)(x - 2)^2$ $\qquad\qquad$ (j) $\dfrac{1}{x}(x - 1)(x + 3)$

5. Find the equations of the tangents to the curve at the points where the graph of
$$y = x(x - 2)(x + 1)$$
cuts the x-axis.

6. Find the equation of the tangent to the graph of
$$y = \tfrac{1}{2}x^3$$
at the point (2, 4).   Show that this tangent is parallel to the tangent to the graph of
$$y = x^2$$
at the point (3, 9).

7. Find the equation of the tangent to the graph of
$$y = 4x^2$$
that is parallel to the line
$$y = 2x + 3.$$

8. Find the equations of the tangents to the curves

$$y = \frac{1}{3}x^2 \quad \text{and} \quad y = \frac{9}{x}$$

at their point of intersection.

9. Find the points where the graph of

$$y = x^3 + x^2 - 5x + 6$$

has zero slope.

10. Find the points on the graph of

$$y = \frac{x^3}{3} - 5x - \frac{4}{x}$$

at which the slope is zero.

Chapter 2

DISTANCE, VELOCITY
AND ACCELERATION

2.1. Average Velocity

If we travel 120 miles in a straight line in two hours at a *constant* velocity, then we know that the velocity is 60 miles per hour. In other words, velocity is a rate that is measured by the ratio of the measure of the distance travelled to the measure of the time taken, *if* the velocity is a constant during that time.

However, 120 miles could be travelled in two hours in many ways if the velocity is not constant; for example,

(i)	.5 hour at 30 m.p.h.,	(ii)	1.0 hour at 90 m.p.h.,
	1.0 hour at 80 m.p.h.,		1.0 hour at 30 m.p.h.,
	.5 hour at 50 m.p.h.,		

are two possible ways in which this could be accomplished. Obviously, in these cases, we cannot find *the* velocity by taking the rate of total distance to total time, as there are several different velocities. However, in these cases, the rate of the total distance to total time still has some significance: it is the *average velocity.*

DEFINITION. The average velocity over a given time interval is the rate of the total directed distance travelled in that time to the total time interval.

We notice that, in case (ii), the arithmetic mean (average) of the two velocities, 90 m.p.h. and 30 m.p.h., is 60 m.p.h., the same as the average velocity. However, in case (i), the arithmetic mean (average) of the three velocities, 30 m.p.h., 80 m.p.h., and 50 m.p.h., is 53.3 m.p.h.! This last is, of course, the unweighted mean; however,

$$\text{the weighted mean} = \frac{.5(30) + 1(80) + .5(50)}{.5 + 1 + .5}$$
$$= \frac{15 + 80 + 25}{2}$$
$$= 60,$$

so that *the weighted mean velocity* is the same as *the average velocity.* Therefore, when we calculate the average, we must be very careful to avoid errors of the type indicated here. We can always avoid such errors by returning to the definition; we find the total distance and the total time and then perform the required division operation. In fact, this is exactly what we do when we calculate the weighted mean velocity.

Example. The following table gives the functional relation between the distance travelled by an airplane and the time. What is the average velocity in each hour? What is the average velocity between the end of the second hour and the start of the sixth hour? What is the average velocity over the whole period of six hours?

Time (in hours)	0	1	2	3	4	5	6
Distance (in miles)	0	300	800	1500	2300	2900	3300

Solution:

In first hour: distance (miles) = 300; average velocity (m.p.h.) = 300.
In second hour: distance (miles) = 500; average velocity (m.p.h.) = 500.
In third hour: distance (miles) = 700; average velocity (m.p.h.) = 700.
In fourth hour: distance (miles) = 800; average velocity (m.p.h.) = 800.
In fifth hour: distance (miles) = 600; average velocity (m.p.h.) = 600.
In sixth hour: distance (miles) = 400; average velocity (m.p.h.) = 400.

Distance travelled (in miles) in 3rd, 4th, 5th hours = 2100.
Average velocity (in m.p.h.) in these three hours =   700.
Total distance (in miles) in six hours = 3300.
Average velocity (in m.p.h.) for whole flight =   550.

EXERCISE 2.1

1. Kingston is 195 miles from Montreal and Toronto 160 miles from Kingston. A train leaves Montreal at 9:00 a.m. and arrives at Kingston at 12:45 p.m. It leaves Kingston at 1:00 p.m. and arrives in Toronto at 3:20 p.m. What is its average velocity (a) from Montreal to Kingston? (b) from Kingston to Toronto? (c) from Montreal to Toronto (including the stop at Kingston)? (d) from Montreal to Toronto (neglecting the time of the stop at Kingston)?

2. A man walks 15 miles from home at 5 miles per hour and then returns at 3 miles per hour. What is (a) his average speed, (b) his average velocity for the whole walk?

3. A car is driven for two hours at 40 miles per hour and then for six hours at 70 miles per hour. What distance does it travel and what is its average velocity over the total distance?

4. An airplane is checked past successive navigational beacons at the following times:

Beacon	Time	Distance from Start (in miles)
A	9:00 a.m.	200
B	9:30 a.m.	350
C	9:50 a.m.	600
D	10:05 a.m.	800
E	10:30 a.m.	1100
F	10:50 a.m.	1250

(a) What is the average velocity of the airplane between each pair of beacons?

(b) What is its overall average velocity between beacon A and beacon F?

(c) Draw a graph to illustrate the flight between beacon A and beacon F.

(d) What do you notice about the slopes of the line segments of the graph?

2.2. Instantaneous Velocity

If we consider the distance fallen by a heavy ball (assuming air resistance to be negligible) under gravity, we obtain the following table (approximately) for distance s in time t . (Figure 2.1 shows the graph of these ordered pairs.)

t (in seconds)	0	1	2	3	4	5	6	7	8	9	10
s (in feet)	0	16	64	144	256	400	576	784	1024	1296	1600

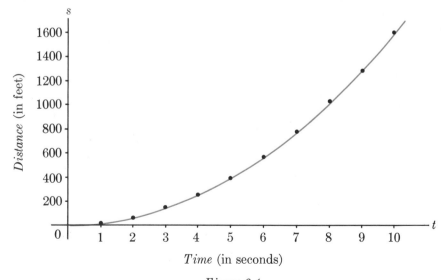

Figure 2.1

From the previous table, we can prepare another table for the average velocity in each one-second interval; for example, in the fourth second, the distance travelled in feet is

$$256 - 144 = 112,$$

and so the average velocity is 112 ft/sec.

One-Second Interval	1st	2nd	3rd	4th	5th	6th	7th	8th	9th	10th
Average Velocity (in ft/sec)	16	48	80	112	144	176	208	240	272	304

Obviously, the actual velocity does not change discontinuously in jumps in this way; it must be changing gradually all the time. If we examine a motion-picture film of the ball falling, we can obtain the values of the distance fallen at the end of each one-tenth of a second. A portion of the table of values near $t = 3$ would look like this:

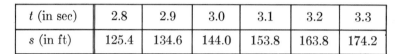

t (in sec)	2.8	2.9	3.0	3.1	3.2	3.3
s (in ft)	125.4	134.6	144.0	153.8	163.8	174.2

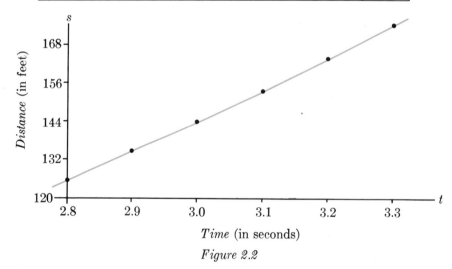

Time (in seconds)

Figure 2.2

We can now calculate the average velocity between 2.8 seconds and 2.9 seconds as follows:

$$\text{average velocity (in ft/sec)} = \frac{134.6 - 125.4}{.1}$$

$$= \frac{9.2}{.1}$$

$$= 92.$$

Similarly,

between 2.9 sec and 3.0 sec, average velocity (in ft/sec) = 94;
between 3.0 sec and 3.1 sec, average velocity (in ft/sec) = 97;
between 3.1 sec and 3.2 sec, average velocity (in ft/sec) = 100;
between 3.2 sec and 3.3 sec, average velocity (in ft/sec) = 104.

The apparent sudden changes in velocity are now appreciably reduced.

If the experiment could be performed with more accurate time and distance measurements, we would obtain the following sequence of values for the average velocities near 3.00 seconds:

t (in sec)	2.98	2.99	3.00	3.01	3.02
s (in ft)	142.09	143.04	144.00	144.96	145.93
Average Velocity (in ft/sec)	95		96	96	97

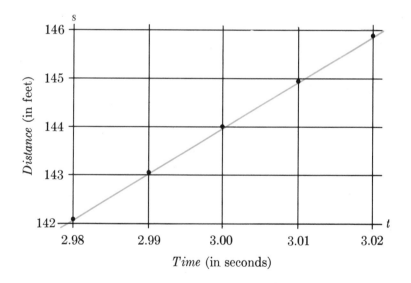

Figure 2.3

Notice that these are again average velocities, in this case average velocities over .01-second intervals, but they are still correct only to the nearest foot per second. Using these values for the average velocities, and the physical intuition that the velocity changes gradually and continuously, we might say that the velocity at $t = 3.00$ is 96 ft/sec to within the experimental accuracy of our results. But even if this is correct, what *do* we mean by velocity at a given time? We have only calculated average velocities over an interval of time so far.

If we wish to speak of velocity at a particular instant of time, we must define *instantaneous velocity* at a given time. To do this, we note that a functional relation exists between distance s in feet and time t in seconds. Thus, if (t, s) is any ordered pair of values of time and distance, we can form a new ordered pair by considering a change in time by a small amount Δt. When the time changes by a small amount Δt, the distance changes by a small amount Δs, and the new ordered pair for time and distance is $(t + \Delta t, s + \Delta s)$. If we calculate the average velocity in the time interval Δt, we find

$$\text{average velocity} = \frac{(s + \Delta s) - s}{(t + \Delta t) - t} = \frac{\Delta s}{\Delta t}.$$

The average velocity can be calculated over a smaller and smaller time interval Δt. If a sequence of values of the average velocities obtained in this way approaches a unique value as the time interval Δt approaches zero, then we can consider this value to be the instantaneous velocity. This value is also called the limit of the sequence of values; in this particular case, we write the limit in the following way:

$$\lim_{\Delta t \to 0} \frac{\Delta s}{\Delta t}.$$

DEFINITION. The instantaneous velocity v of a body that has travelled a distance s in a time t is $\lim\limits_{\Delta t \to 0} \dfrac{\Delta s}{\Delta t}$; that is,

$$v = \lim_{\Delta t \to 0} \frac{\Delta s}{\Delta t}.$$

Note that, from physical considerations, the preceding discussion implies that a functional relation exists between s and t (no body can be in two different places at one time) and also that a functional relation exists between v and t (no body can have two different velocities at the same time). We shall consider these facts from a more mathematical point of view in a later chapter. For the present, we shall accept them intuitively.

Returning to our experiment, we recall the following sequence of values for the average velocities (in feet per second) of the falling ball in .01-second intervals near $t = 3.00$ seconds:

Δt	$2.99 - 2.98$	$3.00 - 2.99$	$3.01 - 3.00$	$3.02 - 3.01$
$\dfrac{\Delta s}{\Delta t}$	95	96	96	97

It would appear that, at $t = 3.00$, the instantaneous velocity is

$$v = \lim_{\Delta t \to 0} \frac{\Delta s}{\Delta t} = 96.$$

However, if we could measure the distances correctly to .0001 foot, we would obtain the following values:

Δt	$2.99 - 2.98$	$3.00 - 2.99$	$3.01 - 3.00$	$3.02 - 3.01$
$\dfrac{\Delta s}{\Delta t}$	95.52	95.84	96.16	96.48

It does not seem so certain now that v is exactly 96 when $t = 3.00$; in fact, we can only estimate that this is true. To decide if the velocity is 96 ft/sec at $t = 3.00$, we would have to continue decreasing the time interval from .01 sec to .0001 sec to 10^{-6} sec and so on, at the same time increasing the accuracy of the distance measurement to correspond.   This is impossible physically, though we may be able to reach .0001 sec with an interrupted spark light.   Physically, we always obtain an average velocity even if the time interval is very small; only theoretically can we obtain an instantaneous velocity.

EXERCISE 2.2

1. In an experiment, a small lead shot is fired vertically with an initial velocity of 96 ft/sec. The following table, which is prepared from the observations, gives the height s in feet at a time t in seconds:

t (in sec)	0	1	2	3	4	5	6
s (in ft)	0	80	128	144	128	80	0

Find the average velocity in each one-second interval.

2. The experiment is repeated using photographic measurement techniques, and the following table is prepared from the observations for $1.90 \leq t \leq 2.10$.

t (in sec)	1.90	1.95	1.98	1.99	2.00	2.01	2.02	2.05	2.10
s (in ft)	124.64	126.36	127.36	127.68	128.00	128.32	128.64	129.56	131.04

Find the average velocity in each interval and estimate the instantaneous velocity at 2.00 sec.

3. For the same experiment, the results near $t = 3$ and $t = 5$ are as follows:

t (in sec)	2.97	2.98	2.99	3.00	3.01	3.02	3.03
s (in ft)	143.99	143.99	144.00	144.00	144.00	143.99	143.99
t (in sec)	4.97	4.98	4.99	5.00	5.01	5.02	5.03
s (in ft)	81.91	81.27	80.64	80.00	79.36	78.71	78.07

Find the average velocities in the various intervals, and estimate the instantaneous velocity at $t = 3.00$ and at $t = 5.00$.

4. Draw a sketch graph of $\{(t, s) \mid t \in Re\}$ from the data of question (1), assuming that the graph is a smooth curve.   What type of function does the graph indicate?   At some times the velocity is positive and at other times negative (see questions (2) and (3)).   What is happening to the values of s as t increases in the different cases that arise?   Is the velocity ever zero?

5. A pearl is dropped into a tall vessel filled with thick glycerine.   The observed times and distances of fall are given in the following table:

t (in sec)	0	1	2	3	4	5	6	7	8	9	10
s (in cm)	0	8.6	33.9	73.9	126.3	188.4	257.8	332.6	411.2	492.4	575.4

Find the average velocity in the successive time intervals.

6. The experiment of question (5) is repeated, and a more detailed study of the observations near the position where $s = 230$ gives the following table:

t (in sec)	5.0	5.2	5.4	5.6	5.8	6.0
s (in cm)	188.39	201.76	215.41	229.31	243.46	257.84

Find the average velocity in the successive intervals and estimate the instantaneous velocity when $s = 230$.

7. A taller vessel than the one in question (5) is now used in the same experiment, and the results for larger values of t are as follows:

t (in sec)	11	13	15	17	19	21	23
s (in cm)	659.7	830.5	1003.0	1176.1	1349.6	1523.2	1696.8

What is the average velocity in each two-second interval?   Can we estimate the instantaneous velocity at these times?   What is the approximate functional relation between s and t when $t > 10$?   Can we say anything about the instantaneous velocity for $t > 10$?

2.3. Velocity as a Derivative

For a body in motion in a straight line, the distance s (in feet) at a time t (in seconds) is the value of a function; we can illustrate this with a graph of s against t. In fact, the graph will consist of a set of discrete points corresponding to the observed times and distances.   In practice, we join these points by a smooth curve because we know that the body changes its distance from an origin in a gradual or continuous way and that time also appears to change continuously.   Although we observe only at a discrete set of values of t, the domain and range of t and s respectively are, in fact, subsets of the real numbers.   In such a case, the values of (t, s) are given by a continuous function of t.   We shall examine this idea more formally in a later chapter.

If we consider a particular case, for example, $s = 16t^2$, $t > 0$ (Figure 2.4), we can take two points $P(t, s)$ and $Q(t + \triangle t, \ s + \triangle s)$ near each other on the curve and obtain

$$s + \triangle s = 16(t + \triangle t)^2.$$

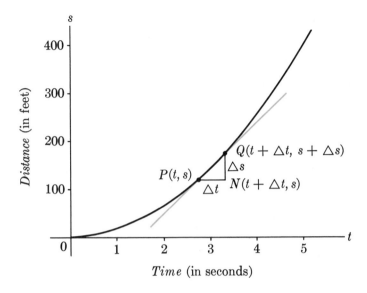

Figure 2.4

If we now calculate the average velocity in the interval $\triangle t$, we obtain

$$\text{average velocity (in interval } \triangle t) = \frac{(s + \triangle s) - s}{(t + \triangle t) - t}$$

$$= \frac{16(t + \triangle t)^2 - 16t^2}{\triangle t}$$

$$= \frac{16t^2 + 32t(\triangle t) + 16(\triangle t)^2 - 16t^2}{\triangle t}$$

$$= \frac{32t(\triangle t) + 16(\triangle t)^2}{\triangle t}$$

$$= 32t + 16(\triangle t) \, .$$

Proceeding to the limit as $\triangle t$ approaches zero, we obtain the instantaneous velocity v at a time t :

$$v = \lim_{\triangle t \to 0} (32t + 16(\triangle t))$$

$$= 32t \, .$$

Note again that this does not mean that we replace $\triangle t$ by 0. It means that $32t + 16(\triangle t)$ can be made to differ from $32t$ by as small a number as we wish. Thus, if $\triangle t = 10^{-6}$, the difference is less than 2×10^{-5}, and if this is not small enough, we can make the difference less than 10^{-24} by making $\triangle t$ less than 5×10^{-26}!

Notice also that, using the rules for derivatives developed in Chapter 1, we can write

$$D_t s = 32t.$$

In this case then,

$$v = D_t s = 32t.$$

In fact, in finding the instantaneous velocity, we are finding the slope of the tangent to the graph of s against t (compare the procedure followed here with that of Chapter 1). It is true in general that

$$v = D_t s.$$

Example. The distance s (in feet) at a time t (in seconds) is given by

$$s = 4t^2 + \frac{64}{t}, \quad t > 0.$$

What is the velocity at any time t? What is the velocity at 1 second and at 2 seconds? At what time (if any) is the velocity zero? What is happening to the distance s at 1 second? 2 seconds? 3 seconds?

Solution:

$$s = 4t^2 + \frac{64}{t}, \quad t > 0;$$

therefore,

$$v = D_t s = 4(2t) + 64\left(-\frac{1}{t^2}\right),$$

$$v = 8t - \frac{64}{t^2}.$$

When $t = 1$,

$$v = 8(1) - \frac{64}{1}$$
$$= 8 - 64$$
$$= -56.$$

At 1 second the velocity is -56 ft /sec.

When $t = 3$,

$$v = 8(3) - \frac{64}{9}$$
$$= 24 - \frac{64}{9}$$
$$= 16\tfrac{8}{9}.$$

At 3 seconds the velocity is $16\tfrac{8}{9}$ ft./sec.

When $v = 0$,

$$0 = 8t - \frac{64}{t^2} ;$$

therefore,

$$8t^3 = 64 ,$$
$$t^3 = 8 ,$$
$$t = 2 .$$

The velocity is zero when the time is 2 seconds.

At 1 second the distance is decreasing as time increases; at 2 seconds the distance has just stopped decreasing as time increases; at 3 seconds the distance is increasing as time increases.

EXERCISE 2.3

In each of the following questions, distance is measured in feet, time in seconds, and velocity in feet per second.

1. If the distance s at any time t is given by

    $$s = 12 - 10t + 2t^2, \quad t \geq 0,$$

    find the velocity v at any time t.
    (a) What is the distance at the end of 1, 2, 3, 4 and 5 seconds?
    (b) What is the velocity when $t = 0, 1, 2, 3, 4, 5, 6$?
    (c) What is the average velocity in the first, second, and third seconds?
    (d) When is the velocity negative?   positive?
    (e) When is the velocity zero?
    (f) What is the value of s when the velocity is zero?

2. Repeat question (1) with

    $$s = t^2 + 4t + 6, \quad t \geq 0.$$

3. Sketch the graphs of s against t and v against t for questions (1) and (2). Indicate the values of t for which the velocity is (a) negative and (b) positive.

4. Find the velocity at any time $t \geq 0$ if the distance s is given by
    (a) $s = 12 + 4t - 5t^2 + 2t^3 ,$ (b) $s = t^3 + 2t^2 + 3t + 4 ,$
    (c) $s = 27t - t^3.$

5. Find the velocity at any time $t > 0$ when the distance s is given by
    (a) $s = 25 - \dfrac{25}{t}$ (b) $s = 2t^2 + 4t - \dfrac{6}{t} ,$
    (c) $s = 2t^3 - 24t + 69 .$

    Does the velocity become zero at any time and, if so, when?   Sketch the graphs determined by the equation in each part.

6. If
$$s = t^2 + 8t$$
find
(a) the average velocity between $t = 2$ and $t = 3$,
(b) the arithmetic mean of the velocities at $t = 2$ and $t = 3$,
(c) the instantaneous velocity at $t = 2\frac{1}{2}$.

7. If
$$s = t^3 + 9t$$
find
(a) the average velocity between $t = 2$ and $t = 3$,
(b) the arithmetic mean of the velocities at $t = 2$ and $t = 3$,
(c) the instantaneous velocity at $t = 2\frac{1}{2}$.

8. Explain why the three results in question (6) are equal while the three results in question (7) are different.

2.4. Acceleration

In physics, acceleration is considered as the rate of change of velocity, but again it is an average acceleration that is measured or calculated. In the most frequently discussed case, that is, acceleration due to gravity, the acceleration is approximately constant; in such cases, the average acceleration is the same as the instantaneous acceleration.

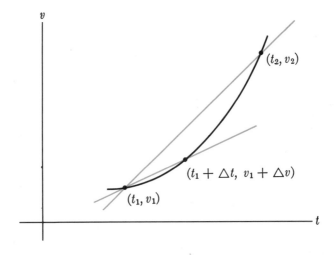

Figure 2.5

DEFINITION.   The average acceleration over a given time interval is the rate of the change in velocity in that time to the time interval itself.   Thus,

$$\text{average acceleration} = \frac{v_2 - v_1}{t_2 - t_1},$$

where

v_1 is the velocity at the beginning of the interval in suitable units,
v_2 is the velocity at the end of the interval in the same units as v_1,
t_1 is the time at the beginning of the interval in appropriate units,
t_2 is the time at the end of the interval in the same units as t_1.

Considering the above definition, we see that the average acceleration is the slope of the chord joining (t_1, v_1) to (t_2, v_2) on the graph of v against t (Figure 2.5).

If we consider two points very near each other on the curve, say (t_1, v_1) and $(t_1 + \triangle t, v_1 + \triangle v)$, then we see that the values of v_1 and $v_1 + \triangle v$ are values of the velocity at two distinct times separated by a small time interval $\triangle t$, and we have

$$\text{average acceleration (in interval } \triangle t) = \frac{(v_1 + \triangle v) - v_1}{(t_1 + \triangle t) - t_1}$$

$$= \frac{\triangle v}{\triangle t}.$$

The limit of this ratio as $\triangle t$ approaches zero gives the slope of the tangent to the curve, and so

$$\lim_{\triangle t \to 0} \frac{\triangle v}{\triangle t} = D_t v.$$

Also, if we use a similar definition to that for instantaneous velocity, we obtain

$$\text{instantaneous acceleration} = a = \lim_{\triangle t \to 0} \frac{\triangle v}{\triangle t},$$

and so

$$a = D_t v.$$

However, v itself is expressible as a derivative, that is, $v = D_t s$, and so the acceleration a is a derivative of a derivative; we say that a is a *second derivative* of s with respect to t.   Symbolically, we may write

$$a = D_t v \quad \text{and} \quad v = D_t s \, ;$$

hence,

$$a = D_t(D_t s) \, ,$$

and, *by analogy* with our exponent laws, we write

$$a = D_t^2 s \, .$$

We must note, however, that D_t^2 does *not* mean that two numbers D_t are multiplied together! In the first place, D_t is *not* a number; it is the symbol for the phrase "the derivative of". Such a symbol is called an *operator*. Therefore, D_t^2 is also *not a number* but an operator, the symbol for the phrase "the derivative of" repeated twice: $D_t^2 = D_t(D_t)$ is short for "the derivative of the derivative of". In the second place, D_t has no mathematical completeness of itself; it must be followed by the value of a function of t in any expression from which a result is wanted. We must have "the derivative of" something; for example,

$$D_t(t^3) = 3t^2$$

and

$$D_t^2(t^3) = D_t(D_t t^3) = D_t(3t^2) = 6t.$$

If the distance is measured in feet and the time in seconds, then we know that the velocity is measured in feet per second, because the velocity is the rate of change of the distance with respect to time. Similarly, as the acceleration is the rate of change of velocity with respect to time, the acceleration stated in terms of the same units is measured in feet per second per second. For brevity, we frequently write the unit of measurement for velocity as ft/sec; similarly, for the unit of measurement for acceleration, we write ft/sec/sec, or even ft/sec².

If we are working in the metric system, we use centimetres and seconds as units of distance and time. The unit of measurement for velocity is written cm /sec , and the unit of measurement for acceleration is written cm/sec/sec or cm/sec².

Example 1. The velocity v of a particle in cm/sec at any time t in seconds is given by the formula

$$v = 16t - 4t^2, \quad t \geq 0.$$

Find the acceleration at any time and its numerical value when $t = 1, 2$ and 4.

Solution:

$$v = 16t - 4t^2 ;$$
$$\therefore \quad a = D_t v = 16 - 8t.$$

When $t = 1$,

$$a = 8 ;$$

When $t = 2$,

$$a = 0 ;$$

When $t = 4$,

$$a = -16.$$

Example 2. The distance s (in feet) of a particle from a fixed point is determined as the value of a function of time t (in seconds) by the equation

$$s = 32 - 2t^2 + t^3, \quad t \geq 0.$$

Find the velocity and acceleration at any time t.   Find also when, if ever, either the velocity or the acceleration is zero.

Solution:

$$s = 32 - 2t^2 + t^3,$$
$$v = D_t s = -4t + 3t^2,$$
$$a = D_t v = D_t^2 s = -4 + 6t.$$

a is zero when $t = \frac{2}{3}$.

v is zero when $t = 0$ and when $t = \frac{4}{3}$.

EXERCISE 2.4

1. In each of the following, the velocity of a particle is given by a formula.   Find the acceleration at any time and its value at the particular times required.

   (a) $v = 10t - t^2,$ $t \geq 0;$ $t = 2$ and $t = 5$

   (b) $v = 2t + 10,$ $t \geq 0;$ $t = 1$ and $t = 3$

   (c) $v = t + \dfrac{4}{t},$ $t \geq 1;$ $t = 2$ and $t = 1\frac{1}{2}$

   (d) $v = (t - 1)^3,$ $t \geq 1;$ $t = 3$ and $t = 5$

   (e) $v = t^3 - 48t,$ $t \geq 1;$ $t = 2$ and $t = 4$

2. The distance in feet that a particle moves in a straight line from a fixed point (time is in seconds, $t \geq 0$) is given by

   (a) $s = t^2 - 2t,$ (b) $s = t^2 - 10t,$ (c) $s = 8t - t^2 - t^3,$

   (d) $s = 2 + 5t,$ (e) $s = \frac{1}{3}t^3 - 4t^2 - 12t + 24.$

   In each case, find the velocity and acceleration in terms of the time.   Find the values of the velocities and accelerations at $t = 2$.   Describe the direction of motion during the first five seconds in each case.

3. The position of a particle (in feet) in terms of the time (in seconds) is given by

   $$s = 4t - 7t^2 + 2t^3,   t \geq 0.$$

   Find the velocity and acceleration at any time.   At what times is the velocity or acceleration zero?   What happens to the direction of motion at the time when the velocity is zero?   Sketch the graphs of the distance, velocity, and acceleration (use only one time scale and a common time axis).

4. The position (in feet) of a particle in terms of the time (in seconds) is given by

   $$s = 16 + 6t - t^2,   0 \leq t \leq 8.$$

   Find the velocity and acceleration at any time.   Find the time, acceleration, and distance when the velocity is zero.   Find the distance at $t = 2$ and $t = 4$.   What do you notice about the distance when the velocity is zero compared with the other distances?   Can you explain your result?

2.5. Stationary Points for Quadratic Functions

If we throw a ball vertically upwards with a velocity of 64 ft/sec, the height s feet at time t seconds is given by the formula

$$s = -\tfrac{1}{2}gt^2 + 64t, \quad t \geq 0,$$

where g is the acceleration due to gravity. If we take $g = 32$ (in ft/sec²), the formula becomes

$$s = -16t^2 + 64t, \tag{1}$$

and so

$$v = D_t s = -32t + 64 \tag{2}$$

and

$$a = D_t v = -32. \tag{3}$$

Obviously, the ball reaches a highest point and then starts to fall back; that is, its direction of motion reverses at the highest point. This point is called a *turning point*, or *stationary point*. At this highest point, where s is therefore greatest, the velocity, v, is zero, and the ball has just ceased to go up and is just beginning to fall back down. Thus, when s is greatest,

$$v = D_t s = 0.$$

We may verify this by finding the maximum value of s as a quadratic function of t by completing the square:

$$
\begin{aligned}
s &= -16t^2 + 64t \\
&= -16(t^2 - 4t) \\
&= -16(t^2 - 4t + 4) + 64 \\
&= -16(t - 2)^2 + 64.
\end{aligned}
$$

We see from this expression for s that s has a maximum value of 64 when $t = 2$. Also, if we examine equation (2), we see that $v = 0$ only when $t = 2$. From this we develop an alternative method of finding the maximum value of s.

To Find the Maximum Value of $s = -16t^2 + 64t$

The maximum value of s occurs when $v = D_t s = 0$, that is, when

$$v = D_t s = -32t + 64 = 0.$$

Therefore,

$$32t = 64,$$

$$t = 2 \quad \text{at the maximum value of } s.$$

So the highest point is reached in two seconds. To find s, we now substitute $t = 2$ in equation (1):

$$s = -16(2)^2 + 64(2)$$
$$= -64 + 128$$
$$= 64 .$$

The maximum value of s is 64 and occurs at $t = 2$; that is, the highest point reached (greatest s) is 64 feet.

When the formula for s determines a quadratic function, we can find the greatest value of s either by completing the square *or* by finding the value of t when $D_t s = 0$ and then calculating the corresponding value of s. If the formula between s and t determines a quadratic function, and if s has a minimum, or smallest, value, we can find this minimum by the same methods that we used to find the maximum value.

EXERCISE 2.5

In the following questions, the distance s is given by the value of a quadratic function of the time t. Find the maximum or minimum value of s by completing the square. Also find $v = D_t s$, the time when $v = 0$, and the value of s at this time. In all cases $t \geq 0$.

1. $s = t^2 - 6t + 21$ 2. $s = 30 + 4t - 4t^2$

3. $s = t^2 + t + 13$ 4. $s = 3t^2 + t - 3\frac{1}{3}$

5. $s = 12t^2 - 60t + 100$ 6. $s = (2t - 3)(3t + 5)$

7. $s = 5t^2 - 3t + 15$ 8. $s = 24 - 6t + 4t^2$

9. $s = 12 + 3t - 12t^2$ 10. $s = 16 - 8t - 4t^2$

2.6. Stationary Points for More General Functions

When the relationship between s and t is not given by a quadratic function, we cannot use the method of completing the square to find a maximum (or minimum) value of s. In most cases, it is still true that, at the maximum or minimum value of s, the velocity is zero. Certainly, at a point where the velocity is zero, the direction of motion of the particle is usually reversed. For, if s increases before the velocity drops to zero, then s decreases after the velocity passes the value zero and becomes negative. And, similarly, if s decreases before the velocity rises to zero, then s increases after the velocity becomes positive. Thus we can use the fact that $D_t s = 0$ at a stationary point to find the time when this point is reached and then use this value of the time to calculate the distance to the stationary point. This distance will be either a maximum (that is, larger than any neighbouring distance) or a minimum (that is, less than any neighbouring distance).

Example 1.   The distance s is given in terms of time t $(t > 0)$ by

$$s = 8t + \frac{72}{t},$$

where s and t are measured in suitable units.   Find the minimum value of s if such a value exists.

Solution:

$$s = 8t + \frac{72}{t},$$

$$v = D_t s = 8 - \frac{72}{t^2}.$$

As a stationary point, $v = 0$; hence,

$$8 - \frac{72}{t^2} = 0,$$

$$t^2 = 9,$$

$$t = 3 \quad (\text{since } t > 0).$$

At this time $t = 3$,

$$s = 8 \times 3 + \frac{72}{3}$$

$$= 24 + 24$$

$$= 48.$$

The minimum value of s is 48.

Note that, in the above example, $s = 48$ must be a minimum value because s is very large both when t is almost zero and when t is very large; only one stationary point exists in the domain $t \in Re^+$.

EXERCISE 2.6

In each of the following, find the maximum or minimum value of the distance s when t (time) is positive.   State whether the value is a maximum or minimum, and why.

1. $s = t^3 - 75t + 100, \quad t > 0$

2. $s = 2t^3 + 3t^2 - 12t + 12, \quad t > 0$

3. $s = 3 - 9t + 6t^2 - t^3, \quad t \geq 2$

4. $s = t^3 - 2t^2 + 6t + 12, \quad t > 0$

5. $s = t^3 + \frac{3}{t}, \quad t > 0$

6. $s = \frac{12}{t} + 3t + 6, \quad t > 0$

7. $s = -t^2 - \frac{54}{t} + 100, \quad t > 0$

8. $s = \frac{16}{t} - t^2 + 10, \quad t > 0$

9. $s = \frac{5}{2}t^2 + 19t + \frac{36}{t}, \quad t > 0$

10. $s = \frac{t^3}{3} - 8t + \frac{9}{t} + 12, \quad t > 0$

2.7. Maximum and Minimum Distances and Velocities

In more general cases than those discussed previously, there may be several stationary points in the linear motion of a particle. For example, a particle may travel to the right, reverse and travel to the left, reverse again and resume travelling to the right. In such a case, the directed distance at its first stationary point is larger than the directed distances just before and just after the reversal of direction. In this case, this value of the distance is said to be a *local maximum value*. Similarly, at the second stationary point, the directed distance is less than the directed distances just before and after the reversal. In this case, this value of the distance is said to be a *local minimum value*. Again we see that the velocity must be zero at the instant of the reversal of direction, and so we again use $D_t s = 0$ to find the times at the stationary points, or to find the maximum or minimum values of s. We then use these times to find the distances of the stationary points.

Example.   The distance $s > 0$ is given by

$$s = 36 - 24t + 9t^2 - t^3$$

for time $t > 0$, the motion ceasing when s becomes zero. Find the maximum and minimum values of s.

Solution:

$$s = 36 - 24t + 9t^2 - t^3\,,$$
$$v = D_t s = -24 + 18t - 3t^2$$
$$= 0 \quad \text{for stationary points}\,.$$

Therefore, at the stationary points,

$$3t^2 - 18t + 24 = 0\,,$$
$$t^2 - 6t + 8 = 0\,,$$
$$(t - 4)\,(t - 2) = 0\,,$$
$$t = 2 \quad \text{or} \quad 4\,.$$

At the stationary point when $t = 2$,

$$s = 36 - 48 + 36 - 8$$
$$= 16\,.$$

At the stationary point when $t = 4$,

$$s = 36 - 96 + 144 - 64$$
$$= 20\,.$$

We must now ascertain that s does not become zero for t in the domain $0 < t < 4$, for if it does so, the motion may cease before the stationary points are reached. We must also decide which point is a maximum and which is a minimum.

To determine which is a maximum and which a minimum, we may examine neighbouring points and also sketch the graph; thus,

$$\text{at } t = 0, \quad s = 36 \, ;$$
$$\text{at } t = 1, \quad s = 36 - 24 + 9 - 1 = 20 \, ;$$
$$\text{at } t = 3, \quad s = 36 - 72 + 81 - 27 = 18 \, ;$$
$$\text{at } t = 5, \quad s = 36 - 120 + 225 - 125 = 16 \, ;$$
$$\text{at } t = 6, \quad s = 36 - 144 + 324 - 216 = 0.$$

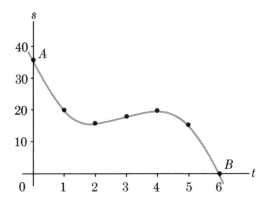

Figure 2.6

We see from Figure 2.6 that 16 is a minimum value, that 20 is a maximum value and that s is not zero until $t = 6$. Note, however, that there *are* points where s is less than 16 and greater than 20, for example, at $t = 6$ and $t = 0$ respectively. However, the stationary points are *local* maxima and minima, and, of course, the points where $t = 0$ and $t = 6$ are *not* stationary points; the points where $t = 0$ and $t = 6$ are the endpoints of the domain of t.

In this case, we do not need the values at any points other than the stationary points and $t = 0$ to see that $t = 2$ gives a minimum and $t = 4$ gives a maximum. We know that, when $t = 0$, $s = 36$, $36 > s > 0$ for $0 < t < 6$, and $s = 0$ when $t = 6$; and so the graph must start at A and end at B in the sketch. Then any continuous curve between A and B with only two stationary points must have the minimum nearer to A than to B and the maximum nearer to B than to A. Some possible curves are shown in red in Figure 2.7; the curves shown in black do not satisfy all the requirements.

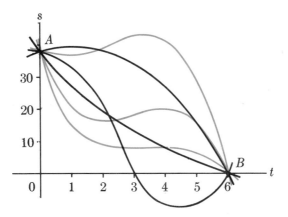

Figure 2.7

By considering the zeros of the acceleration $a = D_t v$ in a similar manner, we can find any maximum or minimum values of v and the times at which they occur. While we can refer to these points as "stationary points" for v as a function of t, "stationary" does not have the same physical interpretation as a reversal of the direction of motion.   However, at such maximum or minimum points, either v stops increasing and starts decreasing (a maximum point) or v stops decreasing and starts increasing (a minimum point).

EXERCISE 2.7

1. The distance s (in feet) that a particle moves in a straight line from a fixed point O at any time t (in seconds) is given by

   $$s = 10 + 36t - 15t^2 + 2t^3, \quad t \geq 0.$$

   Find the velocity at time t seconds.   Find the stationary points of the motion and the distances of these points from O.   For each distance, state whether it is a local maximum or a local minimum distance from O.

2. For the motion described in question (1), find the acceleration at time t seconds. By considering the stationary points for the velocity, that is, the points where $a = D_t v = 0$, find the maximum or minimum values (if any) of the velocity. Are these the largest or smallest values ever attained by the velocity for $t \geq 0$?

3. The distance s (in feet) of a particle at any time t (in seconds) from a fixed point on a line is given by

   $$s = 15 + 2t - 7t^2 + 4t^3, \quad t \geq 0.$$

   Find the velocity and acceleration, the points at which the direction of motion is reversed and the maximum or minimum velocity, if any.

4. The distance s (in feet) of a particle from a fixed point O on a line at any time t (in seconds) is given by

$$s = 40 - 15t + 4t^2 - \tfrac{1}{3}t^3, \quad t \ge 0.$$

Find the velocity and acceleration at any time and the points at which the direction of motion is reversed (if any). By sketching the graph, decide whether the distance at these points is a local maximum or a local minimum. Does the velocity have a maximum or a minimum at any time?

5. The distance s (in centimetres) of a particle from a fixed point O on a line at any time t (in seconds) is given by

$$s = \frac{1}{3}t^3 - 29t - \frac{100}{t}, \quad t \ge 1.$$

Find the velocity and the position of any stationary points of the motion. State whether such points are local maxima or minima of s.

6. The velocity v (in ft/sec) at any time t (in seconds) of a particle moving on a line is given by

$$v = t^2 - 14t - \frac{72}{t}, \quad t > 1.$$

Find the acceleration at any time. Find the times when the velocity attains its maximum or minimum values.

Chapter Summary

Average velocity and acceleration · Instantaneous velocity and acceleration as derivatives of distance and velocity respectively

If
> s is the distance in given units,
> t is the time in given units,
> v is the velocity in appropriate units,

and
> a is the acceleration in appropriate units,

then
> $v = D_t s \quad$ and $\quad a = D_t v = D_t^2 s.$

Stationary points for the distance s occur when $v = D_t s = 0$.

Stationary points for the velocity v occur when $a = D_t v = 0$.

Use condition $v = D_t s = 0$ to find maxima or minima of s.

Use condition $a = D_t v = 0$ to find maxima or minima of v.

REVIEW EXERCISE 2

1. A passenger liner completes a voyage in six days. It travels 360 miles (nautical) the first day, 450 miles the second, 420 the third, 270 the fourth day, 330 the fifth day and 420 the sixth day.   What is the average speed in knots (nautical miles per hour) each day?   What is the average speed for the voyage? Draw a graph of the distance travelled as a function of the time, assuming the actual speed at any time is the average speed for that day.   What does the slope of each segment of the graph represent?

2. In the following, the distance s is given in terms of the time t in suitable units.   In each case, find (i) the velocity, (ii) the acceleration, (iii) the time of occurrence and value of a maximum or minimum value of s (if any).   Also find the time of occurrence and value of a maximum or minimum value of v (if any) for (a), (b) and (c).

(a) $s = t^2 - 7t + 12, \quad t \geq 0$

(b) $s = 6 - 6t^2 + t^3, \quad t \geq 0$

(c) $s = t^3 - 4t + 12, \quad t \geq 0$

(d) $s = 40 - 4t - \dfrac{36}{t}, \quad t \geq 1$

(e) $s = t^3 - \dfrac{24}{t} + 25, \quad t \geq 1$

3. The distance s (in miles) travelled by an airplane in a time t (in hours) is given by
$$s = 600t + 30t^2 - 4t^3, \quad 0 \leq t \leq 5.$$

(a) What is the distance travelled in each of the five hours?

(b) What is the average velocity in each hour and over the whole flight?

(c) What is the velocity at any time t?

(d) What is the velocity when $t = 1, 2, 3, 4$?

(e) What is the velocity when $t = \frac{1}{2}, 1\frac{1}{2}, 2\frac{1}{2}, 3\frac{1}{2}, 4\frac{1}{2}$?

(f) Why is the velocity at $t = 3\frac{1}{2}$ closer to the average velocity in the hour from $t = 3$ to $t = 4$ than the velocity at either $t = 3$ or $t = 4$?   Draw a sketch graph if desired to assist the explanation.

4. (a) Using the relation of time and distance in question (3), find the acceleration at any time.

(b) When, if ever, is the acceleration zero?

(c) What happens to the velocity when the acceleration is zero?

(d) What is the value of the velocity when the acceleration is zero?

(e) Why is the average velocity in the interval from $t = 2$ to $t = 3$ greater than the velocity at either $t = 2$ or $t = 3$?

5. The relation between s and t is given by
$$s = 600t + 30t^2 + 4t^3, \quad 0 \le t \le 5,$$
where s is in miles and t in hours.

(a) Find the velocity and acceleration at any time t.

(b) Does the velocity have a maximum or a minimum?

(c) Find, if possible, an interval of one hour within which the average velocity is higher than the velocity at either end point.

6. The position s (in centimetres) of a particle at time t (in seconds) is given by
$$s = t^2 - 2t + \frac{8}{t} - 7, \quad t \ge 1.$$

(a) Find the velocity at any time t.

(b) Find the times of any maximum or minimum of the distance s, and determine which occurs.

(c) Find the maximum or minimum values of the distance s.

(d) Does the particle ever return to the origin, that is, to the point where $s = 0$?

Chapter 3

MAXIMA AND MINIMA

3.1. Zeros of the First Derivative

At any point $P(x, y)$, the slope of the curve defined by $y = f(x)$ is given by the value of the derivative $D_x y$. When the slope is a positive number, the tangent to the curve, and also the curve, slopes upwards to the right as x increases. Similarly, when the slope is negative, the curve slopes downwards to the right as x increases. Thus, if we consider the graph of $y = f(x)$ in Figure 3.1, we see that in a domain of x where the slope, $D_x y$, is positive, the values of $y = f(x)$ increase as the values of x increase, and where the slope, $D_x y$, is negative, the values of $y = f(x)$ decrease as the values of x increase. If $D_x y = 0$ throughout a domain of x, then the slope is zero and the values of $y = f(x)$ neither increase nor decrease as x changes; consider, for example, the line that is the graph of $y = 2$ in the domain $\{x \in Re\}$. If $D_x y = 0$ for a single value of x, then the graph of $y = f(x)$ is parallel to the x-axis at the point corresponding to that value of x. In Figure 3.1, there are two such points, A and B.

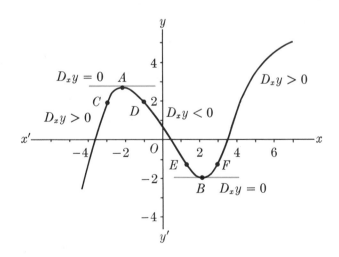

Figure 3.1

49

Figure 3.1 shows that, at A, the value of y is greater than at any neighbouring points, for example, at C or D. To the left of A, that is, between C and A, $D_x y > 0$, and so $f(x)$ is increasing from C to A. Similarly, to the right of A, that is, between A and D, $D_x y < 0$, so that $f(x)$ is decreasing from A to D. The point A is said to be a maximum point, and the curve whose equation is $y = f(x)$ has a maximum value at A. Notice that this is a *local*, or *relative*, maximum.

In Figure 3.1, we show the graph of a smooth continuous function for the domain in which the function is defined; the graph of a smooth continuous function has no sudden changes in slope or jumps in the value of y. In most of our work here, we shall use functions of this kind. The function $f : x \rightarrow 1/x$ near $x = 0$ is an exception to this. For more complicated functions, some of our results may not be true.

DEFINITION. $y = f(x)$ has a maximum value at a point where $D_x y = 0$, if the value of y at this point is greater than its value at all *neighbouring* points.

(We have not attempted a rigorous definition of "neighbouring" in the statement of the definition. For the present, we accept an intuitive meaning of "nearby", or "arbitrarily close to".)

Similarly, at E and F in Figure 3.1, the values of $f(x)$ are greater than those at B, and B is called a *minimum* point.

DEFINITION. $y = f(x)$ has a minimum value at a point where $D_x y = 0$, if the value of y at this point is less than its value at all neighbouring points.

Example. Find the maximum and minimum values of the function determined by

$$y = x^2 - 7x + 10 - \frac{9}{x}, \quad x \neq 0.$$

Solution:

$$y = x^2 - 7x + 10 - \frac{9}{x} \, ;$$

$$\therefore \quad D_x y = 2x - 7 + \frac{9}{x^2}$$

$$= \frac{2x^3 - 7x^2 + 9}{x^2} \, .$$

At a maximum or a minimum, $D_x y = 0$; hence,

$$2x^3 - 7x^2 + 9 = 0,$$
$$(2x - 3)(x - 3)(x + 1) = 0,$$

and the solution set for x is $\{3, \frac{3}{2}, -1\}$.

We now find the values of the functions at these three values of x and then test these values to see which are maxima and which minima.

When $x = 3$,
$$y = 9 - 21 + 10 - 3 = -5.$$

When $x = \frac{3}{2}$,
$$y = \frac{9}{4} - \frac{21}{2} + 10 - 6 = -4\frac{1}{4}.$$

When $x = -1$,
$$y = 1 + 7 + 10 + 9 = 27.$$

To test which points are maxima or minima, we examine the value of y near each of these points.

At $x = 4$,
$$y = 16 - 28 + 10 - 2\frac{1}{4} = -4\frac{1}{4},$$

and at $x = 2$,
$$y = 4 - 14 + 10 - 4\frac{1}{2} = -4\frac{1}{2}.$$

Comparing these values with the value at $x = 3$, we see that
$$-4\frac{1}{4} > -5 \quad \text{and} \quad -4\frac{1}{2} > -5;$$

therefore, the point $(3, -5)$ is a minimum point.

At $x = 1$,
$$y = 1 - 7 + 10 - 9 = -5.$$

Comparing the values of y at $x = 2$ and $x = 1$ with the value at $x = 3/2$, we see that
$$-4\frac{1}{2} < -4\frac{1}{4} \quad \text{and} \quad -5 < -4\frac{1}{4};$$

therefore, the point $(\frac{3}{2}, -4\frac{1}{4})$ is a maximum point.

At $x = -\frac{1}{2}$,
$$y = \frac{1}{4} + 3\frac{1}{2} + 10 + 18 = 31\frac{3}{4},$$

and at $x = -2$,
$$y = 4 + 14 + 10 + 4\frac{1}{2} = 32\frac{1}{2}.$$

Comparing these values with the value at $x = -1$, we see that
$$31\frac{3}{4} > 27 \quad \text{and} \quad 32\frac{1}{2} > 27;$$

therefore, the point $(-1, 27)$ is a minimum point.

Notes: (1) To test the point $(3, -5)$, we used values of y at $x = 4$ and $x = 2$.

(2) We used values of y at $x = 2$ and $x = 1$ to test the point $(\frac{3}{2}, -4\frac{1}{4})$.

(3) We cannot use the values of y at $x = 1$ and $x = -2$ to test the point $(-1, 27)$ because the function is not defined at $x = 0$ (which lies between $x = 1$ and $x = -2$).

(4) We could choose other values of x for test purposes, for example, $x = 3\frac{1}{2}$ and $x = 2\frac{1}{2}$ for $x = 3$; $x = \frac{3}{4}$ and $x = 1\frac{1}{4}$ for $x = 1$; and $x = -.9$ and $x = -1.1$ for $x = -1$. In general, we use the simplest values of x that are close enough to the value we are testing.

(5) We do not always need to evaluate y at the test points accurately; we require only to know that the test values are greater or less than the value being tested. Thus, $\frac{1}{4} + 3\frac{1}{2} + 10 + 18$ is obviously greater than $28 > 27$, and $4 + 14 + 10 + 4\frac{1}{2} > 28 > 27$.

(6) The methods suggested here are adequate in most cases. However, to test more complicated functions, more elaborate methods and precautions may be needed.

EXERCISE 3.1

In all the following questions, $x \in Re$.

1. Find the maximum and/or minimum values of the function determined by
   (a) $y = x^2 + 2x + 2$,
   (b) $y = 1 - 4x - x^2$,
   (c) $y = x^3 - 3x + 4$,
   (d) $y = x^3 + 2x^2 + x - 6$,
   (e) $y = 9x + 3x^2 - x^3$,
   (f) $y = -\frac{1}{2}(x + 2)^2$,
   (g) $y = 1 + 12x - x^3$,
   (h) $y = 2x^3 - 3x^2 + 6x - 9$,
   (i) $y = x + \dfrac{4}{x}$,
   (j) $y = 3x^2 - 7x - \dfrac{1}{x}$.

2. Show that the function given by
$$y = x(x^2 - 3x + 4)$$
has no maxima or minima for real values of x.

3. Show that the function given by
$$y = x - 3 + \frac{4}{x}, \qquad x \neq 0,$$
is such that its maximum is less than its minimum.

4. Show that the graph of
$$y = x^3 + x^2 - 5x + 3 \quad \text{where } y = 0$$
touches the x-axis and find where.

5. Show that the function given by
$$y = x + \frac{4}{x}, \qquad x \neq 0,$$
has a maximum and a minimum. What can be said about the values of y when $x > 0$? when $x < 0$? Use these results to show that y cannot have any value in the range $-4 < y < 4$.

3.2. Maxima and Minima in Geometrical Problems

Many applications of maxima and minima occur in problems that involve geometrical measurement in both two and three dimensions.

Example.   A rectangular metal box without a lid is made from a sheet of tin $16'' \times 6''$.   Equal squares are cut from each of the four corners of the tin sheet, and the edges are turned up and soldered to form the box.   Find the dimensions of the box of maximum volume, and find the maximum volume.

Solution: Let x be the length (in inches) of the side of each square; then $0 < x < 3$.

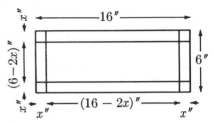

The length of the box (in inches) is $16 - 2x$.
The width of the box (in inches) is $6 - 2x$.
The height of the box (in inches) is x.

Therefore, the volume of the box (in cubic inches) is

$$V = (16 - 2x)(6 - 2x)x$$
$$= 4x^3 - 44x^2 + 96x.$$

$$\therefore \quad D_x V = 12x^2 - 88x + 96.$$

V is a maximum or a minimum when $D_x V = 0$; hence,

$$12x^2 - 88x + 96 = 0,$$
$$3x^2 - 22x + 24 = 0,$$
$$(3x - 4)(x - 6) = 0.$$

Therefore, $x = \frac{4}{3}$ is the only solution in the domain $0 < x < 3$.
This value of x must give a maximum volume because $V = 0$ when $x = 0$ and when $x = 3$, and V must be greater than zero for any x between these two values.   The dimensions of the box of maximum volume are

$$13\tfrac{1}{3}'' \times 3\tfrac{1}{3}'' \times 1\tfrac{1}{3}''$$

and the volume is $V(\tfrac{4}{3}) = 59\tfrac{7}{27}$ cubic inches.

EXERCISE 3.2

1. The perimeter of a rectangle is 24 inches.   What are the dimensions if the area is a maximum, and what is the maximum area?

2. The area of a rectangle is 64 square inches.   What are the dimensions if the perimeter is a minimum, and what is the minimum perimeter?

3. A box has square ends, and the sides are congruent rectangles. The total area of the four sides and two ends is 96 square inches. What are the dimensions of the box if the volume is a maximum, and what is the maximum volume?

4. An open box has a square base and congruent rectangular sides. The total area of the base and sides is 108 square centimetres. What are the dimensions and volume of the box of maximum volume?

5. A box has a square base and top and congruent rectangular sides. It must have a volume of 81 cubic inches. What is the minimum total area of the top, base, and sides, and what are the dimensions corresponding to this minimum area?

6. If a box has a square base, congruent rectangular sides, and no top, the volume is 98 cubic inches. What are the dimensions if the total area of the base and sides is a minimum? What is the minimum area?

7. A man has a one-hundred-foot roll of fencing and four posts. He wishes to enclose the largest possible rectangular area of land with the fence. What shape and size is the area he should enclose?

8. A man wishes to enclose a rectangular area against the wall of a chicken house to form a chicken run. The wall is 50 feet long. He has 60 feet of fencing. What area is the largest he can enclose, and what are its dimensions?

9. Each fruit tree in an orchard requires 100 square feet at maturity. A farmer wishes to plant a rectangular orchard of 400 trees and realizes it will require 40,000 square feet of land. He will have to fence the orchard with rabbit-proof fence at a cost of 50¢ per foot. What is the minimum cost of fencing required, and what are the dimensions of the orchard for this minimum cost?

10. A can has a circular base and top and is in the form of a right circular cylinder. If the total area of the surface of the can is 169.56 square inches, find the dimensions if the volume is a maximum. What is the maximum volume? (Use $\pi \simeq 3.14$.)

11. A can is made in the shape of a cylinder from one rectangular sheet of tin and two square sheets of tin from which the circular ends are made. Neglecting any losses due to joining the three pieces into the cylinder, find the minimum area of tin if the volume of the can has to be 27 cubic inches. What is the ratio of the height to the diameter?

12. In question (11), if the tin for the ends has to be thicker than that for the sides, so that the ends cost 1.5¢ per square inch, and the sides 1¢ per square inch, find the ratio of the height to the diameter for minimum cost, and find the minimum cost.

3.3. Other Applications Involving Maxima and Minima

Many problems in numbers, mechanics, economics and engineering can be solved by the application of derivatives to maxima and minima. Unfortunately, some of the most interesting cases involve scientific and economic theories beyond our present study, and we can consider only some of the simpler situations here.

Example 1. The running cost C in dollars per hour for an aircraft cruising at a height of h feet and at an airspeed of 500 m.p.h. is given by

$$C = 2500 + \frac{h}{40} + \frac{40,000,000}{h}.$$

Find the optimum height for operation, that is, the height at which the cost of operation is a minimum, and also find the minimum cost.

Solution:

$$C = 2500 + \frac{h}{40} + \frac{40,000,000}{h};$$

$$\therefore \quad D_h C = \frac{1}{40} - \frac{40,000,000}{h^2}.$$

For minimum or maximum cost,

$$\frac{1}{40} - \frac{40,000,000}{h^2} = 0,$$
$$h^2 = 1,600,000,000,$$
$$h = 40,000.$$

This value for the height must give a minimum cost because, as h approaches zero and also as h becomes large, the cost increases without limit.

The minimum cost per hour at 40,000 feet is \$4,500.

In many problems, the domain is the set of natural numbers. Up to now, however, each function for which we have found a derivative has a subset of the real numbers for its domain and is smooth and continuous in that domain. To solve problems in maxima and minima when the domain is a subset of the natural numbers, we must form a function of a real variable x which has the same value as that in the problem when x is equal to a natural number in the domain of the problem. The derivative of this function of x, $x \in Re$, can be used to find maxima and minima for the original problem in the domain of the natural numbers.

If the value of x found for a maximum or a minimum is a natural number, then this value provides a solution of the problem. However, the value of x found for a maximum or a minimum value of $f(x)$ may not be a natural number. In this case, the natural number required to satisfy the original problem will be one of the two natural numbers adjacent to the value of x found. The following example illustrates this.

Example 2. Find two natural numbers whose sum is 7 such that their product is a maximum.

Solution: We set up the problem first in the set of real numbers.

Let x be one real number and y be another real number; then the problem requires that

$$x + y = 7.$$

Let

$$P = xy;$$

then

$$P = x(7 - x)$$
$$= 7x - x^2.$$

Now when P is a maximum or a minimum, $D_x P = 0$.

$$D_x P = 7 - 2x;$$

therefore, at a maximum or minimum of P,

$$7 - 2x = 0,$$
$$2x = 7,$$
$$x = 3\tfrac{1}{2}.$$

Thus, $P = x(7 - x)$ has a maximum value of $12\tfrac{1}{4}$ when $x = 3\tfrac{1}{2}$.

In the given problem, the domain is the set of natural numbers; therefore, the maximum value of P will occur when one number is 3 or 4. In this case, the other number is 4 or 3 and the product is 12. Hence, the two natural numbers required are 3 and 4 and the product is 12.

EXERCISE 3.3

1. Find two natural numbers such that their sum is 16 and their product is a maximum.

2. Find two natural numbers such that their sum is 12 and the product of the square of one with the other is a maximum.

3. Find two natural numbers such that their product is 9 and their sum is a minimum.

4. Find two natural numbers whose sum is 15 such that the sum of the squares of the numbers is a minimum.

5. The strength of a beam with a rectangular cross-section is proportional to the product of the breadth and the square of the depth. Find the dimensions of the cross-section that gives the strongest beam that can be cut from a log of circular cross-section of a radius 12 inches.

6. A weight of 100 pounds is to be raised by a lever with the fulcrum at one end and the applied force at the other. The weight is 2 feet from the fulcrum. The lever itself weighs 4 pounds per linear foot. What length of lever is required so that applied force can be as small as possible?

7. If a farmer digs up his potatoes on July 1st, his crop will be 120 bushels, which will sell as new potatoes at $3.00 per bushel. If the crop is allowed to mature further, it will increase at 15 bushels per week. However, the price will drop 20¢ per bushel per week. When should he dig the crop for the maximum cash return?

8. The power W in kilowatts delivered by a 132 kilovolt transmission line 200 miles long with a resistance of 5×10^{-4} ohms per mile is given by

$$W = 132i - \tfrac{1}{10}i^2,$$

where i is the current in amperes. Find the current flowing for the maximum delivered power.

9. A retailer of electrical appliances finds that he can sell 200 refrigerators per month at $250 each. For each reduction of $10 in price, he finds that he sells 10 more refrigerators per month (reductions of less than $10 per unit have no effect on sales). What selling price will produce the maximum gross financial sales per month, and how many refrigerators would he sell at this price?

10. The deflection y inches at a point x feet from the left-hand support of a beam resting on two supports (as shown in the diagram) is given by

$$y = \frac{20}{EI}\left[x(x - 75) \right],$$

where E is a constant called Young's modulus and I is a constant called the second moment of the cross-section of the beam. Show that the deflection has a maximum value at the mid-point of the beam.

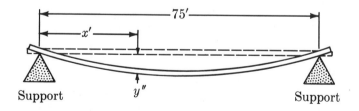

Support $\qquad y''$ $\qquad$ Support

Chapter Summary

$D_x y = 0$ at a maximum or minimum value of $y = f(x)$.

If $f(x_1) > f(x)$ for any x arbitrarily close to x_1, then $f(x_1)$ is a maximum value.

If $f(x_1) < f(x)$ for any x arbitrarily close to x_1, then $f(x_1)$ is a minimum value.

REVIEW EXERCISE 3

1. Determine the maximum and/or minimum values of
   (a) $y = x^2 - 5x + 4$,
   (b) $y = 2 - 9x - 2x^2$,
   (c) $y = 2x^3 - 3x^2 - 12x + 18$,
   (d) $y = x + \dfrac{8}{x}$,
   (e) $y = x^3 + 2 + \dfrac{3}{x}$,
   (f) $y = x^2 + 9 + \dfrac{81}{x}$.

2. Show that, as x increases, the value of y given by
$$y = x^3 - 3x^2 + 3x + 5$$
   never decreases. Does it, in fact, cease to increase at any point? What is the value of $D_x y$ at such a point? Why is there no maximum or minimum?

3. The sum of two natural numbers is 6. What are the numbers if the sum of their cubes is a minimum?

4. The sum of a positive number and its reciprocal is a minimum. What is the number?

5. A box has square ends and a rectangular base but no top, and its volume is 288 cubic centimetres. What is the minimum total area of the sides and base, and what are the corresponding dimensions?

6. Three separate and adjacent rectangular cattle pens each of area 600 square feet are to be formed as shown in the diagram. The farmer naturally wishes to use the least length of fencing he can. What dimensions should he use for the individual pens and what length of fencing would he require?

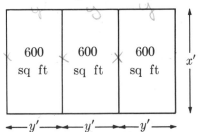

7. A rectangular open-topped bin is to be built in the right-angled corner of a barn so that two sides are formed by the walls of the barn. The other sides are to be four feet high. If the enclosed volume must be 100 cubic feet, find the minimum length of $1'' \times 6''$ boards required in the sides.

8. A vee-shaped water trough has a cross-section the shape of an isosceles right-angled triangle. It is to contain 8 cubic feet of water and is made of sheet metal at a cost of 50¢ per square foot. What is the minimum cost if the labour charges for manufacture are $5.00 irrespective of the dimensions?

9. The base of a chest is a rectangle which is twice as long as it is wide. The top, front, and sides are made of oak, and the back and base are made of pine. The chest has a volume of $12\frac{1}{4}$ cubic feet. Oak costs three times as much per square foot as pine. Find the dimensions of the box for which the lumber has the lowest cost. (Neglect any effects due to the thickness of the sides, top, or base.)

10. A cylindrical tin can has a top seal of aluminum. If aluminum is four times as expensive as tinplate, find the ratio of height to diameter for the most economical shape for the can.

11. A television company agrees to establish a community antenna in a new suburb at a charge of $25 each for 1000 subscribers or less. To encourage more subscribers, it is agreed to give a discount of 10¢ to each subscriber for every additional 10 subscribers in excess of 1000. However, if too many people subscribe, the company finds that it begins to get less than its maximum possible gross income. For the company to receive the maximum gross income, what number of subscribers should it have?

12. A printing company agrees to print 5000 copies of a pamphlet at a rate of $100 per thousand. If more than 5000 copies are printed, it agrees to a discount of 10¢ per thousand *on the whole contract* for each 1000 in excess of 5000. What number of copies give the maximum cash receipts to the printer, and at what price per copy?

13. Even though they are in refrigerated storage, 1000 bushels of apples turn bad at the rate of 20 bushels per month. The September price is $2.50 per bushel, and the price increases at 25¢ per bushel per month. Storage costs are $150.00 per month. If the apples are placed in storage in September, when should they be sold for maximum gross return?

14. The deflection y (in inches) of a cantilever beam from the horizontal at a distance x (in feet) from the support (see diagram below) is given by

$$y = \frac{20}{EI}(x^3 - 15x^2), \quad 0 \le x \le 5,$$

where E and I are defined in (10) Exercise 3.3. Show that, although the deflection does have a *greatest* value, $D_x y \ne 0$ at this point of greatest deflection.

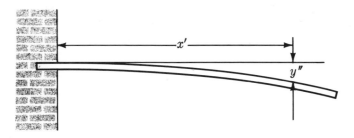

15. The improvement tax assessment on a city lot is calculated at $100 per foot of street frontage.   On a corner lot, full taxes are paid on the front street and 50% of the full taxes on the side street.   If a corner lot of 10,000 square feet is rectangular, find the most economical dimensions.

16. The lot for a business building costs $1,000,000.   The cost of the building itself is given by $(500,000s + 40,000s^2)$ where s is the number of storeys above ground level.   The total investment and any profits thereon are to be recovered over a twenty-year period from rents received.   The present value of the net rentals receivable over the twenty years after construction is estimated at $4,500,000 per storey.   Thus, the building should be constructed so that the possible net gain, measured by

$$\$(4,000,000s - 40,000s^2 - 1,000,000),$$

is a maximum.   Find the optimum number of storeys for the building and its cost.

Chapter 4

SEQUENCES, LIMITS AND DERIVATIVES

4.1. Sequences

DEFINITION. A function f whose domain is a subset of the set of integers defines an ordered set called a *sequence*. The order of the elements of the domain of f is the *natural order* of the integers. The set of values $f(n)$ is called a *sequence*, and each $f(n)$ is a *term* of the sequence.

Some examples of sequences are defined by

$f : n \rightarrow 2n + 1$, $\quad n \in W$, giving the sequence $1, 3, 5, 7, \cdots, 2n+1, \cdots$;

$f : n \rightarrow n^2$, $\qquad n \in N$, giving the sequence $1, 4, 9, 16, \cdots, n^2, \cdots$;

$f : n \rightarrow \dfrac{1}{2^n}$, $\qquad n \in W$ giving the sequence $1, \dfrac{1}{2}, \dfrac{1}{4}, \dfrac{1}{8}, \cdots, \dfrac{1}{2^n}, \cdots$;

$f : n \rightarrow 1 + \dfrac{1}{n^2}$, $\quad n \in N$, giving the sequence $2, 1\dfrac{1}{4}, 1\dfrac{1}{9}, \cdots, 1 + \dfrac{1}{n^2}, \cdots$.

All the above sequences are infinite sequences because the domains are the infinite ordered sets W and N, which are subsets of I. Finite sequences are also possible; for example,

$$f : n \rightarrow 3n + 2, \quad 0 \leq n \leq 10,$$

giving the sequence

$$2, 5, 8, 11, 14, 17, 20, 23, 26, 29, 32.$$

Note that the general term in the sequence is $f(n)$ and that this is the nth term if $n \in N$.

EXERCISE 4.1

In each of the following, give the first six terms of the sequence for which the nth term is $f(n)$, $n \in N$.

1. $f(n) = 2n + 3$
2. $f(n) = n^2 + 1$
3. $f(n) = 2n^2 - n$

4. $f(n) = 1 - \dfrac{2}{n}$
5. $f(n) = \dfrac{n + 2}{5n}$
6. $f(n) = 2^{n+1} - 1$

Give the stated term of the sequences defined by the following functions.

7. 10th term, if $f : n \rightarrow (-1)^n$, $n \in N$

8. 12th term, if $f : n \rightarrow -3n + 15$, $n \in W$

9. 7th term, if $f : n \rightarrow n^2 - 50$, $n \in N$

10. 5th term, if $f : n \rightarrow 1 + \dfrac{1}{3^n}$, $n \in W$

Find a function in each case that would give the following as the first four terms of the corresponding sequence.

11. 2, 4, 6, 8, $\cdots$

12. 4, 2, 1, $\frac{1}{2}$, $\cdots$

13. $\sqrt{3}, \sqrt{21}, 7\sqrt{3}, 7\sqrt{21}, \cdots$

14. log 1, log 3, log 9, log 27, $\cdots$

15. $+1, -1, +1, -1, \cdots$

4.2. Limit of an Infinite Sequence

The sequence given by

$$f : n \rightarrow 1 + \frac{1}{n^2},$$

that is,

$$2, \ 1\frac{1}{4}, \ 1\frac{1}{9}, \ 1\frac{1}{16}, \ \cdots, \ 1 + \frac{1}{n^2}, \ \cdots,$$

is an infinite sequence, and as n increases without bound, $1/n^2$ becomes smaller and smaller. We can choose n so as to make $1/n^2$ as small as we like, and therefore we can make $f(n) = 1 + 1/n^2$ very nearly equal to 1 when we choose n very large. In this case, as n increases without bound, we say that $f(n)$ tends to the "limiting value" 1; that is, $f(n) - 1$ tends to the "limiting value" 0 as n increases without bound. If we examine this situation for specific values of n, we see, for example, that

$$f(10) - 1 = 1 + \frac{1}{10^2} - 1 = 10^{-2},$$

$$f(1000) - 1 = 1 + \frac{1}{10^6} - 1 = 10^{-6},$$

$$f(10^{12}) - 1 = 1 + 10^{-24} - 1 = 10^{-24},$$

$$\cdot \ \cdot \ \cdot \ \cdot \ \cdot \ \cdot \ \cdot \ \cdot \ \cdot \ \cdot \ \cdot \ \cdot$$

In fact, if we wish to require that $|f(n) - 1| < 10^{-50}$ (or any other very small positive real number we choose), then we can find a value n_0 of n such that the inequality is true for *all* values of $n > n_0$. For example, if $f(n) = 1 + 1/n^2$, then

$$f(10^{25}) - 1 = 1 + 10^{-50} - 1 = 10^{-50},$$
$$f(10^{26}) - 1 = 1 + 10^{-52} - 1 = 10^{-52} < 10^{-50},$$
$$f(10^{27}) - 1 = 1 + 10^{-54} - 1 = 10^{-54} < 10^{-50},$$

. . . .

Thus, if we choose $n_0 = 10^{25}$, then $f(n) - 1 < 10^{-50}$ for all $n > 10^{25}$.

Supplementary

We can give a general definition of the limit of a sequence $f(n)$ as n increases without bound:

DEFINITION. A sequence $f(n)$ tends to a limiting value L when n increases without bound if, when we select any positive real number ϵ, no matter how small, we can find an integer n_0 which is such that
$$|f(n) - L| < \epsilon \quad \text{whenever } n > n_0.$$

Example:

(a) If $f(n) = 2\left(1 + \dfrac{1}{2^n}\right)$, show that $|f(n) - 2| < 10^{-12}$ for $n > 50$.

(b) Give some other values of n for which the inequality $|f(n) - 2| < 10^{-12}$ is true.

Solution:

(a)
$$f(n) = 2\left(1 + \frac{1}{2^n}\right):$$

$$\therefore \quad \left|f(n) - 2\right| = \left|2 + \frac{1}{2^{n-1}} - 2\right|$$

$$= \frac{1}{2^{n-1}}.$$

Now
$$\frac{1}{2^{10}} = \frac{1}{1024} < \frac{1}{10^3} = 10^{-3};$$

$$\therefore \quad \frac{1}{2^{40}} < 10^{-12}.$$

Now
$$\left|f(n) - 2\right| < \frac{1}{2^{40}} \quad \text{if} \quad n - 1 > 40;$$

$$\therefore \quad |f(n) - 2| < 10^{-12} \quad \text{if} \quad n - 1 > 40;$$

$$\therefore \quad |f(n) - 2| < 10^{-12} \quad \text{if} \quad n > 41.$$

But
$$50 > 41;$$

$$\therefore \quad |f(n) - 2| < 10^{-12} \quad \text{if } n > 50.$$

(b) The inequality $|f(n) - 2| < 10^{-12}$ is also true for $n > 42$, $n > 60$, or $n > 100$. We do not necessarily use 41, the smallest value of n for which $|f(n) - 2| < 10^{-12}$, but only some suitable value of n so that $|f(n) - 2| < 10^{-12}$ for all n greater than this chosen value.

Examining the definition of a "limiting value" for our example above, we see that the limit L is equal to 2 and that we have chosen $\epsilon = 10^{-12}$. Then we have shown that we can find a suitable value for n_0, either 41, or 50, or in fact any other integer greater than 41. Notice that we must be able to choose *any* small positive real number for ϵ and then find a suitable value for n_0. In our example, if we choose $\epsilon = 10^{-30}$, then $n_0 = 101$ will be suitable; if we choose $\epsilon = 10^{-3000}$, then $n_0 = 10^5$ will serve as a suitable value. What is a suitable n_0 if $\epsilon = 10^{-300}$?

EXERCISE 4.2

By inspection, state what seems to be the limiting value of each of the following sequences as n increases without bound.

1. $f(n) = 2 + \dfrac{4}{n}$

2. $f(n) = -1 + \dfrac{1}{3n}$

3. $f(n) = \dfrac{n + 4}{n}$

4. $f(n) = \dfrac{3 - n}{2n}$

5. $f(n) = \dfrac{n^2 - 1}{n^2 + 1}$

6. $f(n) = \dfrac{n - 1}{n^2 + 1}$

7. $f(n) = 4(1 + 10^{-n})$

8. $f(n) = 3 + 5 \times 10^{-n}$

9. $f(n) = \dfrac{1 + .5}{1 + (.5)^n}$

10. $f(n) = 5\left(\dfrac{1 + .1}{1 - (.1)^{2n}}\right)$

11. For $n > 100$, show that $1 + \dfrac{1}{n}$ differs from its limit by less than 10^{-2}.

12. For $n > 10$, show that $1 + \dfrac{5}{n^3}$ differs from its limit by less than 10^{-2}.

13. For $n > 400$, show that $2 + \dfrac{4}{n}$ differs from its limit by less than 10^{-2}.

14. If $n > 51$, show that $3 + 5 \times 10^{-n}$ differs from its limit by less than 10^{-50}.

15. If $n > 20$, show that $4(1 + 10^{-n})$ differs from its limit by less than 10^{-19}.

Supplementary

16. Find a value n_0 of n so that $\dfrac{n + 4}{n}$ differs from its limit by less than 10^{-2}.

17. Find a value n_0 of n so that $2 + \dfrac{1}{n^2}$ differs from its limit by less than 10^{-4}.

4.3. The Sum of an Infinite Geometric Series

DEFINITION.   The indicated sum of the terms of a finite sequence is called a finite series, and the value of the sum is called the sum of the series.

The general geometric sequence is **defined by**

$$f : n \rightarrow ar^{n-1}, \quad r \in Re, \ n \in N, \text{ where } a \text{ is a fixed real number,}$$

and the finite geometric series is

$$a + ar + ar^2 + ar^3 + \cdots + ar^{n-1} .$$

The sum of n terms of a geometric series is given by

$$S_n = a + ar + ar^2 + \cdots + ar^{n-1},$$

and so

$$rS_n = \quad ar + ar^2 + \cdots + ar^{n-1} + ar^n.$$

By subtraction,

$$(1 - r)S_n = a - ar^n ;$$

therefore,

$$S_n = \frac{a(1 - r^n)}{1 - r}.$$

If $r < 1$, we use the above form to compute the sum; if $r > 1$, then we use

$$S_n = \frac{a(r^n - 1)}{r - 1}$$

as the more convenient form for computation.

Note that $|r| = 1$ is excluded. If $r = 1$, the sum is na; if $r = -1$, the sum is 0 when n is even and a when n is odd.

Example 1. Find the sum of the first six terms of the geometric series
(a) $2 + 2 \cdot 3 + 2 \cdot 3^2 + \cdots$,   (b) $4 + 4(\frac{1}{2}) + 4(\frac{1}{2})^2 + \cdots$.

Solution:

(a)
$$S_6 = \frac{2(3^6 - 1)}{3 - 1}$$
$$= \frac{2(729 - 1)}{2}$$
$$= 728.$$

(b)
$$S_6 = \frac{4[1 - (\frac{1}{2})^6]}{1 - \frac{1}{2}}$$
$$= \frac{4[1 - \frac{1}{64}]}{\frac{1}{2}}$$
$$= 8 - \frac{1}{8}$$
$$= 7.875.$$

The set of values of S_n for different values of n and for a geometric series with given values of a and r forms a sequence. For example, if the geometric series is

$$1 + \frac{1}{2} + \frac{1}{2^2} + \frac{1}{2^3} + \cdots,$$

then

$$S_1 = 1, \; S_2 = 1\tfrac{1}{2}, \; S_3 = 1\tfrac{3}{4}, \; S_4 = 1\tfrac{7}{8}, \; S_5 = 1\tfrac{15}{16}, \; \cdots.$$

If we consider the behaviour of S_n as n increases without bound, we see that, if $|r| > 1$, $|S_n|$ will increase without bound. However, if $|r| < 1$, then $|S_n|$ will not increase without bound but will be less than some real number for all values of n. In fact, if $|r| < 1$, $S_n = a(1 - r^n)/(1 - r)$ tends to a limit $a/(1 - r)$ as n increases without bound; we call this limit S. This result can be proved as follows:

$$\left| S_n - \frac{a}{1 - r} \right| = \left| a\left(\frac{1 - r^n}{1 - r}\right) - \frac{a}{1 - r} \right|$$
$$= \left| \left(\frac{a}{1 - r}\right)(1 - r^n - 1) \right|$$
$$= \left| \frac{ar^n}{1 - r} \right|.$$

Now if $|r| < 1$, then

$$|r^n| < |r^{n-1}| < |r^{n-2}| < |r^{n-2}| < \cdots < |r^2| < |r| < 1,$$

and r^n tends to 0 as n increases without bound; therefore,

$$\left| S_n - \frac{a}{1 - r} \right| \to 0 \qquad \text{as } n \text{ increases without bound.}$$

Hence,

$$S = \lim_{n \to \infty} S_n = \frac{a}{1 - r}, \qquad \text{if } |r| < 1.$$

When the sequence of the sums S_n tends to a limit S, we define S to be the sum of the infinite series.

Example 2. Show that the sequence of the sums of n terms of the geometric series

$$1 + \tfrac{1}{2} + (\tfrac{1}{2})^2 + (\tfrac{1}{2})^3 + \cdots$$

tends to the limit 2, which is by definition the sum of the infinite series.

Solution:
$$S_n = 1 + \tfrac{1}{2} + (\tfrac{1}{2})^2 + \cdots + (\tfrac{1}{2})^{n-1}$$
$$= \frac{1 - (\tfrac{1}{2})^n}{1 - \tfrac{1}{2}}$$
$$= 2\left(1 - \frac{1}{2^n}\right).$$

$$\therefore \quad \left| S_n - 2 \right| = \left| 2 - \frac{1}{2^{n-1}} - 2 \right|$$
$$= \frac{1}{2^{n-1}}.$$

As n increases without bound, $1/2^{n-1}$ tends to zero. Therefore S_n tends to the limit 2 as n increases without bound.

In practice, we use the result $S = a/(1 - r)$, and immediately obtain

$$S = \frac{1}{1 - \frac{1}{2}}$$
$$= 2,$$

unless we wish to establish the result from first principles.

EXERCISE 4.3

Find the sum to n terms of each of the following geometric series and the sum of the infinite series if it exists.

1. $.03 + .003 + .0003 + \cdots$

2. $-\frac{1}{4} + \frac{1}{8} - \frac{1}{16} \cdots$

3. $3 - 6 + 12 - \cdots$

4. $3 + \frac{3}{2} + \frac{3}{4} + \cdots$

5. The sum of the n terms of the series

$$\frac{1}{(1)(3)} + \frac{1}{(3)(5)} + \frac{1}{(5)(7)} + \cdots + \frac{1}{(2n - 1)(2n + 1)}$$

is given by

$$S_n = \frac{n}{2n + 1}.$$

Find the sum of the corresponding infinite series if that sum exists.

6. Find a value of n so that S_n for question (2) differs from S by less than $\frac{1}{2^{10}}$.

7. Find a value of n so that S_n for question (1) differs from S by less than 10^{-20}.

8. Find a value of n so that S_n for question (4) differs from S by less than 10^{-3}.

4.4. The Irrational Numbers as Limits (Supplementary)

The limit of a sequence of values $f(n)$, when n increases without bound, can be used to show that any irrational number is in fact the limit of a sequence of rational numbers. Let us consider $\sqrt{2}$. We shall form the following sequences:

First Sequence	*Second Sequence*	*Third Sequence*
$t_1 = 1.4,$	$s_1 = t_1^2 = 1.96,$	$u_1 = 2 - s_1 = .04,$
$t_2 = 1.41,$	$s_2 = t_2^2 = 1.9881,$	$u_2 = 2 - s_2 = .0119,$
$t_3 = 1.414,$	$s_3 = t_3^2 = 1.999396,$	$u_3 = 2 - s_3 = .000604,$
$t_4 = 1.4142,$	$s_4 = t_4^2 = 1.99996164,$	$u_4 = 2 - s_4 = .00003836,$

Here, each value of t_n is such that, if the last decimal digit is increased by one, the square of that number is greater than 2. It seems evident that the limit of u_n

will be zero, so that the limit of $s_n = t_n^2$ will be 2, and thus the limit of t_n will be $\sqrt{2}$. We can write the result formally in two ways,

$\qquad$ *either* $\qquad$ as n increases without bound,

$\qquad\qquad\qquad$ t_n^2 approaches a limit 2, and

$\qquad\qquad\qquad$ t_n approaches a limit $\sqrt{2}$,

$\qquad$ *or*

$\qquad\qquad\qquad$ as t_n^2 approaches a limit 2,

$\qquad\qquad\qquad$ t_n approaches a limit $\sqrt{2}$.

In fact, many pairs of sequences of rational numbers may be used so that one sequence approaches 2 while the second associated sequence approaches $\sqrt{2}$. Questions (1) and (2) in the exercise following give two examples of such sequences. For any such pairs of sequences, say x_n and y_n, it will be true that

$\qquad\qquad\qquad$ as x_n approaches the limit 2,

$\qquad\qquad$ $y_n = \sqrt{x_n}$ approaches the limit $\sqrt{2}$.

In such cases we usually drop the suffix n and write

$\qquad\qquad\qquad$ as x approaches 2,

$\qquad\qquad$ $y = \sqrt{x}$ approaches $\sqrt{2}$.

EXERCISE 4.4

1. A sequence is formed as follows:

$$1.5, \quad 1.42, \quad 1.415, \quad 1.4143, \quad \cdots.$$

Give a rule for forming the sequence. What appears to be the limit of the sequence?

2. Two sequences are formed as follows:

$$a_1 = 1.5, \quad b_1 = 1.33; \quad a_2 = 1.415, \quad b_2 = 1.4134; \quad \cdots.$$

Note that $b_n \simeq \dfrac{2}{a_n}$ and $a_{n+1} = \dfrac{1}{2}(a_n + b_n)$. Show that each sequence seems

to have $\sqrt{2}$ as its limit (give the first four terms in each sequence). By how much do the fourth terms, a_4 and b_4, differ?

3. Form two sequences similar to these in question (2) for $\sqrt{3}$.

4. (a) If in question (2) it is always true that

$$a_n > \sqrt{2} > b_n,$$

what is the maximum possible error if either a_4 or b_4 is used for an approximation to $\sqrt{2}$?

(b) If in question (3)
$$a_n > \sqrt{3} > b_n,$$
what is the maximum possible error if either a_4 or b_4 is used for an approximation to $\sqrt{3}$?

4.5. Algebraic Functions

If $P(x)$ and $Q(x)$ are polynomials in x, then
$$f : x \rightarrow \frac{P(x)}{Q(x)}$$
is a rational algebraic function. The set of ordered pairs for such a function f over the real numbers x is
$$\left\{ (x, y) \mid y = f(x) = \frac{P(x)}{Q(x)}, \ \ Q(x) \neq 0, \ x \in Re \right\}.$$
For example,
$$\text{(i)} \quad f : x \rightarrow x^3 + 2x^2 + 5x + 5,$$
$$\text{(ii)} \quad f : x \rightarrow \frac{x^2 + 4x - 5}{x^3 - 2x + 3x - 1},$$
$$\text{(iii)} \quad f : x \rightarrow \frac{x^4 + 2x^2 + 3}{x^3 + 3x^2 - 2x - 5}$$
are rational algebraic functions, and (i) is also a polynomial function. If the polynomial in the numerator of $f(x)$ is of the same degree as, or of higher degree than, the denominator, then it is frequently convenient to simplify the expression for $f(x)$ into the sum of a polynomial and a rational algebraic expression with the degree of the numerator less than the degree of the denominator.

Example. Simplify
$$\frac{x^3 - 2x^2 + 3x + 4}{x^2 + 2x - 3}.$$

Solution:

$$
\begin{array}{r}
x - 4 \\
x^2 + 2x - 3 \overline{)\, x^3 - 2x^2 + 3x + 4} \\
\underline{x^3 + 2x^2 - 3x} \\
-4x^2 + 6x + 4 \\
\underline{-4x^2 - 8x + 12} \\
14x - 8
\end{array}
$$

$$\therefore \quad \frac{x^3 - 2x^2 + 3x + 4}{x^2 + 2x - 3} = x - 4 + \frac{14x - 8}{x^2 + 2x - 3}.$$

A function whose defining rule contains roots or fractional powers of poly-nomials is an algebraic function, but it is *not* a rational algebraic function. Some examples are the functions

(i) $f : x \rightarrow \sqrt{3x^2 + 5x - 4}$,

(ii) $f : x \rightarrow (x^2 - 4)\sqrt{x + 2}$,

(iii) $f : x \rightarrow \dfrac{x^2 + 2x + 5}{\sqrt{x^3 + 3x^2 - 5x + 6}}$,

(iv) $f : x \rightarrow \sqrt{\dfrac{x^2 + 3x + 1}{2x^2 + 2x + 5}}$,

(v) $f : x \rightarrow (x + 1)\sqrt{x^3 - 4x^2 + 5x - 7}$.

EXERCISE 4.5

Classify the following functions as (a) polynomial functions, (b) rational algebraic functions, (c) algebraic functions, or (d) non-algebraic functions.

1. $x \rightarrow 3x^3 + 2x + 1$

2. $x \rightarrow 3x^2 + (x + 1)^{1/2}$

3. $x \rightarrow \dfrac{2x + 3}{x^2 + 1}$

4. $x \rightarrow (x + 2)(x + 3)^2$

5. $x \rightarrow \dfrac{x^2 + x + 1}{x - 2}$

6. $x \rightarrow x \sin x$

7. $x \rightarrow \dfrac{(x^2 + 1)^{1/2}}{x - 1}$

8. $x \rightarrow \sqrt{\dfrac{x^4 + x^2 + 1}{x}}$

9. $x \rightarrow \dfrac{1}{x^4} + \dfrac{2}{x^2} + 1$

10. $x \rightarrow (x^2 + x + 1)^{5/2}$

11. $x \rightarrow x^2 e^{-2x}$

12. $x \rightarrow \sin (x + 3)$

13. $x \rightarrow \dfrac{x^{1/2} + 1}{x^{3/2} + x}$

14. $x \rightarrow \left(\dfrac{x + 1}{x + 2}\right)^2$

15. $x \rightarrow \left(\dfrac{x}{x + 1}\right)^x$

16. $x \rightarrow \left(\dfrac{x - 1}{x + 1}\right)^{1/2}$

17. $x \rightarrow \log x$

18. $x \rightarrow x^2 (1 + x^3)$

4.6. Limiting Values of Algebraic Functions

In previous chapters, we introduced the concept of a limit informally as it arose in finding the slope of a graph or in finding the instantaneous velocity or acceleration of a moving object. We shall now examine the concept from a purely algebraic point of view in the same way that we examined the limit of a sequence in Section 4.2.

Consider the rational algebraic function

$$f : x \to \frac{x^2 - 4}{x - 2},$$

which is defined for all real values of x except 2. At $x = 2$, $f(x)$ is not defined because division by zero is not a possible operation. However, for all other values of x not equal to 2,

$$f(x) = \frac{x^2 - 4}{x - 2} = x + 2. \tag{1}$$

Thus we can calculate a table of values such as the following for

$$f(x) = \frac{x^2 - 4}{x - 2} \qquad (x \in Re, \ x \neq 2).$$

x	1	1.5	1.9	1.999	$\cdots$	3	2.5	2.1	2.0001	$\cdots$
$f(x)$	3	3.5	3.9	3.999	$\cdots$	5	4.5	4.1	4.0001	$\cdots$

It is obvious from this table of values that, as $x \to 2$, $f(x) \to 4$, whether $x < 2$ or $x > 2$. In calculating the values for the table, we have used the result of equation (1), which we may use for every value of x except 2 itself. This result, that $f(x) \to 4$ as $x \to 2$, is written more formally as

$$\lim_{x \to 2} \frac{x^2 - 4}{x - 2} = 4.$$

Notice that, while $(x^2 - 4)/(x - 2)$ *does not* have a value for $x = 2$ (it has only a limiting value of 4 as x approaches 2) $x + 2$ *does* have a value at $x = 2$, and this value is 4.

Another more exact way of viewing this result is to estimate that the limit is 4 from the table of values and then to ask this question: for what value of x does $f(x)$ differ from 4 by less than some very small quantity, say 10^{-24}? The last statement in the question, requires that

$$\left| f(x) - 4 \right| = \left| \frac{x^2 - 4}{x - 2} - 4 \right| < 10^{-24}.$$

The question asks for what value of x this is true, and we may proceed as follows:

$$\left| \frac{x^2 - 4}{x - 2} - 4 \right| = \left| x + 2 - 4 \right| \qquad (x \neq 2)$$
$$= \left| x - 2 \right|.$$

Therefore,

$$\left| \frac{x^2 - 4}{x - 2} - 4 \right| < 10^{-24} \quad \text{when} \quad |x - 2| < 10^{-24} \quad (x \neq 2);$$

that is,

$$|f(x) - 4| < 10^{-24} \quad \text{when} \quad 2 - 10^{-24} < x < 2 + 10^{-24}.$$

Example 1. Find the limit of

(a) $f(x) = \dfrac{x^3 - 27}{x - 3}$ as $x \to 3$,   (b) $f(x) = x^2 + x + 1$ as $x \to 1$.

Solution:

(a) If $x \neq 3$, then

$$\frac{x^3 - 27}{x - 3} = \frac{(x - 3)(x^2 + 3x + 9)}{x - 3}$$
$$= x^2 + 3x + 9.$$

$$\therefore \quad \lim_{x \to 3} \frac{x^3 - 27}{x - 3} = 9 + 9 + 9 = 27.$$

(b) If $f(x) = x^2 + x + 1$, then, as x approaches 1, $f(x)$ approaches the value 3. In this case, $f(x) = x^2 + x + 1$ has a value when $x = 1$; that is $f(1) = 3$. In this case, the function is said to be *continuous* at $x = 1$.

Example 2. Show that

(a) if $\left| x - 3 \right| < 10^{-5}$, then $\left| \dfrac{x^3 - 27}{x - 3} - 27 \right| < 10^{-4}$;

(b) if $\left| x - 3 \right| < 10^{-21}$, then $\left| \dfrac{x^3 - 27}{x - 3} - 27 \right| < 10^{-20}$.

Solution:

$$\left| \frac{x^3 - 27}{x - 3} - 27 \right| = \left| x^2 + 3x + 9 - 27 \right|$$
$$= \left| x^2 + 3x - 18 \right|$$
$$= \left| x + 6 \right| \cdot \left| x - 3 \right|.$$

(a) If $\left| x - 3 \right| < 10^{-5}$, then

$$-10^{-5} < x - 3 < 10^{-5},$$
$$3 - 10^{-5} < x < 3 + 10^{-5},$$
$$9 - 10^{-5} < x + 6 < 9 + 10^{-5},$$
$$\left| x + 6 \right| < 9 + 10^{-5} < 10 ;$$
$$\therefore \quad \left| x + 6 \right| \cdot \left| x - 3 \right| < 10(10^{-5}) ;$$
$$\therefore \quad \left| \frac{x^3 - 27}{x - 3} - 27 \right| < 10^{-4} .$$

(b) If $\left| x - 3 \right| < 10^{-21}$, then

$$9 - 10^{-21} < x + 6 < 9 + 10^{-21},$$
$$\left| x + 6 \right| < 10 ;$$
$$\therefore \quad \left| x + 6 \right| \cdot \left| x - 3 \right| < 10(10^{-21}) ;$$
$$\therefore \quad \left| \frac{x^3 - 27}{x - 3} - 27 \right| < 10^{-20} .$$

Supplementary

The critical requirement for a limit L for $f(x)$ to exist as $x \to a$ is that we can always find a value of x near a such that $|f(x) - L|$ is less than a very small positive real number, however small we care to make it, when $|x - a|$ is less than some other very small positive real number. For instance, in the above example,

$$|f(x) - L| < 10^{-20} \quad \text{for} \quad |x - a| < 10^{-21},$$

where $f(x) = \dfrac{x^2 - 27}{x - 3}$ and $L = 27$. If we stated the requirement as

$$|f(x) - L| < 10^{-1000},$$

we could satisfy the requirement by taking

$$|x - a| < 10^{-1001}.$$

Mathematicians state the requirement in the following way:

If, given any real number ϵ, however small, we can find another real number δ such that

$$|f(x) - L| < \epsilon \quad \text{when} \quad 0 < |x - a| < \delta,$$

then the limit of $f(x)$ as x approaches a exists and is equal to L.

EXERCISE 4.6

In each of the following, find the limit L for $f(x)$ as x approaches a if the limit exists.

1. $f(x) = \dfrac{x^2 - 4}{x + 2}$, $a = -2$

2. $f(x) = \dfrac{x^2 - 9}{x - 3}$, $a = 3$

3. $f(x) = \dfrac{x - 3}{x + 3}$, $a = 3$

4. $f(x) = \dfrac{x^2 - 4x + 3}{x - 1}$, $a = 1$

5. $f(x) = \dfrac{4x + 2}{3x + 1}$, $a = \frac{1}{3}$

6. $f(x) = \dfrac{x^2 - 16}{x - 1}$, $a = -4$

7. $f(x) = \dfrac{x^2 + 1}{x - 1}$, $a = 1$

8. $f(x) = \dfrac{x}{x^2 + 1}$, $a = 0$

9. $f(x) = \dfrac{x - 4}{x^2 + x + 1}$, $a = 2$

10. $f(x) = \dfrac{x^3 - 64}{x^2 - 16}$, $a = 4$

11. $f(x) = \dfrac{2 + 1/x}{1 - 1/x}$, $a = 0$

12. $f(x) = \dfrac{2 + 1/x}{1/x^2}$, $a = 0$

13. $f(x) = \dfrac{x^2 - \pi^2}{x - \pi}$, $a = \pi$

14. $f(x) = \dfrac{x^3 - 2\sqrt{2}}{x - \sqrt{2}}$, $a = \sqrt{2}$

15. If $f(x) = \dfrac{x^2 - 9}{x - 3}$ has a limiting value of 6 as x approaches 3, show that

$$|f(x) - 6| < 10^{-10} \quad \text{if} \quad |x - 3| < 10^{-10}.$$

16. If $f(x) = 4\left(\dfrac{x^2 - 4x + 3}{x - 1}\right)$ has a limiting value of -8 as x approaches 1, show that

$$|f(x) + 8| < 10^{-5} \quad \text{if} \quad |x - 1| < 10^{-6}.$$

17. If $f(x) = \dfrac{x^3 - 64}{x^2 - 16}$ has a limiting value of 6 as x approaches 4, show that

$$|f(x) - 6| < 10^{-6} \quad \text{if} \quad |x - 4| < 10^{-6}.$$

4.7. The Derivative of $f : x \to f(x)$, $x \in Re$, as a Limit

In Chapter 1, we considered some simple functions and two points, (x, y) and $(x + h, y + k)$, on the graph of $y = f(x)$. For these functions, k/h approaches a limiting value as h approaches zero. This limit is unique, and by definition its value is $D_x y = f'(x)$, the value of the derivative of the function f at x.

In Chapter 2, we considered the distance of a particle as a function of the time t. By considering the ordered pairs $(t + \triangle t, s + \triangle s)$ and (t, s), we found that $\lim\limits_{t \to 0} \dfrac{\triangle s}{\triangle t}$, if it exists, is by definition the velocity of the particle and that its value at t is given by $D_t s$.

We now define the process algebraically:

DEFINITION. If $f : x \to f(x)$, then the limiting value, if it exists, of the *difference quotient*

$$\frac{f(x + h) - f(x)}{h}$$

as the real number h approaches zero is $f'(x)$, which is called the value of the derivative of f at x. [$D_x y$, y', and $\dfrac{dy}{dx}$ are other notations for $f'(x)$ if $y = f(x)$.] Symbolically: if $f : x \to f(x)$, and so $x + h \to f(x + h)$, then

$$\lim_{h \to 0} \frac{f(x + h) - f(x)}{h} = f'(x) = D_x y = \frac{dy}{dx} = y', \quad \text{where } y = f(x),$$

provided that the limit exists.

$D_x y$, $\dfrac{dy}{dx}$ and y' are used extensively by engineers and scientists while $f'(x)$ is used more by pure mathematicians.

The notation $f'(x)$ implies the value of a function f' at x and, in fact, the derivative is a function. This is one of the reasons why mathematicians favour this notation. We see from our definition that, corresponding to any given value of x, we have at most one value of $f'(x)$. Hence f' is a function over that part of the domain of f for which it exists and is such that,

$$\text{if} \quad f : x \to f(x), \quad \text{then} \quad f' : x \to f'(x),$$

and if f determines $\{(x, f(x))\}$, then f' determines $\{(x, f'(x))\}$ in the respective domains of definition. The function f' is the derivative of the function f, and $f'(x)$ is its value at x. The domain of definition of f' is a subset of the domain of definition of f.

The other notations, $D_x y$ and $\dfrac{dy}{dx}$, do not convey the functional character of the derivative quite so obviously. It must be emphasized that, in the notation $\dfrac{dy}{dx}$, the four letters form one symbol for a distinct mathematical entity, the value of the derivative at x. $\dfrac{dy}{dx}$ is *not* a fraction, and d is *not* a number; so we cannot divide numerator and denominator by d.

EXERCISE 4.7

1. Verify that the definition of this chapter gives the same values for $D_x(x^2)$, $D_x(x^3)$, and $D_x\left(\dfrac{1}{x}\right)$ as those obtained in Chapter 1.

2. With the new notations, rewrite the table of values of the derivatives that we prepared in Chapter 1.

3. Verify that each of the derivatives which we have calculated has the same domain as the original function. (This is not necessarily the case for all functions.)

4.8. Some Theorems about Limits and Derivatives

In the next chapter, we shall make use of the following theorems about the limits of functions:

If $\lim\limits_{x \to a} f(x) = A$ and $\lim\limits_{x \to a} g(x) = B$ exist, then

(1) $$\lim_{x \to a} [f(x) + g(x)] = A + B ,$$

(2) $$\lim_{x \to a} [f(x) - g(x)] = A - B ,$$

(3) $$\lim_{x \to a} [f(x) \cdot g(x)] = A \cdot B ,$$

(4) $$\lim_{x \to a} \frac{f(x)}{g(x)} = \frac{A}{B} , \quad \text{if } \lim_{x \to a} g(x) = B \neq 0.$$

As a special case of (3), we have

(3a) $$\lim_{x \to a} c f(x) = cA , \quad \text{if } c \text{ is a constant.}$$

Although these results may seem to be obvious, they do require proof; however, we shall not prove them rigorously here. The questions in the exercises verify them in certain cases. In the following two theorems for derivatives, it will be seen that the analogous results to Theorem (1) and (2) for limits are true for derivatives. The results for derivatives (see pages 89, 92) corresponding to those of Theorems (3) and (4) for limits are markedly different, and the two must not be confused.

We shall now use Theorem (1) for limits to prove the corresponding theorem for derivatives. We have already used this theorem in Chapters 1 and 2 without realizing that we did so.

Derivative Theorem 1. $D_x[f(x) + g(x)] = D_x f(x) + D_x g(x)$.

Proof: Let f and g be two functions of x, and let $h = f + g$. Now let

$$x \text{ change to } x + \triangle x ;$$

then, correspondingly,

$$f(x) \text{ changes to } f(x + \triangle x) ,$$
$$g(x) \text{ changes to } g(x + \triangle x) ,$$

and
$$h(x) \text{ changes to } h(x + \triangle x) ,$$

and therefore
$$h(x + \triangle x) = f(x + \triangle x) + g(x + \triangle x) .$$

But
$$h(x) = f(x) + g(x) ;$$

therefore
$$h(x + \triangle x) - h(x) = f(x + \triangle x) - f(x) + g(x + \triangle x) - g(x) ,$$

and
$$\frac{h(x + \triangle x) - h(x)}{\triangle x} = \frac{f(x + \triangle x) - f(x)}{\triangle x} + \frac{g(x + \triangle x) - g(x)}{\triangle x} .$$

If the limits of all the difference quotients exist as $\triangle x \to 0$, then

$$\lim_{\triangle x \to 0} \frac{f(x + \triangle x) - f(x)}{\triangle x} = f'(x) \qquad \text{(by definition)},$$

$$\lim_{\triangle x \to 0} \frac{g(x + \triangle x) - g(x)}{\triangle x} = g'(x) \qquad \text{(by definition)},$$

and
$$\lim_{\triangle x \to 0} \frac{h(x + \triangle x) - h(x)}{\triangle x} = h'(x) \qquad \text{(by definition)};$$

therefore,

$$h'(x) = \lim_{\triangle x \to 0} \left[\frac{f(x + \triangle x) - f(x)}{\triangle x} + \frac{g(x + \triangle x) - g(x)}{\triangle x} \right]$$

$$= f'(x) + g'(x) \qquad \text{(Limit Thm. (1))}$$

or

$$D_x h(x) = D_x[f(x) + g(x)] = D_x f(x) + D_x g(x) .$$

This theorem is of course merely the general form of the result that we justified by direct calculation for $ax^3 + bx^2 + cx + d$ in Chapter 1.

We may also prove a similar theorem for the difference of $f(x)$ and $g(x)$:

Derivative Theorem 2. $D_x[f(x) - g(x)] = D_x f(x) - D_x g(x)$.

The proof of this theorem is requested in question (5) below.

Derivative Theorem 3. $D_x[cf(x)] = cD_x f(x)$ if c is any constant.

These theorems for derivatives are easily extended to prove that

$$D_x[f(x) + g(x) + h(x) + \cdots] = D_x f(x) + D_x g(x) + D_x h(x) + \cdots.$$

EXERCISE 4.8

Verify Theorems (1), (2), (3), and (4) for the following pairs of functions.

1. $\dfrac{x+2}{x+3}, \quad \dfrac{x^2-4}{x-2}$ as $x \to 2$

2. $\dfrac{x^3+1}{x+1}, \quad \dfrac{x^2-1}{x+1}$ as $x \to -1$

3. $\dfrac{2x+1}{2x+3}, \quad \dfrac{x+4}{x+2}$ as $x \to 1$

4. $\dfrac{x^2-4}{x+2}, \quad \dfrac{x^2-4}{x-2}$ as $x \to 2$

5. Prove Derivative Theorem 2.

6. Prove Derivative Theorem 3.

Chapter Summary

Limits of sequences · Sum of the infinite geometric series · Irrational numbers as limits (supplemental) · Algebraic functions · Limits of functions · The derivative as a limit · Statement of theorems for limits of functions · The derivative of the sum of several functions

REVIEW EXERCISE 4

Find the stated term for each of the sequences determined by the following functions.

1. 5th term for $f: n \to 2n + 1, \quad n \in N$

2. 3rd term for $f: n \to 2 - \dfrac{1}{5^n}, \quad n \in W$

3. 4th term for $f : n \rightarrow 4\left(1 - \dfrac{1}{10^n}\right)$, $n \in W$

4. 10th term for $f : n \rightarrow n^2 + 1$, $n \in W$

5. 8th term for $f : n \rightarrow \dfrac{1}{n(n+1)}$, $n \in N$

6. Find the limit of each of the sequences in questions (1) to (5) if a limit exists.

7. Find a value of n such that
$$4\left(1 - \frac{1}{10^n}\right)$$
differs from its limit by less than 10^{-30}.

8. Find a value of n such that
$$\frac{1}{n(n+1)}$$
differs from 0 by less than 10^{-2}.

9. Find the sum of the infinite geometric series
$$1 + \frac{1}{4} + \frac{1}{16} + \cdots .$$

10. Give two sequences each of which appears to converge to $\sqrt{10}$ as a limit.

Classify each of the following functions as (a) a polynomial function, (b) a rational algebraic function, (c) an algebraic function, or (d) a non-algebraic function.

11. $x^3 - 3x^2 + 4x - 1$

12. $x^2 + \dfrac{1}{x} - \dfrac{1}{x^2}$

13. $\dfrac{\sin x}{1 + \cos x}$

14. $\sqrt{1 + x^2}$

15. $\dfrac{x^2 + 2x + 1}{x^3 - 5x^2 + 7}$

16. $1 + x^x + x^{2x}$

Evaluate each of the following limits.

17. $\dfrac{x^2 - 4x + 3}{x^2 - 5x + 4}$ as $x \rightarrow 1$

18. $\dfrac{x}{2x - x^2}$ as $x \rightarrow 0$

19. $\dfrac{3x^3 - 2x^2 + 5x}{x^2 - x}$ as $x \rightarrow 0$

20. $\dfrac{x^3 - 8}{x - 2}$ as $x \rightarrow 2$

Chapter 5

DERIVATIVES OF FUNCTIONS

5.1. The Derivative of x^n, $x \in Re$

Consider the function determined by $y = x^n$, $n \in N$.

$$\text{When } x \text{ changes to } x + \triangle x,$$
$$y \text{ changes to } y + \triangle y,$$

and

$$y + \triangle y = (x + \triangle x)^n.$$

Therefore,

$$\triangle y = (x + \triangle x)^n - x^n$$
$$= [(x + \triangle x) - x][(x + \triangle x)^{n-1} + (x + \triangle x)^{n-2}x + \cdots + x^{n-1}]$$
$$= \triangle x[(x + \triangle x)^{n-1} + (x + \triangle x)^{n-2}x + \cdots + x^{n-1}].$$

The factors can be found by direct division:

$$(x + \triangle x) - x \overline{)(x + \triangle x)^n} \quad \frac{(x + \triangle x)^{n-1} + (x + \triangle x)^{n-2}x + \qquad \cdots \qquad + x^{n-1}}{\qquad \qquad - x^n}$$

$$\frac{(x + \triangle x)^n - (x + \triangle x)^{n-1}x}{0 \qquad + (x + \triangle x)^{n-1}x}$$

$$\frac{(x + \triangle x)^{n-1}x - (x + \triangle x)^{n-2}x^2}{0 \qquad \qquad + (x + \triangle x)^{n-2}x^2}$$

$$\cdots \cdots \cdots \cdots \cdots$$

$$(x + \triangle x)x^{n-1} - x^n$$
$$\frac{(x + \triangle x)x^{n-1} - x^n}{0 \qquad + 0}$$

Hence,

$$\frac{\triangle y}{\triangle x} = [(x + \triangle x)^{n-1} + (x + \triangle x)^{n-2}x + \cdots + x^{n-1}].$$

79

Therefore,

$$D_x y = \lim_{\triangle x \to 0} \left(\frac{\triangle y}{\triangle x} \right)$$
$$= \lim_{\triangle x \to 0} [(x + \triangle x)^{n-1} + (x + \triangle x)^{n-2} x + \cdots + x^{n-1}]$$
$$= \lim_{\triangle x \to 0} (x + \triangle x)^{n-1} + \lim_{\triangle x \to 0} [(x + \triangle x)^{n-2} x] + \cdots + \lim_{\triangle x \to 0} x^{n-1} \qquad (3)$$
$$= nx^{n-1},$$

as there are n terms in the series and the limit of each term is x^{n-1}. Thus, if

$$y = x^n, \quad x \in Re, \ n \in N,$$

then

$$D_x y = nx^{n-1}.$$

Note that, in line (3), we have used Theorem 1 for limits to permit the order of the processes of taking a limit and of addition to be interchanged.

An alternative proof can be given using the binomial theorem to expand $(x + \triangle x)^n$.

We have proved the result

$$\text{if } \ y = x^n, \ \text{ then } \ D_x y = nx^{n-1}, \quad x \in Re,$$

for the case when n is a natural number. It can be proved that, if $y = x^r$, $D_x y = rx^{r-1}$, $x \in Re$, for the case when r is any rational number (refer to the supplementary part of this section for a proof), and, in fact, for the case when r is any real number. We may assume this result to be true without proof:

$$\text{if } \ y = x^r, \ \text{ then } \ D_x y = rx^{r-1}, \quad x, r \in Re,$$

or, in the alternative notations,

$$\text{if } \ f(x) = x^r, \ \text{ then } \ f'(x) = rx^{r-1}, \quad x, r \in Re,$$

or

$$\text{if } \ f : x \to x^r, \ \text{ then } \ f' : x \to rx^{r-1}, \quad x, r \in Re,$$

Example 1. Find the derivative of $x^7 + 3x^5 - x^2$.

Solution:

$$D_x(x^7) = 7x^6,$$
$$D_x(3x^5) = 15x^4,$$
$$D_x(x^2) = 2x.$$

$$\therefore \quad D_x(x^7 + 3x^5 - x^2) = 7x^6 + 15x^4 - 2x.$$

Note that we have used the Derivative Theorems 1 and 2 in this example.

Example 2.   Find the derivative of $x^5 + 2x^{5/2} - x^{-5}$.

Solution:

$$D_x(x^5) = 5x^{5-1} = 5x^4,$$
$$D_x(2x^{5/2}) = 2(\tfrac{5}{2}x^{(5/2)-1}) = 5x^{3/2},$$
$$D_x(x^{-5}) = -5x^{-5-1} = -5x^{-6}.$$

$\therefore$ $D_x(x^5 + 2x^{5/2} - x^{-5}) = 5(x^4 + x^{3/2} + x^{-6})$

Example 3.   Find the derivative of $2x^4 - 3x^2 + 5x$.

Solution:

$$D_x(2x^4 - 3x^2 + 5x) = 8x^3 - 6x + 5.$$

Derivative of $y = x^r$, $x \in Re$, $r \in Ra$ (Supplementary)

Theorem.   If $y = x^r$, $x \epsilon Re$, $r \epsilon Ra$, then $D_x y = rx^{r-1}$.

Proof: First, consider r positive.   Let $r = s/t$, where s and t are positive integers.

If $y = x^{s/t}$, then $y^t = x^s$ by the laws of exponents,

and
$$(y + \triangle y)^t = (x + \triangle x)^s.$$

Hence,
$$(y + \triangle y)^t - y^t = (x + \triangle x)^s - x^s.$$

Therefore, as in the main part of this section,

$$(y + \triangle y - y)[(y + \triangle y)^{t-1} + \cdots + y^{t-1}] = (x + \triangle x - x)[(x + \triangle x)^{s-1} + \cdots + x^{s-1}].$$

Hence,
$$\frac{\triangle y}{\triangle x} = \frac{(x + \triangle x)^{s-1} + \ldots + x^{s-1}}{(y + \triangle y)^{t-1} + \ldots + y^{t-1}}$$

and, in the limit as $\triangle x \to 0$,

$$D_x y = \lim_{\triangle x \to 0} \frac{\triangle y}{\triangle x}$$

$$= \lim_{\triangle x \to 0} \left[\frac{(x + \triangle x)^{s-1} + \cdots + x^{s-1}}{(y + \triangle y)^{t-1} + \cdots + y^{t-1}} \right]$$

$$= \frac{sx^{s-1}}{ty^{t-1}}$$

$$= \frac{s}{t} \cdot \frac{x^{s-1}}{x^{(t-1)s/t}}$$

$$= \frac{s}{t} \cdot \frac{x^{s-1}}{x^{s-(s/t)}}$$

$$= \frac{s}{t} \cdot x^{s-1-s+(s/t)}.$$

$$D_x y = \frac{s}{t} \cdot x^{(s/t)-1}.$$

$\therefore$ $D_x y = rx^{r-1}$ if $r \epsilon Ra^+$.

Secondly, consider r negative; then $r = -q$, where q is positive.

$$\text{If} \quad y = x^r = x^{-q}, \text{ and } q = s/t, \text{ then } y = x^{-s/t}.$$

By the laws of exponents,

$$y^t = x^{-s} = \frac{1}{x^s},$$

and

$$(y + \triangle y)^t = \frac{1}{(x + \triangle x)^s}.$$

Hence,

$$(y + \triangle y)^t - y^t = \frac{1}{(x + \triangle x)^s} - \frac{1}{x^s}$$

$$= \frac{x^s - (x + \triangle x)^s}{(x + \triangle x)^s x^s}$$

$$= -\frac{(x + \triangle x)^s - x^s}{(x + \triangle x)^s x^s}.$$

$$\therefore \quad (y + \triangle y - y)\,[(y + \triangle y)^{t-1} + \cdots + y^{t-1}]$$

$$= -\frac{(x + \triangle x - x)\,[(x + \triangle x)^{s-1} + \cdots + x^{s-1}]}{(x + \triangle x)^s x^s}.$$

$$\therefore \quad \frac{\triangle y}{\triangle x} = -\frac{(x + \triangle x)^{s-1} + \cdots + x^{s-1}}{[(y + \triangle y)^{t-1} + \cdots + y^{t-1}]\,(x + \triangle x)^s x^s}.$$

$$\therefore \quad D_x y = \lim_{\triangle x \to 0} \frac{\triangle y}{\triangle x} = -\lim_{\triangle x \to 0} \frac{(x + \triangle x)^{s-1} + \cdots + x^{s-1}}{[(y + \triangle y)^{t-1} + \cdots + y^{t-1}]\,(x + \triangle x)^s x^s}$$

$$= -\frac{s x^{s-1}}{t y^{t-1} x^s \cdot x^s}$$

$$= -\frac{s}{t}\left(\frac{x^{s-1}}{x^{-(t-1)s/t} \cdot x^{2s}}\right)$$

$$= -\frac{s}{t} x^{s-1+s-(s/t)-2s}.$$

$$= -\frac{s}{t} x^{-(s/t)-1}$$

$$= -q x^{-q-1}.$$

$$\therefore \quad D_x y = r x^{r-1} \quad \text{if} \quad r \epsilon R a^-.$$

Thus, using both results and $D_x x^0 = D_x 1 = 0 = 0 x^{-1}$,

$$\text{if} \quad y = x^r, \quad x \epsilon Re, \quad r \epsilon Ra, \quad \text{then} \quad D_x y = r x^{r-1}.$$

It can be proved that this formula for the derivative of x^r is also true if r is any real number.

Note: At various points in the above proofs, we have reversed the order of certain operations involving limits, addition, multiplication, and division. Where has this been done? Quote the appropriate limit theorem in each case.

EXERCISE 5.1

Find the derivatives of the functions determined by the following.

1. $5x$

2. $5x + 7$

3. $4x^2$

4. $4x^2 - 10$

5. $7x^2 - 12x + 6$

6. $3 + 11x - 2x^2$

7. $x^2 - 2x + 3$

8. $2x^2 + x + 1$

9. $3x - x^2$

10. $2x^3 - 7x + 4$

11. $7 - x - 2x^2$

12. $2x^3 + 5x^2 - 2$

13. $3x^2 - 2x + 1$

14. $\frac{1}{3}x^3 + 3x$

15. $\frac{1}{2}x^2 + 2x - 4$

16. $\frac{1}{2}x^4 + x - 2$

17. $x^3 + \frac{1}{2}x^2 - 4$

18. $3x^2(\frac{1}{2}) - x^4$

19. $\frac{1}{3}x^3 + 2x^2 - 5$

20. $\frac{1}{3}x^3 - \frac{1}{2}x^2$

21. $x - \frac{1}{3}x^3 + x^2$

22. $\frac{1}{5}x^5 + 3x^3$

23. $(x + 1)(x + 2)$

24. $(3x - 2)(2x + 3)$

25. $(x + 1)^3$

26. $(x - 1)^2$

27. $(1 - x)^2$

28. $(1 + 2x)^3$

29. $(x^2 - 1)^2$

30. $(4 - x^2)^3$

31. $(x^3 + 1)^2$

32. $(1 - 2x^3)^4$

33. $(1 - 3x^2)^2$

34. $(7 - 3x^2)^3$

35. $2x^{1/2} - 3x^{2/3}$

36. $2x^{3/2} + \sqrt{2x}$

37. $\dfrac{1}{x} + x^{3/4}$

38. $3t^{1/3} - t^{5/2}$

39. $2x^3 + 3x - \frac{3}{2}x^2$

40. $x^3 + \frac{1}{3}x^{1/3}$

41. $\sqrt{2x} + 2\sqrt[3]{x}$

42. $3x^{8/3} - x^{5/4}$

43. $\sqrt{3x} + \sqrt{\dfrac{x}{3}}$

44. $x^3 + \dfrac{1}{x^2}$

45. $\theta + \theta^{-1} - 2\sqrt{\theta}$

46. $4\sqrt{x^3} + \frac{2}{3}x^3$

47. $x^2 - \dfrac{1}{x^4}$

48. $4x + 3 - \dfrac{5}{x^3}$

49. $\dfrac{3x^3 + 2x^2 + 1}{x^3}$

50. $ax + b + \dfrac{c}{x}$

51. In a proof that

$$\text{if } y = x^n, \quad x \in Re, \quad n \in N, \quad \text{then} \quad D_x y = nx^{n-1},$$

use the binomial theorem to expand $(x + \triangle x)^n$ in $\triangle y = (x + \triangle x)^n - x^n$, and complete the proof.

5.2. The Chain Rule for Derivatives

If $\qquad f = \{(x, u) \mid u = x^2 + 2, \; x \in Re\}$,

then f is a function with domain $\{x \in Re\}$ and range $\{u \in Re, \; u \geq 2\}$; and if

$$g = \{(u, y) \mid y = u^3, \; u \geq 2, \; u \in Re\},$$

then g is a function with domain $\{u \in Re, \; u \geq 2\}$ and range $\{y \in Re, \; y \geq 8\}$. Moreover, if we form a function F such that

$$F = \{(x, y) \mid y = (x^2 + 2)^3, \; x \in Re\},$$

then we see that F is a function with domain $\{x \in Re\}$ and range $\{y \in Re, \; y \geq 8\}$. In this example, when $x = 2$,

$$u = 2^2 + 2 = 6, \quad y = 6^3 = 216, \quad \text{and} \quad y = (2^2 + 2)^3 = 216;$$

and when $x = 2.1$,

$$u = (2.1)^2 + 2 = 6.41, \quad y = (6.41)^3 = 263.37, \quad \text{and} \quad y = [(2.1)^2 + 2]^3 = 263.37.$$

In the general case, if $u = f(x)$ determines u for x in a certain domain S_1 of values of x, then u is determined in a range S_2; that is, the function f is such that

$$\{(x, u) \mid u = f(x), \quad x \in S_1, \; u \in S_2\}.$$

If, further, $y = g(u)$ determines y in a range S_3 for all u in the domain S_2, that is, if the function g is such that

$$\{(u, y) \mid y = g(u), \quad u \in S_2, \; y \in S_3\},$$

then y is determined for x in the domain S_1, and y is in the range S_3. Thus, $y = F(x)$, and the function F is such that

$$\{(x, y) \mid y = F(x) = g[f(x)], \quad x \in S_1, \; y \in S_3\}.$$

We see from the example that $F(x) = g[f(x)]$ must mean that $F(a) = g[f(a)]$, for each $a \in Re$, and similarly for all values of x.

Working in the domains and ranges specified, we obtain, in the usual notations,

$$u = f(x) \quad \text{and} \quad u + \triangle u = f(x + \triangle x).$$

$$\therefore \quad \triangle u = f(x + \triangle x) - f(x);$$

$$\therefore \quad \frac{\triangle u}{\triangle x} = \frac{f(x + \triangle x) - f(x)}{\triangle x}, \quad \text{if } \triangle x \neq 0,$$

and

$$y = g(u) \quad \text{and} \quad y + \triangle y = g(u + \triangle u).$$

$$\therefore \quad \Delta y = g(u + \Delta u) - g(u) \; ;$$

$$\therefore \quad \frac{\Delta y}{\Delta u} = \frac{g(u + \Delta u) - g(u)}{\Delta u}, \quad \text{if } \Delta u \neq 0,$$

and

$$\frac{\Delta y}{\Delta u} = \frac{g[f(x + \Delta x)] - g[f(x)]}{f(x + \Delta x) - f(x)} .$$

$$\therefore \quad \frac{\Delta y}{\Delta u} \cdot \frac{\Delta u}{\Delta x} = \frac{g[f(x + \Delta x)] - g[f(x)]}{f(x + \Delta x) - f(x)} \cdot \frac{f(x + \Delta x) - f(x)}{\Delta x}$$

$$= \frac{F(x + \Delta x) - F(x)}{\Delta x} = \frac{\Delta[F(x)]}{\Delta x} .$$

In the limit, if $\Delta x \to 0$,

$$\lim_{\Delta x \to 0} \frac{\Delta u}{\Delta x} = D_x u ,$$

and if $\Delta u \to 0$, but $\Delta u \neq 0$,

$$\lim_{\Delta u \to 0} \frac{\Delta y}{\Delta u} = D_u y ,$$

and also, as $\Delta x \to 0$,

$$\lim_{\Delta x \to 0} \frac{\Delta F(x)}{\Delta x} = D_x[F(x)]$$

provided each of the limits exists. Hence,

$$D_x[F(x)] = \lim_{\Delta x \to 0} \frac{\Delta F(x)}{\Delta x}$$

$$= \lim_{\Delta x \to 0} \left(\frac{\Delta y}{\Delta u} \cdot \frac{\Delta u}{\Delta x} \right)$$

$$= \left(\lim_{\Delta x \to 0} \frac{\Delta y}{\Delta u} \right) \cdot \left(\lim_{\Delta x \to 0} \frac{\Delta u}{\Delta x} \right)$$

$$= \left(\lim_{\Delta u \to 0} \frac{\Delta y}{\Delta u} \right) \cdot D_x u .$$

Therefore,

$$D_x[F(x)] = D_u y \cdot D_x u , \quad \text{or} \quad D_x y = D_u y \cdot D_x u ,$$

if we remember that, in forming $D_u y$, $y = g(u)$, and in forming $D_x y$, $y = F(x)$ $= g[f(x)]$. This is called the *chain rule for derivatives*.

Note: We have again reversed the order of certain operations, and we have also assumed that if $\lim_{\Delta x \to 0} \frac{\Delta u}{\Delta x}$ exists and if $\lim_{\Delta u \to 0} \frac{\Delta y}{\Delta u}$ exists, then $\lim_{\Delta u \to 0} \frac{\Delta y}{\Delta u}$ is the same as $\lim_{\Delta x \to 0} \frac{\Delta y}{\Delta u}$. The conditions under which this is true require very careful statement in order to have a fully rigorous theory. We shall not attempt this here.*

---

*For a proof, consult one of these references: T. M. Apostol, *Calculus* (New York, Blaisdell, 1961), Vol. 1, p. 138; R. Courant and F. John, *Introduction to Calculus and Analysis* (New York, Interscience, 1965), Vol. 1, p. 219.

We may also state the result in the form

$$F' = g' \cdot f',$$

where

$$F(x) = g[f(x)],$$

or in the form

$$\frac{dy}{dx} = \frac{dy}{du} \cdot \frac{du}{dx}.$$

With the notation $\dfrac{dy}{dx} = \dfrac{dy}{du} \cdot \dfrac{du}{dx}$, the result seems more obvious; it looks similar to $\dfrac{a}{c} = \dfrac{a}{b} \cdot \dfrac{b}{c}$, where a, b, and c are real numbers. However, while this is perhaps useful as a mnemonic, or memory aid, we must remember that $\dfrac{dy}{dx}, \dfrac{dy}{du}$ and $\dfrac{du}{dx}$, as we have defined them, are *not* fractions, and so the result for derivatives is a new one and not simply the well-known result for fractions.

We note that, if $y = u^n$ and $u = f(x)$, the chain rule gives

$$D_x y = nu^{n-1} \cdot D_x u.$$

Example 1.   Find the derivative of $(x^3 + 1)^2$ with respect to x.

Solution: Let

$$u = x^3 + 1$$

and

$$y = u^2 = (x^3 + 1)^2.$$

Then

$$D_x u = 3x^2,$$
$$D_u y = 2u,$$
$$D_x y = 3x^2 \cdot 2u$$
$$= 6x^2(x^3 + 1).$$

Example 2.   Find $f'(x)$ if $f(x) = \sqrt{3x + 4}$.

Solution: Let

$$u = 3x + 4$$

so that

$$D_x u = 3;$$

then

$$y = u^{1/2} = \sqrt{3x + 4} = f(x)$$

and

$$D_u y = \frac{1}{2} u^{(1/2)-1}$$

$$= \frac{1}{2} u^{-1/2}.$$

Therefore,

$$f'(x) = D_x y$$

$$= D_u y \cdot D_x u$$

$$= \frac{1}{2} u^{-1/2} \cdot 3$$

$$= \frac{3}{2} (3x + 4)^{-1/2}$$

$$= \frac{3}{2\sqrt{3x + 4}}.$$

Example 3.   Find the derivative with respect to x of

$$y = (3x^3 - x^{3/2} + 2)^{-5/2}.$$

Solution: Put

$$u = 3x^3 - x^{3/2} + 2.$$

Then

$$y = u^{-5/2}.$$

Therefore,

$$D_u y = -\frac{5}{2} u^{-7/2},$$

and

$$D_x u = 9x^2 - \frac{3}{2} x^{1/2}.$$

$$D_x y = D_u y \cdot D_x u$$

$$= -\frac{5}{2} u^{-7/2} \left(9x^2 - \frac{3}{2} x^{1/2} \right)$$

$$= -\frac{5}{2} (3x^3 - x^{3/2} + 2)^{-7/2} \left(9x^2 - \frac{3}{2} x^{1/2} \right).$$

EXERCISE 5.2

Differentiate each of the following.

1. $(2x + 1)^5$ 2. $(1 - x)^3$

3. $(3 - x)^4$ 4. $(x + 6)^7$

5. $(6 - x^2)^2$ 6. $(x^2 + 2x - 1)^2$

7. $(x^3 - 2x)^2$

8. $(x^3 - 1)^4$

9. $(4 - 2x^3)^3$

10. $(2 - x^4)^2$

11. $(2x - x^3)^4$

12. $\dfrac{1}{x + 1}$

13. $\dfrac{1}{1 - x}$

14. $\dfrac{1}{(2x + 3)^2}$

15. $\sqrt{2x + 3}$

16. $\sqrt{2 - 3x}$

17. $\dfrac{1}{\sqrt{2x + 3}}$

18. $\dfrac{1}{(3 - 2x)^2}$

19. $(x^3 - 4x^2 + 5)^2$

20. $(x^3 - 4x^2 + 5x + 7)^3$

21. $10t - 3t^2$

22. $720v^{-1}$

23. $\dfrac{720}{v^{3/2}}$

24. $\dfrac{4}{x + 3}$

25. $1 + 3t + 2t^2$

26. $\sqrt{3u - 4}$

27. $\dfrac{1}{\sqrt{3u - 4}}$

28. $3u(u - 5)$

29. $2t + 1 + \dfrac{4}{t}$

30. $\dfrac{1}{v^{1.4}}$

31. $\sqrt{x^2 - 1}$

32. $\sqrt{1 - x^2}$

33. $\sqrt{25 - x^2}$

34. $\sqrt{x^2 - 4}$

35. $\sqrt{3x^2 + 5}$

36. $\sqrt{5 - 3x^2}$

37. $\sqrt{x^2 + 9}$

38. $\sqrt{27 - x^3}$

39. $\sqrt{x^2 + 2x - 3}$

40. $\sqrt{3x^2 - 4x + 5}$

41. $\sqrt{5 + 4x - 3x^2}$

42. $\sqrt{x^2 + 3x + 5}$

43. $\dfrac{1}{\sqrt{x^2 + 1}}$

44. $\dfrac{1}{\sqrt{1 - x^2}}$

45. $\dfrac{1}{\sqrt{5x^2 - 10x + 6}}$

46. $\dfrac{1}{\sqrt{3x^2 + x + 4}}$

47. $\sqrt{x^2 + 1}$

48. $\sqrt[3]{x^3 + 8}$

49. $\dfrac{1}{\sqrt[3]{x^3 + 1}}$

50. $\dfrac{1}{\sqrt[3]{3x^3 + 2x + 1}}$

51. $4x^3 - 3x^2 + 6x$

52. $(1 + 4x^2)^{-3/2}$

53. $(1 - x^5)^{-2/5}$

54. $s = \sqrt{1 - 2t^3}$

55. $R = 2\sqrt[3]{(1 + t^2)^2}$

56. $x = \dfrac{5}{(3 - 2t)^2}$

57. $x = \dfrac{5}{\sqrt[3]{3t^2 - 6t}}$

58. $x = \dfrac{4}{\sqrt{6t - t^2}}$

59. $x = 3\sqrt[5]{5t^2 - t^5}$

60. $y = \sqrt{4x^3 - 3x^2 + 6x}$

5.3. Derivative of a Product

Consider $y = uv$, where $u = f(x)$ and $v = g(x)$ determine two functions of x, and so $y = f(x) \cdot g(x)$. In consequence,

when x is changed to $x + \triangle x$,

u is changed to $u + \triangle u$,

v is changed to $v + \triangle v$,

y is changed to $y + \triangle y$,

and

$$y + \triangle y = (u + \triangle u)(v + \triangle v)$$

when the value of the independent variable is $x + \triangle x$.   Thus we obtain

$$\triangle y = (u + \triangle u)(v + \triangle v) - uv$$
$$= uv + v\triangle u + u\triangle v + \triangle u\triangle v - uv$$
$$= v\triangle u + u\triangle v + \triangle u\triangle v.$$

Dividing by $\triangle x$, we have

$$\frac{\triangle y}{\triangle x} = v\frac{\triangle u}{\triangle x} + u\frac{\triangle v}{\triangle x} + \frac{\triangle u\triangle v}{\triangle x\triangle x}\triangle x.$$

We now take the limit as $\triangle x$ tends to zero and obtain

$$D_x y = \lim_{\triangle x \to 0}\frac{\triangle y}{\triangle x}$$

$$= \lim_{\triangle x \to 0}\left(v\frac{\triangle u}{\triangle x} + u\frac{\triangle v}{\triangle x} + \frac{\triangle u\triangle v}{\triangle x\triangle x}\triangle x\right)$$

$$= \lim_{\triangle x \to 0} v\left(\frac{\triangle u}{\triangle x}\right) + \lim_{\triangle x \to 0} u\left(\frac{\triangle v}{\triangle x}\right) + \left(\lim_{\triangle x \to 0}\frac{\triangle u}{\triangle x}\right)\left(\lim_{\triangle x \to 0}\frac{\triangle v}{\triangle x}\right)\left(\lim_{\triangle x \to 0}\triangle x\right)$$

$$= vD_x u + uD_x v + (D_x u)(D_x v)\cdot 0,$$

and therefore,

$$D_x y = vD_x u + uD_x v.$$

Note: Again we have reversed some operations, all of which can be proved to be correct. Note also that we have used correctly the theorem that the limit of $(u \cdot v) =$ (the limit of u) $\times$ (the limit of v), but we have proved that the derivative of $(u \cdot v) \neq$ (the derivative of u) $\times$ (the derivative of v). Thus we have very different rules for the limit of a product and the derivative of a product.

In the alternative notations,

$$\frac{d(uv)}{dx} = v\frac{du}{dx} + u\frac{dv}{dx}, \quad \text{or} \quad (fg)' = fg' + f'g.$$

Thus the derivative of a product of two functions is given by the sum of the product of the first function with the derivative of the second and the product of the second function with the derivative of the first.

Example 1. If

$$y = (x + 1)^3 \cdot x^5$$

find $D_x y$ (a) by expanding y and writing it as a sum of terms, (b) by using the product rule.

Solution:

(a)
$$y = (x + 1)^3 \cdot x^5$$
$$= (x^3 + 3x^2 + 3x + 1)x^5$$
$$= x^8 + 3x^7 + 3x^6 + x^5.$$
$$\therefore \quad D_x y = 8x^7 + 21x^6 + 18x^5 + 5x^4.$$

(b) Let
$$u = (x + 1)^3$$
so that
$$D_x u = 3(x + 1)^2,$$
and let
$$v = x^5$$
so that
$$D_x v = 5x^4.$$
Therefore,
$$D_x y = x^5 \cdot 3(x + 1)^2 + (x + 1)^3 \cdot 5x^4$$
$$= x^4(x + 1)^2[3x + 5(x + 1)]$$
$$= x^4(x + 1)^2[8x + 5].$$

These two forms of $D_x y$ are seen to be identical when the second result is expanded.

Example 2. Find $D_x y$ if
$$y = (x+1)\sqrt{x+2}.$$

Solution: Let
$$u = x + 1;$$
then
$$D_x u = 1.$$
Let
$$w = x + 2$$
so that
$$D_x w = 1,$$
and let
$$v = w^{1/2}$$
so that
$$D_w v = \frac{1}{2} w^{-1/2}.$$

Then
$$D_x v = D_w v \cdot D_x w$$
$$= \frac{1}{2}(x+2)^{-1/2}(1).$$

Therefore,
$$D_x y = u D_x v + v D_x u$$
$$= (x+1) \cdot \frac{1}{2}(x+2)^{-1/2} + (x+2)^{1/2} \cdot 1$$
$$= \frac{1}{2}(x+1)(x+2)^{-1/2} + (x+2)^{1/2}$$
$$= \frac{1}{2}(x+2)^{-1/2}[x+1+2(x+2)]$$
$$= \frac{1}{2}(x+2)^{-1/2}(3x+5).$$

EXERCISE 5.3

Differentiate each of the following.

1. $(x^2 + 4x + 3)(x^2 - 4x + 3)$

2. $(2x^2 + x - 1)(x^3 + x)$

3. $(x^3 + 2x - 1)(x^2 + 5x - 3)$

4. $(3 - x^2)(4 + 6x + x^2)$

5. $(5x - 3x^2)(2 - 3x^2 - 6x^3)$

6. $x(x+1)(x^2 + 2)$

7. $(x+1)(x^2 + 2)(x^3 + 3)$

8. $(2x - 1)^2(3x + 4)^2$

9. $(x^2 + 1)^2(x^3 + 8)$

10. $(x^2 + x)^2(2x + 5)^2$

11. $(3x + 2)^3(5 - x^2)$

12. $(2 + x)^{-1}(x^2 + 4)$

13. $(x - 1)^{-2}(x + 4)$

14. $(2x - 1)^{-1}(x + 2)^{-2}$

15. $x\sqrt{1-x^2}$

16. $(x+3)\sqrt{x^2+2x}$

17. $(3x+1)\sqrt{x^2-5}$

18. $(3-5t)\sqrt{1-3t^2}$

19. $(5t-3)\sqrt{3t^2-2t}$

20. $(3-t)\sqrt{5t^2+3t+1}$

21. $(x^2+3x)\sqrt{3x+5}$

22. $\sqrt{1-3x}\sqrt{3x^2-5}$

23. $\sqrt{1+x^3}\sqrt{1-x^2}$

24. $\sqrt{x^2-3x}\sqrt{x^3-5}$

25. $\sqrt[3]{3x+x^3}\sqrt{x^2-2}$

5.4. Derivative of a Quotient

The rule for the derivative of a quotient is sometimes convenient, and so it is developed here.   Consider

$$y = \frac{u}{v}, \quad \text{where } u = f(x) \text{ and } v = g(x).$$

When x changes to $x + \triangle x$,
u changes to $u + \triangle u$,
v changes to $v + \triangle v$,
y changes to $y + \triangle y$,

and

$$y + \triangle y = \frac{u + \triangle u}{v + \triangle v}$$

when the value of the independent variable is $x + \triangle x$.

$$\therefore \quad \triangle y = \frac{u + \triangle u}{v + \triangle v} - \frac{u}{v}$$

$$= \frac{(u + \triangle u)v - u(v + \triangle v)}{(v + \triangle v)v}$$

$$= \frac{v\triangle u - u\triangle v}{(v + \triangle v)v}.$$

$$\therefore \quad \frac{\triangle y}{\triangle x} = \frac{v\left(\dfrac{\triangle u}{\triangle x}\right) - u\left(\dfrac{\triangle v}{\triangle x}\right)}{(v + \triangle v)v}.$$

In the limit, when $\triangle x \to 0$,

$$D_x y = \lim_{\triangle x \to 0} \frac{\triangle y}{\triangle x}$$

$$= \lim_{\triangle x \to 0} \frac{v\left(\dfrac{\triangle u}{\triangle x}\right) - u\left(\dfrac{\triangle v}{\triangle x}\right)}{(v + \triangle v)v}. \qquad \text{(See note.)}$$

$$D_x y = \frac{v D_x u - u D_x v}{v^2}.$$

Alternatively,

$$\frac{dy}{dx} = \frac{v \dfrac{du}{dx} - u \dfrac{dv}{dx}}{v^2},$$

or

$$\left(\frac{f}{g}\right)' = \frac{g f' - f g'}{g^2}.$$

Thus the derivative of the quotient of two functions is given by the difference between the product of the second function and the derivative of the first, and the product of the first function and the derivative of the second, all divided by the square of the second function.

Note: Operations are reversed at several points in taking the limit. Write out the procedure in full (as is done above for the product) and show clearly where any of the theorems for limits are used.

It should be noted that, as in the case of the product, we have used correctly the theorem that the limit of $u/v = $ (the limit of u) $\div$ (the limit of v), but we have proved that the derivative of $u/v \neq$ (the derivative of u) $\div$ (the derivative of v).

The rule developed here for the derivative of a quotient is the most complicated that we have obtained. We can avoid using it by rewriting

$$y = \frac{u}{v}$$

as

$$y = u \cdot v^{-1}$$

and using the product formula.

Example. If

$$y = \frac{x^2 + 1}{x^3 - 1},$$

find $D_x y$ (a) by using the quotient rule, (b) by rewriting y as a product and using the product rule.

Solution:

(a)
$$y = \frac{x^2 + 1}{x^3 - 1}.$$

Put $u = x^2 + 1$ so that

$$D_x u = 2x,$$

and $v = x^3 - 1$ so that

$$D_x v = 3x^2 .$$

Therefore, using the quotient rule, we obtain

$$D_x y = \frac{v D_x u - u D_x v}{v^2}$$

$$= \frac{(x^3 - 1) \cdot 2x - (x^2 + 1) \cdot 3x^2}{(x^3 - 1)^2}$$

$$= \frac{2x^4 - 2x - 3x^4 - 3x^2}{(x^3 - 1)^2}$$

$$= \frac{-x^4 - 3x^2 - 2x}{(x^3 - 1)^2} .$$

(b) $\qquad y = \dfrac{x^2 + 1}{x^3 - 1} = (x^2 + 1) \cdot (x^3 - 1)^{-1} .$

Put

$$u = x^2 + 1$$

so that

$$D_x u = 2x ,$$

and put

$$w = x^3 - 1$$

and

$$v = w^{-1}$$

so that

$$D_w v = -w^{-2}$$

and

$$D_x w = 3x^2 .$$

$\therefore \quad D_x v = -3x^2 (x^3 - 1)^{-2} .$

Hence, using the product rule, we have

$$D_x y = u D_x v + v D_x u$$

$$= (x^2 + 1) \cdot (-3x^2) (x^3 - 1)^{-2} + (x^3 - 1)^{-1} \cdot 2x$$

$$= x (x^3 - 1)^{-2} [-3x (x^2 + 1) + 2(x^3 - 1)]$$

$$= x (x^3 - 1)^{-2} [-3x^3 - 3x + 2x^3 - 2] .$$

$\therefore \quad D_x y = x (x^3 - 1)^{-2} [-x^3 - 3x - 2] .$

EXERCISE 5.4

Differentiate each of the following.

1. $\dfrac{3x + 4}{5x + 6}$

2. $\dfrac{2x - 3}{x + 5}$

3. $\dfrac{x + 1}{x^2 + 1}$

4. $\dfrac{x^2}{x^2 + 1}$

5. $\dfrac{1 + 3x - x^2}{2 + 5x + x^2}$

6. $\dfrac{(3x + 2)^2}{2x - x^2}$

7. $\dfrac{3x + 5}{1 - x^2}$

8. $\dfrac{3x^2 + 5x}{1 + 3x}$

9. $\dfrac{t^2 - 5t - 1}{5t - 1}$

10. $\dfrac{t^3 + 2}{1 + 3t}$

11. $\dfrac{5 - x^3}{3x^2 + 1}$

12. $\dfrac{3t^2 - 2t}{5 - 3t^2}$

13. $\dfrac{x^3 - 1}{x^2 - 5x}$

14. $\dfrac{x}{\sqrt{x^2 - 1}}$

15. $\dfrac{\sqrt{x - 1}}{x^2}$

16. $\dfrac{x^2 - x}{\sqrt{1 - x^2}}$

17. $\dfrac{\sqrt{5 - t}}{t^3}$

18. $\dfrac{5 - x}{\sqrt{x^2 - 6x}}$

19. $\dfrac{\sqrt{1 + 3t^2}}{2t + 3}$

20. $\dfrac{\sqrt{1 - 5x^2}}{x^2}$

Chapter Summary

Rules for Derivatives:

$$D_x(x^r) = rx^{r-1}, \quad \text{where } x \in Re \text{ and } r \in Re$$
$$D_x(u \pm v) = D_x(u) \pm D_x(v)$$
$$D_x(uv) = u D_x v + v D_x u$$
$$D_x\left(\frac{u}{v}\right) = \frac{v D_x u - u D_x v}{v^2}$$

If $u = f(x)$ and $y = g(u)$ so that

$$y = F(x) = g[f(x)],$$

then

$$D_x y = D_u y \cdot D_x u, \quad \text{or} \quad F' = g'f'. \qquad \text{(Chain rule)}$$

REVIEW EXERCISE 5

Differentiate each of the following.

1. $x^3 - 3x^2 - \dfrac{3}{\sqrt{x}}$

2. $\dfrac{x^{3/2} - x^{1/2} + 3}{x^{1/2}}$

3. $\dfrac{2}{\sqrt{x}} + \dfrac{x}{\sqrt{3}} + \sqrt{\dfrac{x}{2}}$

4. $\dfrac{2}{\sqrt[3]{x}} + \dfrac{3}{x^3}$

5. $\sqrt{3x^3 + 5x - 4}$

6. $\sqrt{3x + \dfrac{1}{x}}$

7. $\sqrt{3t - 6} + \sqrt{6 - 2t}$

8. $(x - 1)\sqrt{x^2 - 3x + 3}$

9. $(2x + 3)\sqrt{1 - 3x - x^2}$

10. $(2 - 3x)\sqrt[3]{x^3 - 2x}$ $(x^3 - 2x)^{1/3}$

11. $(x + x^2)\sqrt[3]{1 - x^3}$

12. $\dfrac{2 - x^3}{3x^2 + 4}$

13. $\dfrac{2 - x}{x^2 - 7x}$

14. $\dfrac{\sqrt{1 + 3t^2}}{3t + 2}$

15. $7t\sqrt{t - 3} - 5(t - 3)^{3/2}$

16. $x\sqrt{3x + 5} - \tfrac{1}{3}(3x + 5)^{3/2}$

17. $3t\sqrt{1 - 5t} + \dfrac{1}{6}(1 - 5t)^{3/2}$

18. $\dfrac{3t}{\sqrt{1 + t}} - 5\sqrt{1 + t}$

19. $\dfrac{x^2}{\sqrt{1 + 2x}} + x\sqrt{1 + 3x}$

20. $\dfrac{\sqrt{1 + 3x}}{3x} - \dfrac{1}{\sqrt{1 + 3x}}$

21. $\dfrac{3x}{\sqrt{x + 6}} + x\sqrt{1 + 3x}$

22. $x^2\sqrt[3]{2x^2 - 7}$

23. $\dfrac{2}{x - 6} + \dfrac{x + 6}{2x}$

24. $\dfrac{3x + 2}{(x^2 + 5)^2}$

25. $\left(\dfrac{x^2 + 4}{3x + 2}\right)^2$

26. $\sqrt{\dfrac{2t + 1}{2t - 1}}$

27. $\dfrac{\sqrt{x + 4}}{3x} + \dfrac{3x}{\sqrt{x + 4}}$

28. $\dfrac{\sqrt[3]{x + \dfrac{2}{x}}}{\sqrt[3]{x - \dfrac{2}{x}}}$

29. $\dfrac{5}{\sqrt[3]{2x^2 - 7x + 5}}$

30. $(6 + t)\sqrt{2 - 3t + t^2}$

Chapter **6**

TANGENTS, DERIVATIVES AND GRAPHS

6.1. Derivatives for Relations

As we know, the graphs of some simple curves represent relations, not functions. For example,

the graph of $x^2 + y^2 = 9$ is a circle,

the graph of $\dfrac{x^2}{9} + \dfrac{y^2}{4} = 1$ is an ellipse,

the graph of $\dfrac{x^2}{25} - \dfrac{y^2}{16} = 1$ is a hyperbola,

and the graph of $y^2 = 4ax$ is a parabola.

However, each of these relations determines two continuous functions; for example, in the case of the ellipse $x^2/9 + y^2/4 = 1$,

$$y = 2\sqrt{1 - \frac{x^2}{9}} \quad \text{and} \quad y = -2\sqrt{1 - \frac{x^2}{9}},$$

and each equation determines a function of x in the domain $-3 \le x \le +3$. Similar results exist for the other relations. Thus, at any given point on the graph, the value of y is the value of a function of x. Also, at any point on these curves, a tangent exists, and so we would expect that $D_x y$ exists at any point except where the tangent is parallel to the y-axis.

Before we try to use the various formulae that we have developed to evaluate derivatives, we shall examine the case of the ellipse from basic principles.

Let $P(x_1, y_1)$ and $Q(x_1 + \triangle x, y_1 + \triangle y)$ be two points on the graph of

$$\frac{x^2}{a^2} + \frac{y^2}{b^2} = 1 \; ;$$

then

$$\frac{x_1^2}{a^2} + \frac{y_1^2}{b^2} = 1 = \frac{(x_1 + \triangle x)^2}{a^2} + \frac{(y_1 + \triangle y)^2}{b^2}.$$

97

Therefore,

$$\frac{(x_1 + \triangle x)^2 - x_1^2}{a^2} + \frac{(y_1 + \triangle y)^2 - y_1^2}{b^2} = 0,$$

$$\frac{2x_1\triangle x + (\triangle x)^2}{a^2} + \frac{2y_1\triangle y + (\triangle y)^2}{b^2} = 0.$$

Dividing by $\triangle x \neq 0$ and taking the limit as $\triangle x \to 0$, we have

$$\lim_{\triangle x \to 0} \left[\frac{2x_1 + \triangle x}{a^2} + \frac{2y_1 \dfrac{\triangle y}{\triangle x} + \dfrac{\triangle y}{\triangle x}\triangle y}{b^2} \right] = 0.$$

$$\therefore \quad \lim_{\triangle x \to 0} \left(\frac{2x_1}{a^2}\right) + \lim_{\triangle x \to 0} \frac{\triangle x}{a^2} + \lim_{\triangle x \to 0} \left(\frac{2y_1}{b^2} \cdot \frac{\triangle y}{\triangle x}\right) + \lim_{\triangle x \to 0} \left(\frac{\triangle y}{\triangle x} \cdot \frac{\triangle y}{b^2}\right) = 0;$$

$$\therefore \quad \frac{2x_1}{a^2} + 0 + \frac{2y_1}{b^2}\left(\lim_{\triangle x \to 0} \frac{\triangle y}{\triangle x}\right) + \left(\lim_{\triangle x \to 0} \frac{\triangle y}{\triangle x}\right)\left(\lim_{\triangle x \to 0} \frac{\triangle y}{b^2}\right) = 0.$$

Now if y is the value of a function of x at (x_1, y_1) and $\lim\limits_{\triangle x \to 0} \dfrac{\triangle y}{\triangle x}$ exists, then the limit is equal to $D_x y$, and $\triangle y \to 0$ as $\triangle x \to 0$. Therefore,

$$\frac{2x_1}{a^2} + \frac{2y_1}{b^2} \cdot D_x y + D_x y \cdot 0 = 0,$$

and

$$\frac{2x_1}{a^2} + \frac{2y_1}{b^2} \cdot D_x y = 0.$$

$$\therefore \quad D_x y = -\frac{b^2 x_1}{a^2 y_1}.$$

This is the value of the derivative of y with respect to x at (x_1, y_1).

The value of the derivative at any point (x, y) on the graph of a function determined by

$$\frac{x^2}{a^2} + \frac{y^2}{b^2} = 1$$

will be given by

$$D_x y = -\frac{b^2 x}{a^2 y}.$$

Thus, in this case where y is not given explicitly as a function of x, we have evaluated the derivative of y with respect to x wherever the derivative exists. (Where does the derivative not exist?)

We see that we can use our standard results for differentiation if we use the interpretation that the relation does determine y as a function of x in the neighbourhood of any given point (x, y) at which the derivative exists. Under this interpretation, we can differentiate an expression such as y^2 by using the chain rule. Thus,

$$D_x(y^2) = D_y(y^2) \cdot D_x y = 2y \cdot D_x y \,.$$

We may differentiate each member of the relation $x^2/a^2 + y^2/b^2 = 1$, and the derivative of the L.H.S. will be equal to the derivative of the R.H.S.

$$D_x\left(\frac{x^2}{a^2} + \frac{y^2}{b^2}\right) = D_x(1) \,,$$

$$D_x\left(\frac{x^2}{a^2}\right) + D_x\left(\frac{y^2}{b^2}\right) = 0 \,,$$

$$\frac{2x}{a^2} + D_y\left(\frac{y^2}{b^2}\right) D_x y = 0 \,,$$

$$\frac{2x}{a^2} + \frac{2y}{b^2} \cdot D_x y = 0 \,,$$

$$D_x y = -\frac{b^2 x}{a^2 y} \,.$$

This agrees, of course, with the result we calculated previously from basic principles.

Example.   Find the derivative of y with respect to x for a function determined by

$$x^2 - xy + 2y^2 = 4 \,.$$

Find the value of the derivative at $(-1, 1)$ and state also where, if anywhere, the derivative does not exist.

Solution:

$$x^2 - xy + 2y^2 = 4 \,.$$

Differentiating, we get

$$D_x(x^2) - D_x(xy) + 2D_x(y^2) = 0 \,,$$
$$2x - x \cdot D_x y - 1 \cdot y + 4y \cdot D_x y = 0 \,,$$
$$(2x - y) - (x - 4y) D_x y = 0 \,;$$

therefore,

$$\text{if } \ x - 4y \neq 0, \quad D_x y = \frac{2x - y}{x - 4y} \,.$$

At $(-1, 1)$

$$D_x y = \frac{2(-1) - 1}{-1 - 4(1)}$$

$$= \frac{-2 - 1}{-1 - 4}$$

$$= \frac{3}{5} \,.$$

$D_x y$ will not be defined at any point where $x - 4y = 0$.

EXERCISE 6.1

Find $D_x y$ for each of the following.

1. $2xy + x^2 + y^2 = 4$

2. $x^2y - 2y^2 = 0$

3. $3xy^2 + 4x - 2y^3 = 0$

4. $y^3 - 3xy + y^2 = x^2$

5. $x^2y^2 + 3y^2 + x^2 = 8$

6. $x^4 + 2xy^2 - y^3 = 0$

7. $x^{1/2} + y^{1/2} = a^{1/2}$

8. $x^{1/2}y^{3/2} + ax + by = 0$

9. $\dfrac{x^{2/3}}{a^{2/3}} + \dfrac{y^{2/3}}{a^{2/3}} = 1$

10. $\dfrac{x}{\sqrt{x^2 + y^2}} = \dfrac{y^2}{a^2}$

11. $3x^3 - xy^2 - 2y = 0$

12. $x^2y + 2xy + y^2 = 100$

13. $y^2 - 2xy^2 + x^2y^2 = 4$

14. $xy^2 + 4x^2y + 3xy = 5$

15. $\dfrac{x^4}{a^4} + \dfrac{2x^2y^2}{b^4} + \dfrac{y^2}{c^2} = 0$

16. $\dfrac{x^2}{16} - \dfrac{xy}{12} + \dfrac{y^2}{9} = 1$

17. $xy^2 = x + \dfrac{1}{x}$

18. $\dfrac{(x^2 + a^2)^{1/2}}{x} = \dfrac{y}{(y^2 + b^2)^{1/2}}$

19. $(x + y)(x^2 - xy + y^2) = 1$

20. $\sqrt{(x^2 + 1)(y^2 - 1)} = xy$

6.2. Tangents

When we have found the value of the derivative $D_x y$ at a point on the graph of a function, we can find the equation of the tangent at that point by using the point-slope form of the equation of a line.

Example 1. Find the equation of the tangents to the ellipse given by

$$\frac{x^2}{16} + \frac{y^2}{25} = 1$$

at the point where $x = 2\sqrt{2}$.

Solution: When $x = 2\sqrt{2}$,

$$\frac{8}{16} + \frac{y^2}{25} = 1,$$

$$\frac{y^2}{25} = \frac{1}{2},$$

$$y^2 = \frac{2(25)}{4};$$

therefore,

$$y = +\tfrac{5}{2}\sqrt{2} \quad \text{or} \quad y = -\tfrac{5}{2}\sqrt{2}.$$

The required points are $A(2\sqrt{2}, \frac{5}{2}\sqrt{2})$ and $B(2\sqrt{2}, -\frac{5}{2}\sqrt{2})$.

Differentiating, we have

$$\frac{2x}{16} + \frac{2y}{25} D_x y = 0 \,,$$

$$D_x y = -\frac{25x}{16y} \quad \text{if} \quad y \neq 0 \,.$$

Therefore, at A,

$$D_x y = -\frac{25 \cdot 2\sqrt{2}}{16 \cdot \frac{5}{2}\sqrt{2}}$$

$$= -\frac{5}{4} \,.$$

Similarly, at B,

$$D_x y = +\frac{5}{4} \,.$$

At A, the equation of the tangent is

$$y - \tfrac{5}{2}\sqrt{2} = -\tfrac{5}{4}(x - 2\sqrt{2}) \,,$$
$$y = -\tfrac{5}{4}x + 5\sqrt{2} \,,$$

and, at B, the equation of the tangent is

$$y + \tfrac{5}{2}\sqrt{2} = \tfrac{5}{4}(x - 2\sqrt{2}) \,,$$
$$y = \tfrac{5}{4}x - 5\sqrt{2} \,.$$

Example 2.   Find the equation of the tangent to the graph of

$$y = \frac{x+2}{x+1}$$

at the point $(3, \frac{5}{4})$.   If there is a second tangent to the curve that is **parallel** to this first tangent, find its equation also.

Solution: If $\qquad y = \dfrac{x+2}{x+1} \,,$

then

$$D_x y = \frac{(x+1)D_x(x+2) - (x+2)D_x(x+1)}{(x+1)^2}$$

$$= \frac{(x+1)1 - (x+2)1}{(x+1)^2}$$

$$= \frac{-1}{(x+1)^2} \,.$$

Therefore, at $(3, \frac{5}{4})$,

$$D_x y = \frac{-1}{(3 + 1)^2} = -\frac{1}{16}.$$

Hence, the equation of the tangent to $y = (x + 2)/(x + 1)$ at $(3, \frac{5}{4})$ is

$$y - \frac{5}{4} = -\frac{1}{16}(x - 3),$$

$$y = -\frac{x}{16} + \frac{23}{16}.$$

If $D_x y = -1/16$ for another value of x and a corresponding value of y exists, then there is a second tangent parallel to the first with slope $-1/16$. If

$$-\frac{1}{16} = \frac{-1}{(x + 1)^2},$$

$$16 = (x + 1)^2 ;$$

therefore,

$$x + 1 = +4 \quad \text{or} \quad x + 1 = -4 ;$$

$$x = 3 \quad \text{or} \quad x = -5 .$$

$x = 3$ corresponds to the given point on the curve,

and

$x = -5$ corresponds to the point $(-5, \frac{3}{4})$ on the curve.

Therefore at $(-5, \frac{3}{4})$ on the curve, the equation of the tangent is

$$y - \frac{3}{4} = -\frac{1}{16}(x + 5),$$

$$y = -\frac{1}{16}x + \frac{7}{16}.$$

EXERCISE 6.2

Find the equation of the tangent to the graph of each of the following relations at the point indicated.

1. $x^2 + y^2 = 25$ at $(3, 4)$ 2. $\dfrac{\dot{x}^2}{25} + \dfrac{y^2}{16} = 1$ at $(4, 1\frac{2}{5})$

3. $\dfrac{x^2}{20} - \dfrac{y^2}{16} = 1$ at $(-5, 2)$ 4. $\dfrac{y^2}{10} - \dfrac{x^2}{4} = 1$ at $(6, -10)$

5. $y^2 = 100x$ at $(4, 20)$ 6. $xy = 56$ at $(-7, -8)$

7. $x^2 + y^2 = 9$ at $(3, 0)$

8. $2x^2 + 4y^2 - 4xy + 2x = 8$ at $(2, 1)$

Find the equation of the tangent to the graph of each of the following functions at the point indicated.

9. $y = \dfrac{x}{1 - x^2}$ at $(\frac{1}{2}, \frac{2}{3})$

10. $y = \sqrt{2 + x}$ at $(2, 2)$

11. $y = x^{1/2} + x^{-1/2}$ at $(4, 2.5)$

12. $y = \dfrac{2}{x + 1}$ at $(1, 1)$

13. $y = \dfrac{6(x - 1)}{x^2 + 3}$ at $(3, 1)$

14. $y = (x^2 + 4)^{1/2}$ at $(-2, 2\sqrt{2})$

15. $y = x^{-1/2}$ at $(4, \frac{1}{2})$

16. $y = \dfrac{1}{(x^2 + 1)^{1/2}}$ at $\left(1, \dfrac{1}{\sqrt{2}}\right)$

17. $y = x(x^2 + 4)^{1/2}$ at $(2, 4\sqrt{2})$

18. $y = x^2 + \sqrt{x^4 + 16}$ at $(0, 4)$

6.3. The Tangents to the Standard Conics (Supplementary)

The standard equations of the conics, given in terms of literal constants a and b, are as follows:

$$\text{ellipse:} \qquad \frac{x^2}{a^2} + \frac{y^2}{b^2} = 1 \, ;$$

$$\text{hyperbola:} \qquad \frac{x^2}{a^2} - \frac{y^2}{b^2} = 1 \, ;$$

$$\text{parabola:} \qquad y^2 = 4ax \, ;$$

$$\text{circle:} \qquad x^2 + y^2 = a^2 \, .$$

We can find an equation for the tangent at any point (x_1, y_1) on a conic in terms of the same constants.

Example.   Find the tangent to the ellipse

$$\frac{x^2}{a^2} + \frac{y^2}{b^2} = 1$$

at a point (x_1, y_1) on the ellipse.

Solution: Differentiating, we obtain

$$\frac{2x}{a^2} + \frac{2y}{b^2} \cdot D_x y = 0 \ ;$$

therefore,

$$D_x y = -\frac{b^2 x}{a^2 y},$$

and so, at (x_1, y_1),

$$D_x y = -\frac{b^2 x_1}{a^2 y_1}.$$

The equation of a tangent at (x_1, y_1) is given by

$$y - y_1 = -\frac{b^2 x_1}{a^2 y_1}(x - x_1) \ ,$$

$$(y - y_1)\frac{y_1}{b^2} = -(x - x_1)\frac{x_1}{a^2}.$$

$$\therefore \quad \frac{yy_1}{b^2} - \frac{y_1^2}{b^2} = -\frac{xx_1}{a^2} + \frac{x_1^2}{a^2} \ ;$$

$$\therefore \quad \frac{xx_1}{a^2} + \frac{yy_1}{b^2} = \frac{x_1^2}{a^2} + \frac{y_1^2}{b^2}.$$

But (x_1, y_1) is on the ellipse; therefore,

$$\frac{x_1^2}{a^2} + \frac{y_1^2}{b^2} = 1 \ .$$

Thus the equation of the tangent at (x_1, y_1) on the ellipse

$$\frac{x^2}{a^2} + \frac{y^2}{b^2} = 1$$

is

$$\frac{xx_1}{a^2} + \frac{yy_1}{b^2} = 1 \ .$$

EXERCISE 6.3

1. Find the equation of the tangent to the hyperbola

$$\frac{x^2}{a^2} - \frac{y^2}{b^2} = 1$$

at (x_1, y_1) on the hyperbola.

2. Find the equation of the tangent to the parabola

$$y^2 = 4ax$$

at (x_1, y_1) on the parabola.

3. Find the equation of the tangent to the rectangular hyperbola

$$xy = k^2$$

at the point (x_1, y_1) on the hyperbola.

4. Find the equation of the tangent to the conic

$$ax^2 + 2hxy + by^2 = c$$

at (x_1, y_1) on the conic.

5. Find the equation of the tangent to the general conic which is given by

$$ax^2 + 2hxy + by^2 + 2gx + 2fy + c = 0$$

at (x_1, y_1) on the conic.

6.4. Graph Sketching: the First Derivative

The first derivative gives us valuable additional data from which to sketch a graph:

   (i) The derivative shows where y is increasing with respect to x and where y is decreasing.

  (ii) The zeros of the derivative show where the maxima and minima occur.

 (iii) The points where the derivative does not exist indicate where the slope of the graph is parallel to the y-axis, or where the graph has a cusp, or crosses itself, or has a discontinuity (see Figure 6.1).

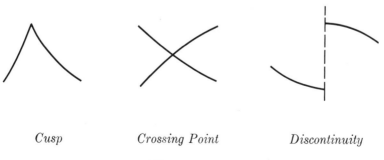

Cusp   *Crossing Point*   *Discontinuity*

Figure 6.1

Example 1.   Give the domains of x for which the values of y given by the following equations increase and decrease:

(a) $y = x^3 + 2x$,   (b) $y = \dfrac{1}{x+2}$,   (c) $y = x^2 - x$.

Solution:

(a)   For $y = x^3 + 2x$,

$$D_x y = 3x^2 + 2.$$

Therefore, for all real values of x, $D_x y > 0$, and so y increases as x increases for all real values of x.

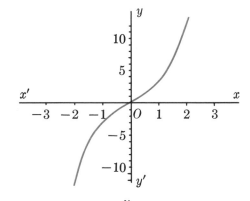

(b)   For $y = \dfrac{1}{x+2}$, $x \neq -2$,

$$D_x y = -\dfrac{1}{(x+2)^2}, \qquad x \neq -2.$$

Therefore, for all real x ($x \neq -2$), $D_x y < 0$, and so y decreases as x increases for all real values of x ($x \neq -2$).

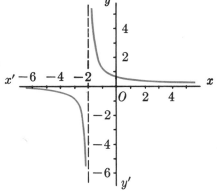

(c)   For $y = x^2 - x$,

$$D_x y = 2x - 1.$$

Hence, for $x > \frac{1}{2}$, $D_x y > 0$, and, for $x < \frac{1}{2}$, $D_x y < 0$. Thus, for $x > \frac{1}{2}$,

   y increases as x increases,

but, for $x < \frac{1}{2}$,

   y decreases as x increases.

When $x = \frac{1}{2}$, $D_x y = 0$; therefore the point $(\frac{1}{2}, -\frac{1}{4})$ is a minimum point.

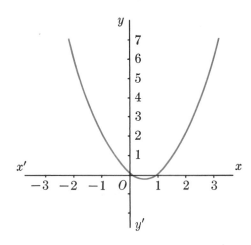

Example 2. Find the maximum and minimum points of the graph of

$$y = 4\left(\frac{x}{x^2 + 1}\right).$$

Sketch the graph of this equation.

Solution: If $y = 4\left(\frac{x}{x^2 + 1}\right)$,

$$D_x y = 4\left[\frac{(x^2 + 1)\cdot 1 - x \cdot 2x}{(x^2 + 1)^2}\right]$$

$$= 4\left[\frac{1 - x^2}{(x^2 + 1)^2}\right].$$

At a stationary point, $D_x y = 0$; that is,

$$1 - x^2 = 0.$$

Therefore, the maximum and minimum points occur at $x = 1$ and $x = -1$.

At $x = 1$,

$$y = 2,$$

and at $x = \frac{1}{2}$,

$$y = 4\left(\frac{\frac{1}{2}}{\frac{1}{4} + 1}\right) = 4\left(\frac{\frac{1}{2}}{\frac{5}{4}}\right) = \frac{8}{5} < 2,$$

and at $x = 2$,

$$y = 4\left(\frac{2}{4 + 1}\right) = \frac{8}{5} < 2.$$

Therefore, $(1, 2)$ is a maximum point. Similarly, $(-1, -2)$ is a minimum point.

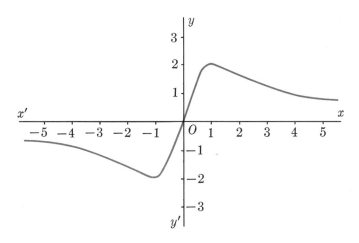

Example 3.   Find the points on each of the following graphs where the derivative does not exist, and discuss the behaviour of the graph near such points:

(a) $y = |x|$,

(b) $xy = 16$,

(c) $y = \dfrac{2}{(x-1)^2}$,

(d) $y^2 = x^3$.

Draw a sketch graph for each case.

Solutions:

(a) If $y = |x|$,   then

$$y = x \qquad \text{for} \qquad x > 0,$$
$$y = 0 \qquad \text{at} \qquad x = 0,$$
$$y = -x \qquad \text{for} \qquad x < 0.$$

For $x > 0$,

$$D_x y = 1 ;$$

for $x < 0$,

$$D_x y = -1 ;$$

and at $x = 0$, $D_x y$ is not uniquely defined.   The graph has a cusp at $(0, 0)$.

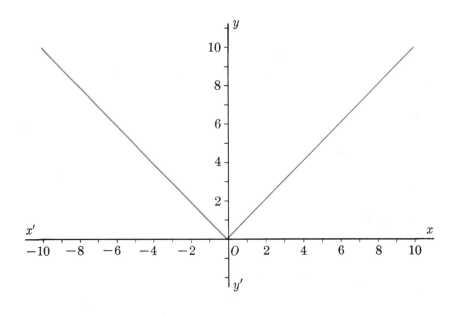

(b) If $xy = 16$,   then

$$xD_x y + 1 \cdot y = 0 \; ;$$

therefore,

$$D_x y = -\frac{y}{x}$$

and $D_x y$ is not defined for $x = 0$.

As $x \rightarrow 0$ with x positive,

y is positive and increases without bound,

and

$D_x y$ is negative and decreases without bound.

As $x \rightarrow 0$ with x negative,

y is negative and decreases without bound,

and

$D_x y$ is ~~positive~~ and ~~increases~~ without bound.

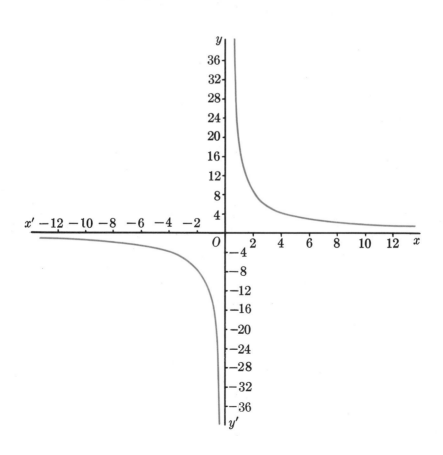

(c) If $y = \dfrac{2}{(x-1)^2}$,

$$D_x y = -\frac{4}{(x-1)^3}$$

and $D_x y$ is not defined for $x = 1$.

As $x \to 1$ with $x > 1$, or $x - 1 > 0$,

y is positive and increases without bound,

and

$D_x y$ is negative and decreases without bound.

As $x \to 1$ with $x < 1$, or $x - 1 < 0$,

y is positive and increases without bound,

and

$D_x y$ is positive and increases without bound.

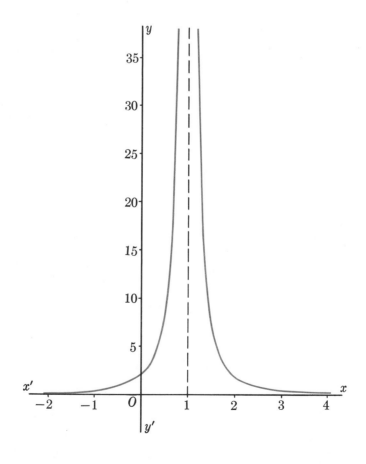

(d) If $y^2 = x^3$, then

$$y = +x^{3/2}, \quad x \notin Re^-, \quad \text{and} \quad y = -x^{3/2}, \quad x \in Re^+,$$

determine the two functions that together are equivalent to the original relation.

For $y = +x^{3/2}, \quad D_x y = \frac{3}{2}x^{1/2}, \quad x \notin Re^-,$ and

y is real and positive for all $x > 0$,

$D_x y$ is real and positive for all $x > 0$,

and
$$D_x y = 0 \quad \text{at} \quad x = 0, \quad y = 0.$$

For $y = -x^{3/2}, \quad D_x y = -\frac{3}{2}x^{1/2}, \quad x \in Re^+,$ and

y is real and negative for all $x > 0$,

$D_x y$ is real and negative for all $x > 0$,

and
$$D_x y \to 0 \quad \text{as} \quad x \to 0.$$

The graph has a cusp at $(0, 0)$.

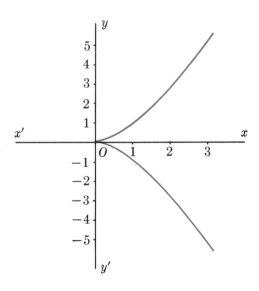

Example 4.   Sketch the graph of

$$y = \tfrac{1}{3}(x^3 - 9x).$$

Solution: The domain of x is all the real numbers, and the range of y is all the real numbers.   When x is large and positive, $y \simeq \tfrac{1}{3}x^3$ and y is large and positive. When x is large and negative, $y \simeq \tfrac{1}{3}x^3$ and y is large and negative.

$$y = \tfrac{1}{3}x(x^2 - 9),$$

and when $y = 0$,

$$x(x^2 - 9) = x(x - 3)(x + 3) = 0.$$

Thus,

the intercepts on the x-axis are $-3, \ 0, \ 3,$

the intercept on the y-axis is $0,$

and

the curve is symmetrical with respect to the origin.

$$D_x y = x^2 - 3,$$

and when $D_x y = 0$,

$$x^2 - 3 = 0.$$

Therefore, stationary points occur at $x = -\sqrt{3}$ and $x = +\sqrt{3}$. The point $(\sqrt{3}, -2\sqrt{3})$ is a minimum as nearby points are $(1, -\tfrac{8}{3})$ and $(2, -\tfrac{10}{3})$. The point $(-\sqrt{3}, +2\sqrt{3})$ is a maximum as nearby points are $(-1, \tfrac{8}{3})$ and $(-2, \tfrac{10}{3})$.

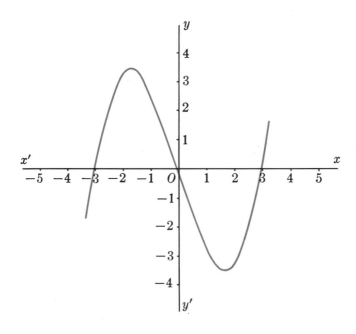

EXERCISE 6.4

Find the stationary points of the function determined by each of the following expressions, and state the domains of x in which the function is increasing and in which it is decreasing.

1. $y = x^2 + 6x + 3$
2. $y = -x^2 + 4x + 5$
3. $y = x^3 - 6x^2 + 9x + 10$

4. $y = x^4 + 4x^3$
5. $y = x + x^{-1}$
6. $y = 1 + |x - 1|$

7. $y = \dfrac{x + 1}{x - 1}$
8. $y = \dfrac{x}{x^2 - 4}$
9. $y^3 = x^2$

10. State the values of x for which the derivative is not defined, and identify any cusps that occur in the graphs of the functions in questions (1) to (9).

11. Using all the data found above and any other factors, such as symmetries, sketch the graphs of the functions in questions (1) to (9).

6.5. Graph Sketching: the Second Derivative

The second derivative, $D_x^2 y$ or $f''(x)$, measures the rate of change of the first derivative, $D_x y$ or $f'(x)$, as x changes. $D_x y$ measures the rate of change of $y = f(x)$ as x changes, and so it is a measure of the slope of the graph of $y = f(x)$. Thus, $D_x^2 y$ is a measure of the rate of change of the slope of the graph of $y = f(x)$. In particular, if the slope has been increasing for $x < a$ as x increases and then at $x = a$ the slope starts decreasing as x increases, then, at $x = a$, $D_x y$ will have a maximum value, and $D_x^2 y$ will be zero. Notice that this does not require $D_x y$ to be zero, though it is possible for both the first and second derivatives to be zero for the same value of x.

DEFINITION.   A point (x_1, y_1) on the graph of $y = f(x)$ at which $D_x^2 y = 0$ and $D_x y$ has a maximum or a minimum value is called a *point of inflection*.

It will be noted that when $D_x^2 y > 0$, as between A and B in Figure 6.2, the curve is concave upwards. When $D_x^2 y < 0$, as between C and D in Figure 6.2, the curve is concave downwards. At E in Figure 6.2, $D_x^2 y = 0$, and E is a point of inflection. Note that, at the point of inflection E, the curve and the tangent cross each other, while at any other point on the curve, the curve, in the immediate neighbourhood of the point, lies entirely on one side of the tangent (as at B or C).

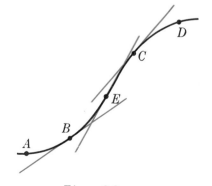

Figure 6.2

The value of the second derivative at a stationary point is also important. As we already know, $D_x y = f'(x) = 0$ at a maximum or a minimum of the function determined by $y = f(x)$. If a maximum occurs when $x = a$, then the graph of the function is as illustrated in Figure 6.3. We can see that, near the maximum point P, the slope of the graph is positive for $x < a$ and negative for $x > a$; that is, $f'(x) > 0$ for $x < a$, and $f'(x) < 0$ for $x > a$. Thus, the values of the derived function $f'(x)$ decrease near $x = a$; that is, the rate of change of $f'(x)$ as x increases is negative. Therefore, $D_x^2 y = f''(x)$ is negative at $x = a$ if a maximum occurs at $x = a$.

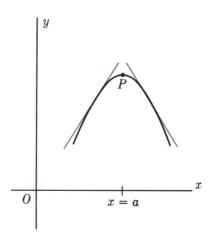

Figure 6.3

Thus, the conditions at a *maximum* are

$$f'(x) = D_x y = 0 \quad \text{and} \quad f''(x) = D_x^2 y < 0.$$

In a similar way, we may show that the conditions at a *minimum* are

$$f'(x) = D_x y = 0 \quad \text{and} \quad f''(x) = D_x^2 y > 0.$$

Example 1. Find the maximum and minimum values of

$$y = f(x) = \tfrac{1}{3}(x^3 - 9x).$$

Solution:

$$f(x) = \tfrac{1}{3}(x^3 - 9x);$$
$$\therefore \quad f'(x) = x^2 - 3,$$
$$f''(x) = 2x.$$

At a stationary point, $f'(x) = 0$; hence, the abscissae of the stationary points are given by

$$x^2 - 3 = 0,$$
$$x^2 = 3.$$

Therefore, the stationary points are at $x = \sqrt{3}$ and $x = -\sqrt{3}$.

At $x = \sqrt{3}$,

$$y = f(\sqrt{3})$$
$$= -2\sqrt{3}$$

and

$$f''(x) = 2\sqrt{3}$$
$$> 0.$$

Therefore, $(\sqrt{3}, -2\sqrt{3})$ is a minimum point.

At $x = -\sqrt{3}$,

$$y = f(-\sqrt{3})$$
$$= 2\sqrt{3}$$

and

$$f''(x) = -2\sqrt{3}$$
$$< 0.$$

Therefore, $(-\sqrt{3}, 2\sqrt{3})$ is a maximum point.

Example 2.   Find the points of inflection on the graph of

(a) $y = x^3 + x$, (b) $y = (x-1)^2(x-3)$.

Solutions:

(a) If $$y = x^3 + x,$$

$$D_x y = 3x^2 + 1,$$

and

$$D_x^2 y = 6x.$$

Hence, there is a point of inflection when $x = 0$, where $D_x^2 y = 0$. The point of inflection is $(0, 0)$ and the slope at this point is 1.

(b) If $$y = (x-1)^2(x-3),$$

$$D_x y = 2(x-1)(x-3) + (x-1)^2$$
$$= (x-1)(3x-7),$$

and

$$D_x^2 y = 1(3x-7) + 3(x-1)$$
$$= 6x - 10.$$

Hence, there is a point of inflection when $x = \frac{5}{3}$, where $D_x^2 y = 0$. The point of inflection is $(\frac{5}{3}, -\frac{16}{27})$ and the slope at this point is $-\frac{4}{3}$.

EXERCISE 6.5

Find the points of inflection on the graph of each of the following.

1. $y = x^3 - 5x + 1$

2. $y = x^3 - 2x^2 + 3$

3. $y = x^4 + 4x^3$

4. $y = x^4 + 2x^3 - 12x^2 + 8x$

5. $y = 2x^2 + \dfrac{1}{x^2}$ 6. $y = x\sqrt{x + 2}$

7. $y = x^{1/2}$ 8. $y = x^{4/3} + 2x^{1/3}$

Find the positions of the maxima and minima of the following, using the second derivative test to distinguish them.

9. $y = 2x^3 - 9x^2 - 24x - 12$ 10. $y = x^3 + 12x^2 + 36x - 50$

11. $y = (x - 2)^2(x - 3)^2$ 12. $y = x - \dfrac{4}{x^2}$

13. $y = \dfrac{x^3 - 16}{x}$ 14. $xy = y - x^2$

Sketch the graph of each of the following, making full use of stationary points and points of inflection.

15. $y = \frac{1}{5}(x^4 - 4x^3)$ 16. $y = \frac{1}{3}x(4 - x)^2$

17. $y = \frac{1}{100}(x^5 - 5x^4)$ 18. $y = x^3 - 3x^2 + 4x$

19. $y = 12\left(\dfrac{4 - x^2}{x}\right)$ 20. $y^2 = 3\left(\dfrac{4 - x}{x}\right)$

21. $y = \dfrac{(x - 3)}{(x - 1)}$ 22. $y = 2\left(\dfrac{x - 4}{x^2}\right)$

23. $y = \dfrac{x^2}{x + 2}$ 24. $y = \dfrac{2x}{x^2 + 4}$

6.6. Graph Sketching: Asymptotes (Supplementary)

DEFINITION.   If the graph whose equation is $y = f(x)$ and the line whose equation is $y = mx + b$ are such that

$$\lim_{x \to \infty} [f(x) - mx - b] = 0 \quad \text{and} \quad \lim_{x \to \infty} [f'(x) - m] = 0,$$

then the line $y = mx + b$ is an *asymptote* to the graph of $y = f(x)$.
   When $m = 0$, so that the line is given by $y = b$, the asymptote is a *horizontal* asymptote.

   This definition is valid for all asymptotes except vertical asymptotes for which we need a separate definition.

DEFINITION.   If the graph whose equation is $y = f(x)$ is such that $|f(x)|$ and $|f'(x)|$ increase without bound as x approaches a, then the line $x = a$ is a *vertical* asymptote to the graph of $y = f(x)$.

Example 1. Find a horizontal asymptote to

$$y = \frac{1}{x^2}.$$

Solution:

$$f(x) = \frac{1}{x^2},$$

and

$$f'(x) = -\frac{2}{x^3};$$

therefore,

$$\lim_{x \to \infty} [f(x) - 0] = \lim_{x \to \infty} \left(\frac{1}{x^2}\right) = 0,$$

and

$$\lim_{x \to \infty} [f'(x) - 0] = \lim_{x \to \infty} \left(-\frac{2}{x^3}\right) = 0.$$

Hence, $y = 0$ is a horizontal asymptote to $y = 1/x^2$.

Example 2. Show that

$$y = 2x + 3$$

is an asymptote to

$$y = \frac{2x^2}{x+1} + 5.$$

Solution: In this case,

$$f(x) = \frac{2x^2}{x+1} + 5,$$

and

$$\begin{aligned} f'(x) &= \frac{(x+1)4x - 2x^2 \cdot 1}{(x+1)^2} \\ &= \frac{4x^2 + 4x - 2x^2}{(x+1)^2} \\ &= \frac{2x^2 + 4x}{x^2 + 2x + 1}. \end{aligned}$$

Now

$$\begin{aligned} f(x) - (2x + 3) &= \frac{2x^2}{x+1} + 5 - 2x - 3 \\ &= \frac{2x^2 + 5x + 5 - 2x^2 - 5x - 3}{x+1} \\ &= \frac{2}{x+1}, \end{aligned}$$

and

$$\lim_{x \to \infty} \left(\frac{2x^2}{x+1} + 5 - 2x - 3\right) = \lim_{x \to \infty} \left(\frac{2}{x+1}\right) = 0.$$

Also

$$f'(x) - 2 = \frac{2x^2 + 4x}{x^2 + 2x + 1} - 2$$

$$= \frac{2x^2 + 4x - 2x^2 - 4x - 2}{x^2 + 2x + 1}$$

$$= \frac{-2}{x^2 + 2x + 1};$$

therefore,

$$\lim_{x \to \infty} \left(\frac{2x^2 + 4x}{x^2 + 2x + 1} - 2 \right) = \lim_{x \to \infty} \left(\frac{-2}{x^2 + 2x + 1} \right) = 0.$$

Hence, $y = 2x + 3$ is an asymptote to $y = \dfrac{2x^2}{x + 1} + 5$.

Example 3.   Find a vertical asymptote to the graph of

$$y = \frac{1}{x}.$$

Solution: As x approaches 0,

$$|f(x)| = \frac{1}{|x|}$$

increases without bound, and

$$|f'(x)| = \left| -\frac{1}{x^2} \right|$$

$$= \frac{1}{|x^2|}$$

increases without bound.   Therefore, $x = 0$ is a vertical asymptote to $y = 1/x$.

EXERCISE 6.6

1. Find vertical asymptotes to the graph of

(a) $y = \dfrac{2}{x + 1}$,

(b) $y = \dfrac{3}{2x - 1}$,

(c) $y = x + \dfrac{1}{2x}$,

(d) $y = \dfrac{3}{x} + 2$,

(e) $y = \dfrac{1}{x - 1} + 2$,

(f) $y = \dfrac{x}{x^2 - 4} + 1$.

2. Find horizontal asymptotes to the graph of

(a) $y = \dfrac{2}{x + 1}$,

(b) $y = \dfrac{2}{x} + 1$,

(c) $y = 2 - \dfrac{3}{x^2}$,

(d) $y = \dfrac{4}{x^2 + 1}$

(e) $y = \dfrac{1}{x^2 - 4} + 1$,

(f) $y = \dfrac{x^2 - 1}{x^2 + 1}$.

3. In each of the following show that

    (a) $y = x$ is an asymptote to $y = x + \dfrac{1}{2x}$;

    (b) $y = 2(x+1)$ is an asymptote to $y = \dfrac{2x^2}{x-1}$;

    (c) $y = 3 - x$ is an asymptote to $y = \dfrac{-(x-1)^2}{x+1}$;

    (d) $y = 2x$ is an asymptote to $y = \dfrac{2x^3 + 1}{x^2}$;

    (e) $y = x + 1$ is an asymptote to $y = \dfrac{x^3 + x^2 + 2x + 3}{x^2 + 1}$.

4. Sketch the graph of

    (a) $y = \dfrac{2}{x+1}$,   (b) $y = x + \dfrac{1}{2x}$,

    (c) $y = \dfrac{x}{x^2 - 4} + 1$,   (d) $y = 1 + \dfrac{2}{x}$,

    (e) $y = \dfrac{4}{x^2 + 1}$,   (f) $y = \dfrac{2x^2}{x-1}$,

    (g) $y = \dfrac{2x^3 + 1}{x^2}$,   (h) $y = \dfrac{x^2 - 1}{x^2 + 1}$.

Chapter Summary

Derivatives of functions defined implicitly by relations · Tangents to graphs determined by relations and functions · Curve sketching using first and second derivatives

At a maximum of $y = f(x)$, $D_x y = 0$ and $D_x^2 y < 0$.

At a minimum of $y = f(x)$, $D_x y = 0$ and $D_x^2 y > 0$.

At a point of inflection of $y = f(x)$, $D_x^2 y = 0$.

Asymptotes (Supplementary)

$y = mx + b$ is an asymptote to $y = f(x)$

    if $\lim_{x \to \infty} [f(x) - mx - b] = 0$ and $\lim_{x \to \infty} [f'(x) - m] = 0$.

$x = a$ is an asymptote to $y = f(x)$

    if $|f(x)|$ and $|f'(x)|$ increase without bound as x approaches a.

REVIEW EXERCISE 6

Find $D_x y$ for each of the following.

1. $x^2 - 3xy + 4y^2 = 25$

2. $x^2 + y^2 = 2(x + y) - 4$

3. $x^{1/2} - y^{1/2} = 9$

4. $(x^2 + y^2)^{1/3} = x + y - 1$

Find the equations of the tangents to the graphs determined by the following equations at the points indicated.

5. $\dfrac{x^2}{8} + \dfrac{y^2}{50} = 1$ at $(2, 5)$

6. $xy = 28$ at $(4, 7)$

7. $y = x + \sqrt{x^2 - 25}$ at $(13, 25)$

8. $y = \dfrac{2}{x + 3}$ at $(2, .4)$

9. $x^4 - 8x^2 y^2 + 4y^4 = 16$ at $(2, 0)$

10. $y^2 = \dfrac{x^3}{4 - x}$ at $(2, -2)$

For each graph determined by the following equations, identify the stationary points as maxima or minima, and find the points of inflection. Sketch each graph.

11. $y = x^4 - 6x^2 + 8x$

12. $y = 4 - x^3$

13. $y = 1 - |x - 1|$

14. $x^2 y = x - 4$

15. $y^2 x = 4 - x$

16. $y = x^4 - 4x^3$

Chapter 7

FURTHER APPLICATIONS OF DERIVATIVES

7.1. Distance, Velocity and Acceleration

In Chapter 2, we found that if the distance s moved by a body on a line is given by a function of the time t, then $D_t s$ is the velocity v of the body, and $D_t v = D_t^2 s$ is the acceleration a. We also found that if $v = D_t s = 0$ at a particular time, then the corresponding distance s was a maximum or minimum distance if the direction of the velocity reversed at this point. Similarly, if $a = D_t v = 0$ at a particular time, then at that time the velocity generally attained either a maximum or a minimum value. In our earlier work, s and v were given by polynomial functions of the time. We can now apply our greater knowledge of derivatives to problems where the distance or velocity is any algebraic function of the time.

Example 1. In the time interval $0 < t < 100$, the velocity v is given by

$$v = \frac{t}{1+t}.$$

Find the acceleration at any time t for $0 < t < 100$.

Solution:

$$v = \frac{t}{1+t};$$

$$\therefore \quad a = D_t v$$

$$= \frac{(1+t)(1) - t(1)}{(1+t)^2}$$

$$= \frac{1 + t - t}{(1+t)^2}$$

$$= \frac{1}{(1+t)^2}.$$

121

Example 2. A particle is moving so that, at any time t, the relation between the distance s and the velocity v is given by

$$s^2 + c^2v^2 = k^2,$$

where c and k are constants. Find the relation between the acceleration a and the distance s.

Solution:

(1) $$s^2 + c^2v^2 = k^2$$

and s and v are each values of functions of t. Therefore, differentiating equation (1), we obtain

$$D_t(s^2) + D_t(c^2v^2) = D_t(k^2) \ ;$$

$$\therefore \quad D_s(s^2)D_ts + D_v(c^2v^2)D_tv = 0 \ ;$$

$$\therefore \quad 2s \cdot v + c^2 2v \cdot a = 0 \ .$$

Now, in general, $2v \neq 0$; hence,

$$s + c^2a = 0 \ ,$$

which determines the relation between the acceleration a and the distance s.

EXERCISE 7.1

1. The velocity v of a particle is given in terms of the time t by

$$v = \frac{20t}{1 + t^2} \ .$$

   Find the acceleration in terms of the time, and find the maximum velocity.

2. The distance s of a particle from a given origin at any time t is given by

   $$s = 10\sqrt{4 + t}$$

   Find the velocity and acceleration at any time.

3. The velocity v of a particle at any time t is given by

   $$v = 20(1 + t^2)^{1/2} + 100 \ .$$

   What is the acceleration at any time?

4. The velocity v of a body is given by the equation   —implicitly

   $$10v^2 = 64s + 1000 \ ,$$

   where s is the distance from a fixed origin. Find the acceleration (remember that $D_ts = v$).

5. The velocity v in ft/sec of a shell in the barrel of a gun is given by

$$v = \frac{5000s}{5 + s},$$

where s is the distance of the shell from the breech block along the barrel. Find the acceleration in terms of the distance s.

6. If the relation between the velocity v and time t is given by

$$\frac{1}{v} - \frac{1}{v_0} = kt$$

where v_0 is the velocity when $t = 0$ and k is a positive constant, show that the acceleration is negative (that is, a retardation) and that it is proportional to the square of the velocity.

7. The thickness x in cm of an oxide layer on many metals is given as a function of the time t by

$$x = kt^{1/2}.$$

Find the rate of growth v and the rate of change of the rate of growth a as functions of the time. Show that a varies as the reciprocal of the cube of the thickness x.

8. The total energy H of a certain particle of mass m that has moved a distance s and has attained a velocity v is given by

$$H = \tfrac{1}{2}mv^2 + mfs$$

where f is a constant. If the total energy is a constant of the motion, show that the acceleration is equal to the constant $-f$.

9. The energy equation for a particle of constant mass m moving under gravity g with a vertical velocity v at a height x near the earth's surface is

$$H = \tfrac{1}{2}mv^2 + mgx$$

where H is the constant total energy and where H, m, v, g, and x are in suitable units. Show that the acceleration is constant and equal to $-g$.

10. The velocity v of a rocket moving vertically after the burnout of its motors is given as a function of s, the distance from the centre of the earth, by

$$v^2 = v_0^2 + k \left(\frac{1}{s} - \frac{1}{s_0} \right)$$

where k is a positive constant,
$\quad\quad v_0$ is the velocity at the time of motor burnout,
$\quad\quad s_0$ is the distance from the centre of the earth at motor burnout.

Show that the deceleration due to gravity is inversely proportional to the square of the distance. If $v_0^2 < k\dfrac{1}{s_0}$, find the maximum height reached by the rocket. What happens if $v_0^2 > k\dfrac{1}{s_0}$?

7.2. Rate Problems

In many situations in science and engineering, it is very difficult to measure directly the rate of change of the property we wish to study. However, it may be relatively easy to measure the rate of change of some other property or quantity. If the two properties can be related to each other mathematically, then from the measurement of the rate of change of the simply observed quantity, we can calculate the rate of change of the other quantity that we wish to study.

Example 1. The velocity of an airplane when climbing to cruising altitude is 300 m.p.h. (440 ft/sec), and the angle of climb is 45°. How rapidly does the altitude of the plane increase?

Solution: Let s feet be the distance travelled by the airplane in time t seconds, and let y feet be the altitude of the airplane. Then

$$y = s \sin 45°,$$

$$y = \frac{s}{\sqrt{2}}. \tag{1}$$

Also,

$$s = 440t. \tag{2}$$

Equation (1) determines y as a function of s, and equation (2) determines s as a function of t.

Rate of increase of altitude in feet per second is

$$D_t y = (D_s y)(D_t s) \qquad \text{(chain rule)}$$

$$= \left[D_s\left(\frac{s}{\sqrt{2}}\right) \right] (D_t s)$$

$$= \left(\frac{1}{\sqrt{2}}\right)(440)$$

$$= 220(\sqrt{2})$$

$$\simeq 311.$$

The altitude increases at 311 feet per second (approximately).

In this example, we can check the result by a simple velocity diagram which shows that the rate of climb is

$$v = 440 \sin 45°$$

$$= 220\sqrt{2}$$

$$\simeq 311.$$

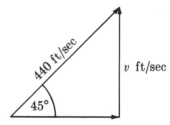

Example 2. A sphere is expanding, and the measured rate of increase of its radius is 5 inches per minute. At what rate is its volume increasing when the radius is 5 inches?

Solution: Let the radius of the sphere at any time t minutes be given by r inches, and let the volume be V cubic inches. Then

$$V = \tfrac{4}{3}\pi r^3 \tag{1}$$

and

$$D_t r = 5 . \tag{2}$$

Now (1) gives V as a function of r, and (2) gives the rate of change of r with respect to time.

Rate of change of the volume with respect to time is

$$
\begin{aligned}
D_t V &= (D_r V)(D_t r) && \text{(chain rule)}\\
&= [D_r(\tfrac{4}{3}\pi r^3)](D_t r)\\
&= (4\pi r^2)(5)\\
&= 20\pi r^2 .
\end{aligned}
$$

Therefore, when the radius of the sphere is 5 inches, the volume is increasing at 500π cubic inches per minute.

Example 3. A conical glass vase is being filled with liquid at a rate of 10 cubic inches per second. The vase is 20 inches high and 3 inches in radius at the top. Find the rate at which the water level is rising when the depth is 10 inches.

Solution: Let V be the volume of water in cubic inches at time t seconds, and let h be the height of the water in inches above the vertex and r the radius of the water surface in inches. Then

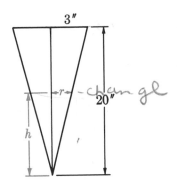

$$V = \frac{1}{3}\pi r^2 h ,$$

and

$$\frac{r}{h} = \frac{3}{20} .$$

Therefore,

$$V = \frac{1}{3}\pi \left(\frac{3}{20}\right)^2 h^3 ,$$

$$V = \frac{3\pi}{400}\, h^3 ,$$

and

$$D_h V = \frac{9\pi}{400}\, h^2 .$$

Also,

$$D_t V = 10 .$$

But

$$D_t V = (D_h V)(D_t h) ; \qquad \text{(chain rule)}$$

hence,

$$10 = \frac{9\pi h^2}{400}(D_t h) ,$$

and

$$D_t h = \frac{4000}{9\pi h^2} .$$

When $h = 10$,

$$D_t h = \frac{4000}{9\pi(100)}$$

$$= \frac{40}{9\pi} .$$

The rate at which the water level rises when the depth is 10 inches is $40/9\pi$ inches per second.

EXERCISE 7.2

1. A cylindrical tank has a radius of 3 feet and a depth of 10 feet. It is being filled at a rate of 5 cubic feet per minute. How fast is the surface rising?

2. A rectangular prismatic tank has the following dimensions: length is 10 feet, width is 6 feet, and depth is 8 feet. It is being filled with water, and the surface level is rising at 6 inches per minute. What is the rate of inflow of water to the tank?

3. A pond that lies in a crater is being drained at a rate of 1000 cubic feet per minute. If the crater has the shape of an inverted cone of radius 200 feet (at the original water level) and original depth 50 feet (at centre), find that rate at which the water level begins to fall. How fast is it falling when the water at the centre is only 20 feet deep?

4. A water trough on a farm has an isosceles triangular cross section which is 24 inches across the top and 8 inches deep. The trough is 8 feet long. If it is empty and then is filled at a rate of 4 cubic feet of water per minute, how fast does the water level rise when the deepest point is 7 inches?

5. A spherical weather balloon has a diameter of 5 feet when it is 5000 feet high. It is observed that the diameter increases at a constant rate of 2 inches per minute as it continues to rise. At what rate is the volume increasing when the diameter is 10 feet? At what rate is the surface area increasing then?

6. The trough down the centre of a cattle barn is 2 feet wide at the top and 1 foot at the bottom. It is 1 foot deep and 80 feet long. It is filled at a rate of 10 cubic feet per minute. What is the rate of rise of the water level? What is the rate when the water is 10 inches deep?

7. A 20-foot ladder which is leaning against a wall begins to slip. If the top slips down the wall at a rate of 2 feet per second, how fast is the bottom moving when it is 16 feet from the wall?

8. A man who is 6 feet tall is walking straight away from a lamppost at a rate of 4 miles per hour. The lamppost is 24 feet high. How fast is the end of his shadow moving when he is 24 feet from the foot of the lamppost?

9. A rocket rises from its launching pad with a velocity given by .25 h feet per second, where h feet is the height reached by the rocket at that time. The rocket is observed from a point 10,000 feet away from the launch pad. At what rate is the distance of the rocket from the observer changing when the rocket is at an altitude of 30,000 feet?

10. Two ships start out from harbour at the same time; one travels northeast and the other southeast. If the first has a speed of 16 knots and the second 12 knots, how fast are they separating after 1 hour?

11. A rocket is being tracked from a radar post that is 10 miles from the launch pad. The rocket rises vertically to a height of 17.32 miles and then turns through an angle of 30° from the vertical directly away from the radar post. It then travels at the constant speed of 12,000 miles per hour along a straight path for 2 minutes. How fast is it then receding from the radar post?

12. An aircraft flying at 10,000 feet and at a ground speed of 450 m.p.h. passes over the control tower and heads east. At a beacon check point 20 minutes later, it turns to head northeast. At what rate is it now receding from the control tower? At what rate is it receding from the control tower 10 minutes later? (Neglect any effects of altitude or curvature of the earth.)

13. Two railroad tracks intersect at an angle of 60° and are straight for ten miles on either side of the intersection. One train is travelling at 60 m.p.h. and another at 90 m.p.h. The slower train passes the intersection on one track 3 minutes ahead of the second on the other track. What is their minimum distance apart? How fast is the distance between them changing when they are a minimum distance apart?

14. An airplane flying due east at 400 m.p.h. passes over an airport 12 minutes before a second airplane flying south 30° west at 500 m.p.h. If the airplanes are at the same altitude, how fast will they be separating when the second plane is over the airport? When will they be nearest?

15. One plane is flying due east straight and level at 30,000 feet and at 420 m.p.h. A second plane flies due north at 40,560 feet and at 480 m.p.h. The second plane crosses above the flight path of the first plane 2 minutes after the first plane passes that point. How fast are the planes receding from each other after another 5 minutes? How fast were they approaching each other when they were a minimum distance apart?

7.3. Maxima and Minima Problems

Example 1. The velocity of a wave of length l in deep water is given by

$$v = k\sqrt{\frac{l}{a} + \frac{a}{l}} ,$$

where k and a are known positive constants. What is the length of the wave (in terms of a) for the velocity to be a minimum?

Solution:

$$v = k\sqrt{\frac{l}{a} + \frac{a}{l}} , \quad k, l, a \in Re^{+} .$$

Let

$$u = \frac{l}{a} + \frac{a}{l} ;$$

then

$$v = ku^{1/2}.$$

Therefore,

$$D_l v = D_u v \cdot D_l u$$

$$= \frac{1}{2} ku^{-1/2} \left(\frac{1}{a} - \frac{a}{l^2} \right)$$

$$= k \frac{\dfrac{1}{a} - \dfrac{a}{l^2}}{2\sqrt{\dfrac{l}{a} + \dfrac{a}{l}}} .$$

$D_l v = 0$ when $0 = \dfrac{1}{a} - \dfrac{a}{l^2}$; hence,

$$\frac{1}{a} = \frac{a}{l^2} ,$$

$$l^2 = a^2 ,$$

$$l = a .$$

A stationary value of v occurs when $l = a$, and this is the only stationary value of v for l in the domain of the problem.

As $l \to 0$, v increases without bound, and as l increases without bound, so does v; therefore, the value $v = \sqrt{2}\, k$ when $l = a$ must be a minimum.

Example 2. Two point sources of light, A and B, are 8 feet apart. The light at A is twice as strong as that at B. The intensity of light at a point is equal to the power of the light in suitable units divided by the square of the distance of the point from the light source. Find where the light intensity on the line segment AB is a minimum.

Solution: Let   the power of the light at B be W ;
then
$$\text{the power of the light at A is } 2W.$$

Let P be a point at a distance x feet from A, $0 < x < 8$.

The light intensity at P from A is $\dfrac{2W}{x^2}$.

The light intensity at P from B is $\dfrac{W}{(8 - x)^2}$.

Therefore, the total light intensity at P is

$$I = \frac{2W}{x^2} + \frac{W}{(8 - x)^2}.$$

$$\therefore \bullet \ \ D_x I = -\frac{4W}{x^3} - \frac{2W(-1)}{(8 - x)^3}$$

$$= 2W\left(-\frac{2}{x^3} + \frac{1}{(8 - x)^3}\right).$$

When $D_x I = 0$ at a maximum or minimum,

$$\frac{2}{x^3} - \frac{1}{(8 - x)^3} = 0,$$

$$\frac{2}{x^3} = \frac{1}{(8 - x)^3},$$

$$2(8 - x)^3 = x^3,$$

$$\sqrt[3]{2}\,(8 - x) = x,$$

$$(\sqrt[3]{2} + 1)x = 8\sqrt[3]{2},$$

$$x = \frac{8\sqrt[3]{2}}{\sqrt[3]{2} + 1},$$

$$x \simeq 4.46,$$

and

$$8 - x \simeq 3.54.$$

$$D_x^2 I = 2W\left(+\frac{6}{x^4} + \frac{3}{(8 - x)^4}\right)$$

$$> 0 \text{ for all } x \text{ in } 0 < x < 8.$$

Therefore, $x = 4.46$ gives a minimum value of I.

This result, that the intensity at the point is a minimum, may be inferred from the fact that the intensity increases without bound as $x \to 0$ and $x \to 8$, and the point at $x = 4.46$ is the only stationary point.

EXERCISE 7.3

1. The annual cost C (in dollars) of a natural gas pipe line of radius r (in feet) is given approximately by

$$C = ar^2 + br^{-5}$$

where a and b are constants. Determine the radius in terms of a and b for which the annual cost is a minimum.

2. A dam spillway is 100 feet wide, and the flow of water over it is h feet deep. The "head" of water which causes the flow is 10 feet. Find the value of h that makes the flow q (in cubic feet per second) a maximum if q is given by

$$q = 100h\sqrt{64(10 - h)}.$$

3. The efficiency E of a screw in mechanics is given as a function of h by

$$E = \frac{h(1 - \tfrac{1}{2}h)}{(h + \tfrac{1}{2})}$$

where h is the tangent of the angle of pitch of the screw. For what value of h is E a maximum?

4. An electric generator of internal resistance of 1 ohm produces a 12-volt output. The efficiency e of the generator when it yields a current of I amperes is given as a function of I by the formula

$$e = \frac{12I}{P_0 + 12I + I^2},$$

where P_0 is a constant intrinsic power loss. For what value of I is e a maximum?

5. The power P (in foot-pounds per second) transmitted by a particular belt drive to a machine is given as a function of the linear velocity v of the belt by the formula

$$P = v(100 - \tfrac{3}{16}v^2).$$

For what value of v is P a maximum, and what is the maximum value of P?

6. An electric current of 1 amp. flows in a circular coil 5 cm in radius. The force F on a small magnet at a point on the axis of the coil at a distance x cm from the centre of the coil is given by

$$F = \frac{100x}{(25 + x^2)^{5/2}}.$$

Find the maximum value of F.

7. The cost in dollars per hour of running a steam boat is $2v^3$, where v is the speed in knots relative to the water-current speed. A voyage of 100 nautical miles has to be made against a current of 4 knots. What is the minimum cost of the voyage, and at what speed is it travelled?

8. Two lights A and B are 140 feet apart, and their powers are 216 watts and 512 watts respectively. The intensity of illumination at a point is given by the power of the source of light divided by the square of the distance of the point from the source. At what point between A and B is the intensity of illumination a minimum?

9. In a laboratory experiment, n observed measurements of a certain quantity are found to be $m_1, m_2, m_3, \cdots, m_n$. If each measurement were to be taken as m instead of its observed value, then the differences from the observed values would be $m_1 - m, m_2 - m, \cdots, m_n - m$. Show that

$$V = (m_1 - m)^2 + (m_2 - m)^2 + \cdots + (m_n - m)^2$$

is a minimum, if V is considered as the value of a function of m, when

$$m = \frac{m_1 + m_2 + \cdots + m_n}{n}.$$

7.4. Maxima and Minima Problems in Geometry

Example 1. An open topped box in the shape of a rectangular prism with square ends has to be constructed with 54 sq ft of 1″ lumber. Neglecting the effects of the thickness of the sides, find the dimensions of the box of maximum volume.

Solution: Let x represent the width or depth in feet and y represent the length in feet. Then volume V of the box in cubic feet is given by

$$V = x^2 y, \quad x, y \in Re^+.$$

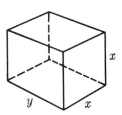

The surface area S in square feet is given by

$$S = 3xy + 2x^2 = 54 ;$$
$$\therefore \quad 3xy = 54 - 2x^2 ,$$
$$y = \frac{54 - 2x^2}{3x} .$$

Therefore,

$$V = x^2 \frac{54 - 2x^2}{3x} ,$$

$$V = 18x - \frac{2}{3}x^3 ,$$

$$D_x V = 18 - 2x^2 .$$

When $D_xV = 0$ at a maximum or minimum,

$$2x^2 = 18 \,,$$
$$x^2 = 9 \,,$$
$$x = 3 \,, \quad \text{as } x \in Re^+.$$

Therefore,

$$y = \frac{54 - 2(3^2)}{3(3)}$$
$$= \frac{54 - 18}{9}$$
$$= \frac{36}{9}$$
$$= 4 \,.$$

The box is 4 feet long and 3 feet wide and deep.

We can verify the fact that this value is a maximum by considering the value of D_x^2V.

$$D_x^2V = -4x \,,$$

and, when $x = 3$,

$$D_x^2V = -12 \,.$$

D_x^2V is negative when $x = 3$; therefore, the value found is a maximum.

For reference, we now present a solution of one of the more complicated examples that can arise. The complication is in the algebraic manipulation, not in the basic calculus concepts of the conditions for maxima and minima.

Example 2. Two towns A and B are 4 miles and 8 miles from the straight shore of a lake. D and E are the points on the shore line nearest to A and B respectively, and D and E are 9 miles apart. A water pipeline is to be laid from a pumping station P on the lake shore. Find the position of the pumping station so that the length of pipe required is a minimum.

Solution: Let the distance of DP in miles be x, $x \in Re^+$, and let the length of pipe in miles be y, $y \in Re^+$. Then

and

$$AP^2 = 4^2 + x^2$$

$$BP^2 = 8^2 + (9 - x)^2$$
$$= 64 + 81 - 18x + x^2$$
$$= 145 - 18x + x^2 \,.$$

$$y = AP + PB ;$$

$$\therefore \quad y = \sqrt{16 + x^2} + \sqrt{145 - 18x + x^2}$$
$$= (16 + x^2)^{1/2} + (145 - 18x + x^2)^{1/2} ;$$

$$\therefore \quad D_x y = \tfrac{1}{2}(16 + x^2)^{1/2} \cdot 2x + \tfrac{1}{2}(145 - 18x + x^2)^{-1/2} \cdot 2(x - 9)$$
$$= \frac{x}{\sqrt{16 + x^2}} + \frac{x - 9}{\sqrt{145 - 18x + x^2}} .$$

For y to be a minimum, $D_x y = 0$; hence, for a minimum,

$$\frac{x\sqrt{145 - 18x + x^2} + (x - 9)\sqrt{16 + x^2}}{\sqrt{16 + x^2}\sqrt{145 - 18x + x^2}} = 0 ,$$

and this is zero only if the numerator is zero. .Therefore,

$$x\sqrt{145 - 18x + x^2} + (x - 9)\sqrt{16 + x^2} = 0 ;$$

$$\therefore \quad x\sqrt{145 - 18x + x^2} = (9 - x)\sqrt{16 + x^2} ,$$

$$x^2(145 - 18x + x^2) = (9 - x)^2(16 + x^2) ,$$

$$145x^2 - 18x^3 + x^4 = (81 - 18x + x^2)(16 + x^2)$$
$$= (81)(16) - (18)(16)x + 16x^2 + 81x^2 - 18x^3 + x^4 .$$

$$\therefore \quad (145 - 81 - 16)x^2 + (18)(16)x - (81)(16) = 0 ,$$
$$48x^2 + (18)(16)x - (81)(16) = 0 ,$$
$$x^2 + \quad 6x \quad - \quad 27 \quad = 0 ,$$
$$(x - 3)(x + 9) = 0 ,$$

and, since $x \in Re^+$, $x = 3$.

The corresponding value of y is given by

$$y = \sqrt{16 + 9} + \sqrt{145 - 54 + 9}$$
$$= \sqrt{25} + \sqrt{100}$$
$$= 5 + 10$$
$$= 15 .$$

If the pumping station were to be built at D,

$$y = 4 + \sqrt{81 + 64} = 4 + \sqrt{145} > 4 + \sqrt{144} = 16 > 15 ,$$

and if the pumping station were to be built at E,

$$y = 8 + \sqrt{81 + 16} = 8 + \sqrt{97} > 8 + \sqrt{81} = 17 > 15 .$$

Now $x = 3$ gives the *only* stationary value of y in the domain of x; therefore this value must be a minimum. The pumping station is built 3 miles from D and 6 miles from E.

EXERCISE 7.4

1. What is the maximum possible area of an isosceles triangle if the two equal sides are each 6 inches long?

2. The perimeter of a triangle is 16 inches. One side is 6 inches long. What are the lengths of the other two sides if the triangle has the largest possible area? (Use

$$A = \sqrt{s(s-a)(s-b)(s-c)}$$

where a, b, c are the lengths of the sides and $2s = a + b + c$.)

3. A memorial window is in the form of a rectangle surmounted by an equilateral triangle with each side equal to the width of the rectangle. The perimeter of the window is 30 feet. What is the maximum area of the window?

4. A Norman window is in the form of a rectangle surmounted by a semicircle with diameter equal to the width of the rectangle. If the perimeter of the window is 40 feet, what is the maximum area?

5. A line through the point $P(2, 2)$ cuts the x and y axes at A and B respectively. Find the minimum length of the line segment AB.

6. If, in question (5), the position of the point P is changed to $(3, 4)$, what is the length of the minimum line segment intercepted by the axes?

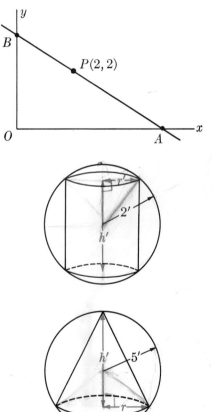

7. A right circular cylinder has to be designed to fit inside a sphere of 4 feet diameter so that each of the top and bottom touches the sphere along its complete circular edge. What are the dimensions of the cylinder of maximum volume, and what is the maximum volume?

8. The vertex of a right circular cone and the circular edge of its base lie on the surface of a sphere. The sphere has a radius of 5 feet. Find the dimensions of the cone of maximum volume that can be fitted into the sphere.

9. A ship is sailing due north at 12 knots when it observes another ship dead ahead at a distance of 15 nautical miles. The second ship is sailing due east at 9 knots. What is the closest distance of approach of the two ships?

10. A power house, P, is on one bank of a straight river 200 feet wide, and a factory, F, is on the opposite bank 400 feet downstream from P. The cable has to be taken across the river under water at a cost of $2.00 per foot. On land the cost is $1.00 per foot. What path should be chosen so that the cost is minimized?

11. A man in a boat is 3 miles off shore and wishes to go to a point on the shore that is 5 miles from his present position. The man can walk at 4 miles per hour and can row the boat at 2 miles per hour. To what point on the shore should he row so that he can reach his destination as soon as possible?

Chapter Summary

Derivatives of algebraic functions and functions defined implicitly applied to problems of kinematics, rates of change, and maxima and minima

REVIEW EXERCISE 7

1. The velocity v of a body at any time t is given by
$$v = 5(1 + t^3)^{1/2}.$$
Find the acceleration in terms of the time.

2. The distance s of a particle from a fixed origin at any time t is given by
$$s = \frac{500t}{10 + t}.$$
Find the velocity and acceleration in terms of t.

3. The velocity v and distance travelled s of a moving body are related by
$$5v^2 = 10s^2 - 1000.$$
Find the acceleration in terms of s.

4. Sand is contained in a hopper that is in the shape of an inverted cone with its axis vertical. The vertex angle of the cone is 90°. Sand flows out of the vertex at a rate of 10 cubic feet per minute. Find the rate at which the surface level of the sand is falling when the depth of sand above the vertex is 10 feet. Assume that the top surface is always flat and horizontal.

5. An observer is 4 miles from a straight railroad track on which a train is travelling at a constant speed of 60 m.p.h. How fast is the distance from the train to the observer decreasing when the train is 5 miles from the observer?

6. A tethered observation balloon is drifting downwind, without changing its altitude, at 6 m.p.h. We assume that the tethering cable runs from the ground to the balloon in a straight line. If the balloon is at a height of 1000 feet, how fast is the cable unwinding when 4000 feet of cable has been let out?

7. (a) The rate v of a chemical reaction involving the transformation of one compound into another new compound is given by

$$v = kx(a - x),$$

where k and a are constants and x is the concentration of the new compound. For what value of x is v a maximum, and what is the maximum value?

(b) In a more complex reaction,

$$v = k(a - x)(b + x)$$

where k, a and b are constants. For what value of x is v a maximum, and what is the maximum value?

8. A trophy is to be made in the shape of a cone, and its volume has to be 288π cubic inches. Find the dimensions of the cone so that the cost of covering its lateral area with gold leaf is a minimum. (Lateral area is

$$S = 2\pi rs,$$

where r is the radius of base and s is the slant height of surface.)

9. A spring is located inside a forest area 200 yards from the nearest point on a straight road. This nearest point is 1000 yards from a crossroads where a structure housing a filling station and a restaurant is to be built. A water pipeline can be laid along the side of the road at a cost of $10 per hundred feet, but in the forest area, the cost rises to $12 per hundred feet. At what point on the road should the pipeline start into the forest area if the cost of laying the pipeline from the spring to the structure is to be a minimum?

10. A line through the point $P(2, 3)$ cuts the x-axis at A and the y-axis at B. If O is the origin, find the equation of the line so that $OA + OB$ is a minimum.

11. $P(3, 1)$ and $Q(-2, 4)$ are two points of the ellipse given by the equation

$$3x^2 + y^2 = 28.$$

Find the co-ordinates of a point R on the ellipse so that the area of $\triangle PQR$ is a maximum.

Chapter 8

SOLUTIONS OF $D_x y = f(x)$

8.1. Primitives

If F is a function of x in a given domain of definition, then at each value of x in that domain we have a unique value $F(x)$ of F, and we have a unique value $F'(x)$ of the derivative F' if it exists for that value of x.

Example 1. If
$$F : x \rightarrow x^2 ,$$
then
$$y = F(x) = x^2$$
and
$$D_x y = F'(x) = 2x .$$

We may now investigate the following problem: If we are given a function $f : x \rightarrow f(x)$, can we find a function F such that $F'(x) = f(x)$?

Example 2. If
$$f : x \rightarrow 2x ,$$
then
$$f(x) = 2x ,$$
and
$$F : x \rightarrow x^2$$
is a function such that
$$F'(x) = f(x) .$$

However, note that $F : x \rightarrow x^2$ is not the only function for which $F'(x) = 2x$. $F : x \rightarrow x^2 + 2$, $F : x \rightarrow x^2 - 5$, or indeed any function $F : x \rightarrow x^2 + c$, where c is a constant, has the derivative $F' : x \rightarrow 2x$ and so satisfies $F'(x) = f(x)$ where $f : x \rightarrow 2x$. In this case, certainly, there is not a unique function F such that $F'(x) = f(x)$ for a given function $f : x \rightarrow f(x)$, although to each given function F there does correspond a unique derivative F'.

137

In general, if we are given

$$D_x y = f(x) \,,$$

and if we recognize $f(x)$ as the value of the derivative of some function, either from tables of derivatives or from an example we have worked previously, then we can find

$$y = F(x)$$

such that

$$D_x y = F'(x) = f(x) \,.$$

More sophisticated methods are used if $f(x)$ is complicated, but for the present, we shall be content to find $F(x)$ by trying to recognize $f(x)$ as a known derivative. When we find $y = F(x)$ such that $D_x y = f(x) = F'(x)$ where we know $f(x)$, we say we have found *a solution* of the equation $D_x y = f(x)$.

Example 3.   Find a solution of $D_x y = 8x$.

Solution:

$$D_x(x^2) = 2x \; ;$$
$$\therefore \quad D_x(4x^2) = 8x \,.$$

Therefore, $y = 4x^2$ is a solution of $D_x y = 8x$.

Example 4.   Find a function F such that F' is the function

$$F' : x \rightarrow 3x^2 \,.$$

Solution:

$$D_x(x^3) = 3x^2 \,.$$

Therefore, $F : x \rightarrow x^3$ is such that $F' : x \rightarrow 3x^2$.

Example 5.   Find a solution of $D_x y = 2x + 5$.

Solution:

$$D_x(x^2) = 2x \,,$$
$$D_x(x) = 1 \,,$$
$$D_x(5x) = 5 \,,$$

and so

$$D_x(x^2 + 5x) = 2x + 5 \,.$$

Therefore, $y = x^2 + 5x$ is a solution of $D_x y = 2x + 5$.

DEFINITION.   Any function $F : x \rightarrow F(x) = y$ which is such that

$$F'(x) = D_x y = f(x) \quad \text{for} \quad x \in Re$$

s called a *primitive*, or anti-derivative, of $f : x \rightarrow f(x)$.

Theorem.   If $F : x \rightarrow F(x)$ is a primitive of $f : x \rightarrow f(x)$, then

$$G : x \rightarrow G(x) = F(x) + c,$$

where c is an arbitrary constant, is also a primitive of f.

Proof:

$$G : x \rightarrow F(x) + c,$$

$$\therefore \quad G' : x \rightarrow F'(x) + 0 \qquad \text{(derivative of sum)},$$

and

$$F'(x) = f(x) \qquad \text{(definition of primitive)}.$$

$$\therefore \quad G' : x \rightarrow f(x),$$

but

$$G' : x \rightarrow G'(x) \qquad \text{(definition of derivative)};$$

$$\therefore \quad G'(x) = f(x).$$

Therefore, by the definition of a primitive, G is a primitive of f.

The function

$$G : x \rightarrow F(x) + c$$

is called the *general primitive* of f if

$$G'(x) = F'(x) = f(x) :$$

$$y = F(x) + c$$

is called the *general solution* of

$$D_x y = F'(x).$$

Example 6.   Find the general primitive determined by $D_x y = x^2 + 5x$.

Solution:

$$D_x(x^3) = 3x^2 ;$$

$$\therefore \quad D_x\left(\frac{x^3}{3}\right) = x^2.$$

$$D_x(x^2) = 2x ;$$

$$\therefore \quad D_x\left(\frac{5x^2}{2}\right) = 5x.$$

$$\therefore \quad D_x\left(\frac{x^3}{3} + \frac{5x^2}{2}\right) = x^2 + 5x.$$

Thus,

$$F : x \rightarrow \frac{x^3}{3} + \frac{5x^2}{2} + c$$

is the general primitive determined by $D_x y = x^2 + 5x$.

Example 7. Solve $$D_x y = 3 - \frac{2}{x^2}.$$

Solution:
$$D_x x = 1 ,$$
$$D_x\left(\frac{1}{x}\right) = \frac{-1}{x^2} .$$

Therefore, the required solution is

$$y = 3x + \frac{2}{x} + c .$$

Example 8. Solve $$D_x y = 4(x + 1)^3 .$$

Solution:
$$D_x(x + 1)^4 = 4(x + 1)^3 \cdot 1 . \qquad \text{(chain rule)}$$

Therefore, the required solution is

$$y = (x + 1)^4 + c .$$

Example 9. Solve $$D_x y = (2x + 3)^2 .$$

Solution (i):
$$(2x + 3)^2 = 4x^2 + 12x + 9 ;$$

$$\therefore \quad D_x y = 4x^2 + 12x + 9 .$$

Therefore, the required solution is
$$y = \tfrac{4}{3}x^3 + 6x^2 + 9x + c .$$

Solution (ii):
$$D_x(2x + 3)^3 = 3(2x + 3)^2 \cdot D_x(2x + 3) \qquad \text{(chain rule)}$$
$$= 3(2x + 3)^2 \cdot 2$$
$$= 6(2x + 3)^2 .$$

Now
$$D_x y = (2x + 3)^2 .$$

Therefore, the required solution is
$$y = \tfrac{1}{6}(2x + 3)^3 + k .$$

Note that, from Solution (ii),
$$y = \tfrac{1}{6}(8x^3 + 36x^2 + 54x + 27) + k$$
$$= \tfrac{4}{3}x^3 + 6x^2 + 9x + \tfrac{9}{2} + k .$$

Thus, we see that both solutions determine general primitives of $x \to (2x + 3)^2$, as they differ at most by a constant.

The General Primitive of $f:x \to ax^n$, where a is any constant

If $y = ax^{n+1}$, then $D_x y = (n+1)ax^n$, and so

$$D_x\left(\frac{ax^{n+1}}{n+1}\right) = ax^n.$$

Hence, the general primitive of $f:x \to ax^n$ is

$$F:x \to \frac{ax^{n+1}}{n+1} + c,$$

and the general solution of $D_x y = ax^n$ is

$$y = \frac{ax^{n+1}}{n+1} + c.$$

EXERCISE 8.1

Find a solution for each of the following. (The general result for the primitive of x^n is not to be used in questions (1) to (10).)

1. $D_x y = x^7$

2. $D_x y = x^5 + x^3$

3. $D_t s = t^4 + 2t^2$

4. $D_u v = u^3 - 5u^2$

5. $D_x y = \frac{3}{5}x^{2/3}$

6. $D_x y = -2x^{-3}$

7. $D_x y = (\sqrt{x})^4$

8. $D_x y = \sqrt{5x}$

9. $D_x y = (2x+1)^2$

10. $D_t s = (2+4t)^{1/2}$

Find the general primitive for each of the following.

11. $f:x \to 6x^2 + 8x^3$

12. $f:x \to \frac{2}{3}x^{-1/3}$

13. $f:x \to x^{5/2} + 1$

14. $f:x \to (x+2)^{1/3}$

15. $g:x \to (x-3)^{-2}$

16. $g:t \to \frac{1}{3}t^{-4/3} + t$

Solve each of the following.

17. $D_x y = \sqrt{x} + \dfrac{1}{\sqrt{x}}$

18. $D_x y = \dfrac{x^2 + 4}{x^4}$

19. $D_t s = (t^{1/2} + 2)^2$

20. $D_t v = (t^2 + 2t + 1)^2$

21. $D_x y = x(x^2 + 9)$

22. $D_x y = 3x^2(x^3 - 8)$

23. $D_x y = x^2(x^3 + 2)$

24. $D_x y = x(x^2 + 1)^{1/2}$

25. $D_x y = \dfrac{2x}{(x^2 + 1)^3}$

8.2. Families of Curves

The slope of the curve determined by $y = F(x)$ in the Cartesian plane is given by $D_x y = F'(x)$. If we are told that the slope of a certain curve at x is $f(x)$, then *any* curve determined by $y = F(x) + c$, where c is a constant and $D_x y = F'(x) = f(x)$, has this slope at x. The set of curves determined by $y = F(x) + c$ for a set of values of the real number c is called a *family* of curves. One curve of the family corresponds to each value of c. The real number c is referred to as the *parameter* of the family of curves.

Example 1. Find the family of curves if the slope of any one of the curves at x is given by $2x - 1$.

Solution: For the family of curves,

$$y = F(x) + c,$$

and

$$D_x y = F'(x) = 2x - 1 ;$$

therefore,

$$y = x^2 - x + c$$

is the equation of the required family of curves.

(Check: $D_x y = 2x - 1 + 0$.)

The partial graphs of $y = x^2 - x + c$ are shown in Figure 8.1 for some values of c.

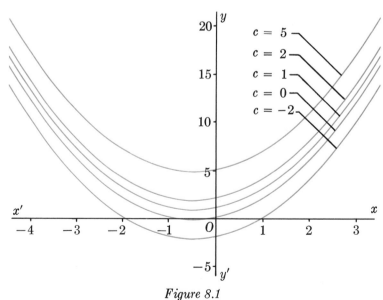

Figure 8.1

Example 2. Find the family of curves whose slope is given by

$$D_x y = 3(x + 2)^2.$$

Solution (i):

$$D_x y = 3(x + 2)^2$$
$$= 3x^2 + 12x + 12 \; ;$$

therefore,

$$y = x^3 + 6x^2 + 12x + c \, ,$$

where c is a constant, is the equation of the required family of curves.

(Check: $D_x y = 3x^2 + 6(2x) + 12 + 0$.)

Solution (ii): If we put

$$u = x + 2 \, ,$$

then

$$D_u(u^3) = 3u^2 \, ,$$
$$D_x u = 1 \; ;$$

$$\therefore \quad D_x[(x + 2)^3] = 3u^2 \cdot 1 \qquad \text{(chain rule)}$$
$$= 3(x + 2)^2 \, .$$

Hence,

$$y = (x + 2)^3 + k \, ,$$

where k is a constant, is the equation of the required family of curves. (Check that this solution does satisfy $D_x y = 3(x + 2)^2$.)

Note that $(x + 2)^3 + k = x^3 + 6x^2 + 12x + 8 + k$ so that Solution (ii) may be written as

$$y = x^3 + 6x^2 + 12x + 8 + k \, .$$

At first sight, this does not appear to agree with Solution (i):

$$y = x^3 + 6x^2 + 12x + c \, .$$

However, the two forms of solution are in fact the same, for although c and k are constants, they are not necessarily identical; the solutions are the same if the equation $c = 8 + k$ is used to determine c in terms of k, or k in terms of c. The numbers c and k are referred to as *arbitrary* constants because, in the general solution, the value of c or k is not determined.

The arbitrary constant in the general solution for a family of curves becomes determined if a particular curve of the family is required, for example, the curve that passes through the origin, or through the point $(1, 2)$, or through any *fixed* point in the plane.

Example 3.   Find the equation of the curve passing through the origin whose slope is given by

$$D_x y = 2x - 1.$$

Solution: From Example 1, the family of curves with the given slope is given by

$$y = x^2 - x + c.$$

The required curve passes through $(0,0)$; that is, $y = 0$, $x = 0$ satisfy the equation of the curve.   Therefore,

$$0 = 0 - 0 + c,$$
$$c = 0.$$

Hence, the required curve has the equation

$$y = x^2 - x.$$

(The graph of this equation is the curve marked $c = 0$ in Figure 8.1.)

Example 4.   Find the equation of the curve passing through $(-1, 3)$ whose slope is given by

$$D_x y = 3(x + 2)^2.$$

Solution (i):   By Example 2, Solution (i),

$$y = x^3 + 6x^2 + 12x + c$$

is the equation of the family of curves with the given slope.   The required curve passes through $(-1, 3)$; therefore,

$$3 = (-1)^3 + 6(-1)^2 + 12(-1) + c,$$
$$3 = -1 + 6 - 12 + c,$$
$$c = 10.$$

Hence, the required curve is the graph of the equation

$$y = x^3 + 6x^2 + 12x + 10.$$

Solution (ii):   By Example 2, Solution (ii),

$$y = (x + 2)^3 + k$$

is the equation of the family of curves with the given slope.   The required curve passes through $(-1, 3)$.   Therefore,

$$3 = (-1 + 2)^3 + k,$$
$$3 = 1 + k,$$
$$k = 2.$$

Hence, the required curve is the graph of the equation

$$y = (x + 2)^3 + 2 \, .$$

(Check that these two results are identical and that the curve does pass through $(-1, 3)$.)

EXERCISE 8.2

Find the families of curves the slopes of which are given by the following.

1. $\frac{2}{3}$

2. $4x + 2$

3. x^2

4. $(x + 2)^3$

5. $\dfrac{-1}{8x^2}$

6. $\dfrac{-2}{(x + 1)^3}$

7. $x^{1/2} + 1$

8. $\frac{1}{2}x^{-1/2}$

9. $\dfrac{x}{\sqrt{25 - x^2}}$

10. $\dfrac{x}{\sqrt{x^2 - 25}}$

11. For each of the families of curves in questions (1) to (10), find (if possible) the equation of the curve that passes through
    (a) $(0, 0)$,   (b) $(4, 3)$,   (c) $(-1, 1)$.
    Sketch the graph of the equation in each case.

12 Show that

$$x^2 + y^2 = c^2 \, ,$$

where c is an arbitrary real number, is a family of circles and that the equation is a general solution of

$$D_x y = -\frac{x}{y} \, .$$

8.3. Acceleration, Velocity and Distance

We recall that if s feet represents the distance of a body from a given origin of measurement, v feet per second represents the velocity, and a feet per second per second represents the acceleration, then $D_t s = v$ and $D_t v = a$. (In other systems of units for measurement of distance and time, corresponding units must be used for velocity and acceleration, for example, (a) miles, miles per hour, and miles per hour per hour, or (b) centimetres, centimetres per second, centimetres per second per second.)   Thus, to find v when we are given a, we have to solve $D_t v = a$, and to find s when we are given v, we have to solve $D_t s = v$. To determine v uniquely from given values for a, we must also know one ordered pair of values (t, v). To determine s uniquely from given values of v, we must also know one ordered pair of values (t, s).

Example 1.   The acceleration of a particle in units of ft/sec^2 is given by $a = -32$. The velocity is v ft/sec and the distance from a given origin is s feet. The time t is measured in seconds. Find v at any time t if $v = 64$ when $t = 0$. Also find s at any time t if $s = 16$ when $t = 0$.

Solution:

$$a = -32 ,$$
$$D_t v = -32 ,$$
$$v = -32t + c .$$

When $t = 0$, $v = 64$; hence,

$$64 = 0 + c ,$$
$$c = 64 .$$

Therefore,

$$v = -32t + 64$$

is the required velocity.

$$D_t s = -32t + 64 ,$$
$$s = -16t^2 + 64t + k .$$

When $t = 0$, $s = 16$; hence,

$$16 = 0 + 0 + k ,$$
$$k = 16 .$$

Therefore,

$$s = -16t^2 + 64t + 16$$
$$= 16(1 + 4t - t^2)$$

is the required distance.

Example 2.   A ball is thrown vertically upwards at 64 ft/sec against the constant acceleration of 32 ft/sec^2 due to gravity. Find the velocity and height at any time t if height is measured upwards from the point of projection. When does the ball return to its starting point?

Solution: Let s represent the height in feet at time t seconds, v the velocity upwards in ft/sec at time t seconds, and a the acceleration upwards in ft/sec^2 at time t seconds; then

$$D_t v = a = -32 ,$$
$$v = -32t + c .$$

When $t = 0$, $v = 64$; hence,

$$64 = 0 + c .$$

Therefore,
$$v = D_t s = -32t + 64 ,$$
$$s = -16t^2 + 64t + k .$$

When $t = 0$, $s = 0$; hence,
$$0 = 0 + 0 + k .$$
Therefore,
$$s = -16t^2 + 64t .$$

At the starting point, $s = 0$; therefore, the time back to the starting point is given by
$$0 = -16t^2 + 64t ,$$
that is,
$$t = 4, \quad \text{or} \quad t = 0 \quad \text{(the original starting time).}$$

Hence, the ball returns to the starting point after 4 seconds.

Example 3. The acceleration of a particle is $16(t + 2)^{-2}$ ft/sec². Find the velocity at any time if the velocity at time $t = 0$ (in seconds) is 8 ft/sec.

Solution:
$$a = D_t v = 16(t + 2)^{-2} ,$$
$$v = -16(t + 2)^{-1} + c .$$

When $t = 0$, $v = 8$; hence,
$$8 = -16(\tfrac{1}{2}) + c ,$$
$$c = 16 .$$
Therefore,
$$v = 16[1 - (t + 2)^{-1}]$$
$$= 16\left(1 - \frac{1}{t + 2}\right)$$
$$= 16\left(\frac{t + 1}{t + 2}\right)$$

is the required velocity.

Example 4. The velocity of a particle is given by $t(1 - t^2)^{1/2}$ cm/sec. Find the distance s in centimetres at any time t in seconds if $s = 1$ when $t = 0$.

Solution: Now
$$D_t(1 - t^2)^{3/2} = \tfrac{3}{2}(1 - t^2)^{1/2} \cdot D_t(1 - t^2) \qquad \text{(chain rule)}$$
$$= \tfrac{3}{2}(1 - t^2)^{1/2} \cdot (-2t)$$
$$= -3t(1 - t^2)^{1/2} .$$
But
$$D_t s = t(1 - t^2)^{1/2} ;$$
therefore,
$$s = -\tfrac{1}{3}(1 - t^2)^{3/2} + c .$$

When $t = 0$, $s = 1$; hence,

$$1 = -\tfrac{1}{3} + c,$$
$$c = \tfrac{4}{3}.$$

Therefore,

$$s = \tfrac{1}{3}[4 - (1 - t^2)^{3/2}]$$

is the required distance.

Example 5.   The acceleration of a spring-driven model car is initially 20 cm/sec², and it decreases at a constant rate of 2 cm/sec² per second as the spring runs down.   Find the velocity in cm/sec at any time if the car is at rest when $t = 0$.

Solution: Let v represent the velocity in cm/sec at time t seconds and a the acceleration in cm/sec² at time t seconds. Then the rate of increase of a is $D_t a$. But the rate of decrease of a is 2 cm/sec³; therefore, the rate of increase of a is -2 cm/sec³.   That is,

$$D_t a = -2 \, ;$$

therefore,

$$a = -2t + c.$$

When $t = 0$, $a = 20$; hence,

$$20 = 0 + c.$$

Therefore,

$$a = D_t v = -2t + 20 \, ;$$
$$v = -t^2 + 20t + k.$$

When $t = 0$, $v = 0$; hence,

$$0 = 0 + 0 + k.$$

Therefore,

$$v = 20t - t^2.$$

is the required velocity.

EXERCISE 8.3

Find the formula for the distance, giving the distance in terms of the time, if

1. $v = 1 + 2t$ and $s = 3$ when $t = 0$;

2. $v = t^2 - 2t + 3$ and $s = 8$ when $t = 1$;

3. $v = 1 - 2t^{-2}$ and $s = 4$ when $t = 1$;

4. $v = t^2 + t^{-2}$ and $s = 1$ when $t = 1$;

5. $v = (t + 1)(t - 5)$ and $s = 0$ when $t = 0$.

Find the formula for the velocity and the distance in terms of time if

6. $a = 2 + 36t$ and $v = 3,$ $s = 0$ when $t = 0$;

7. $a = 4 - 2t + 3t^2$ and $v = 10,$ $s = 4$ when $t = 1$;

8. $a = 1 - 2t^{-3}$ and $v = 4,$ $s = 6$ when $t = 1$;

9. $a = (t + 2)(t - 4)$ and $v = 2,$ $s = 0$ when $t = 0$;

10. $a = 10 - 2t$ and $v = 0,$ $s = 0$ when $t = 0$.

(Formulae for velocity and distance must *not* be used in any of the following questions.   The acceleration due to gravity may be taken as 32 ft/sec².)

11. An object is dropped from a height of 576 feet under the constant acceleration of gravity.   Find the velocity and distance fallen at any time.

12. An object is to be thrown upwards and is to reach a height of 400 feet.   Find the least initial upward velocity required for the object to reach this height.

13. A ball is thrown upwards against gravity with a velocity of 40 ft/sec.   Find its velocity and height at any time t.   Find also its highest point and when it returns to its starting point.

14. A ball rolls freely down a sloping trough with a constant acceleration of 12 ft/sec².   Find its velocity v and the distance s travelled at any time t if $v = 0$ and $s = 0$ when $t = 0$.

15. A car rolls down a slope inclined at 30° to the horizontal so that its constant acceleration due to gravity is $32 \sin 30°$.   If the car starts to roll from rest, find its speed when it has rolled 2000 feet.

16. The acceleration in cm/sec² of a moving object is given by $a = 1000 - 10t$.   Find the velocity and distance travelled at any time t if the object is at rest when $t = 0$.

17. The velocity of an object in ft/sec is given by $v = (t + 1)^{1/2}$.   Find the distance travelled between the times in seconds when $t = 3$ and $t = 8$.

18. The acceleration in ft/sec² of a moving body is given by $a = (1 + t)^{-1/2}$.   The initial velocity (at $t = 0$) is 2 ft/sec, and the initial distance is zero.   Find the velocity and distance at any time t and, in particular, the distance when $t = 3$.

19. The acceleration produced on a model aircraft by an unwinding elastic-band motor is $(2 - .5t)$ ft/sec², where t is the time in seconds from the beginning of the flight.   What is the velocity reached when the motor has run down (when the acceleration is equal to zero) if the aircraft is initially given a forward velocity of 20 ft/sec?   What distance is travelled in that time?

20. The retro-rockets of a space capsule provide a constant deceleration of 200 ft/sec². If they are fired for 10 seconds and the motion is assumed to be in a straight line, what is the decrease in velocity produced? What distance does the capsule travel in these 10 seconds if its initial velocity is 20,000 ft/sec?

8.4. The Primitive as an Area

One of the important applications of the primitive is to evaluate areas. The simplest area to calculate is the area bounded above by the graph of $y = f(x)$, below by the x-axis, on the left by the line $x = a$, and on the right by the line $x = b$, where a and b $(a < b)$ are given real numbers. Such an area is shown as the shaded region in Figure 8.2.

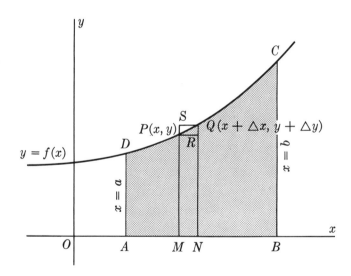

Figure 8.2

Consider first the area bounded above by the graph, to the left by the line $x = a$, below by the x-axis, and to the right by the line PM through $P(x, y)$ and perpendicular to the x-axis. Obviously, this area changes if the position of P is changed on the graph; in fact, if none of the other boundaries is changed, the area is uniquely determined by the position of P. Also, the position of P on the graph is determined by the value of x at P; P is the point with co-ordinates (x, y), or $(x, f(x))$. Thus, the area bounded on the right by PM is a function of x; therefore, we write $A(x)$ for the measure of the area $AMPD$.

Now consider a point $Q(x + \triangle x, y + \triangle y)$ close to $P(x, y)$ on the curve. The area $PMNQ$ is written in the usual notation as $\triangle A$, that is, as the change in the value of the area $A(x)$ as x changes to $x + \triangle x$. If we draw PR perpendicular to QN and QS perpendicular to PM, then

$$\text{Area } PMNR \leq \text{Area } PMNQ \leq \text{Area } SMNQ.$$

Now,

$$\text{Area } PMNR = PM \times MN$$
$$= y \triangle x,$$

and

$$\text{Area } SMNQ = QN \times MN$$
$$= (y + \triangle y) \triangle x$$

Therefore,

$$y \triangle x \leq \triangle A \leq (y + \triangle y) \triangle x,$$

and so

$$y \leq \frac{\triangle A}{\triangle x} \leq y + \triangle y.$$

If we now consider the limit of these inequalities as $\triangle x$ approaches zero,

$$\lim_{\triangle x \to 0} \frac{\triangle A}{\triangle x} = D_x A,$$

and

$$\lim_{\triangle x \to 0} (y + \triangle y) = y.$$

Therefore, in the limit $\triangle x \to 0$,

$$y \leq D_x A \leq y;$$

hence,

$$D_x A = y,$$

or

$$A'(x) = f(x).$$

Thus, the area is given by the value of some primitive of $f(x)$, and the general primitive is

$$F : x \to F(x) + c,$$

where F is any particular primitive of f; therefore,

$$A(x) = F(x) + c.$$

Obviously, if P coincides with D, then $x = a$ and the value of $A(x)$ is 0; that is,

$$A(a) = 0$$

and so

$$F(a) + c = 0 ,$$
$$c = -F(a) .$$

Therefore,

$$A(x) = F(x) - F(a) .$$

We may now evaluate the area shaded in Figure 8.2, that is, the area bounded above by the graph of $y = f(x)$, below by the x-axis, on the left by the line $x = a$, and on the right by the line $x = b$ $(a < b)$. We shall write $_aA_b$ for the value of this area. This is the value of $A(x)$ when P coincides with C, that is, when $x = b$; therefore,

$$_aA_b = F(b) - F(a) .$$

Note that F may be *any* primitive of f and that no arbitrary constant need be added.

Example.   Find the area between the graph of $y = 3x^2$, the x-axis, and the lines $x = 1$ and $x = 2$.

Solution: The shaded area in the diagram is the area required.

$$f(x) = F'(x) = 3x^2 ,$$
$$F(x) = x^3 .$$

Therefore,

$$_1A_2 = F(2) - F(1)$$
$$= 2^3 - 1^3$$
$$= 8 - 1$$
$$= 7 .$$

Hence, the area is $_1A_2 = 7$.

EXERCISE 8.4

1. If the graph of $y = f(x)$ is shown in the diagram, show that $A'(x) = f(x)$ is still true and that

$$_aA_b = |F(b) - F(a)| ,$$

where F is any primitive of f.

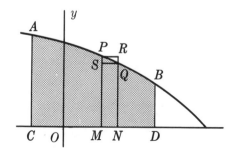

In each of the following questions (2) to (19), find the area between the graph of $y = f(x)$, the x-axis and the given lines.

2. $f(x) = x,$ $\qquad\qquad x = 2,$ $\qquad x = 5$

3. $f(x) = x + 2,$ $\qquad\qquad x = -2,$ $\qquad x = 2$

4. $f(x) = 1 - x,$ $\qquad\qquad x = 0,$ $\qquad x = 1$

5. $f(x) = 6 - 2x,$ $\qquad\qquad x = -1,$ $\qquad x = 3$

6. $f(x) = 2x^2 + 4,$ $\qquad\qquad x = 0,$ $\qquad x = 2$

7. $f(x) = 2x^2 + 4,$ $\qquad\qquad x = -2,$ $\qquad x = 0$

8. $f(x) = 2x^2 + 4,$ $\qquad\qquad x = -2,$ $\qquad x = 2$

9. $f(x) = 4(x^2 + 1),$ $\qquad\qquad x = -1,$ $\qquad x = 1$

10. $f(x) = x^2 + x + 1,$ $\qquad x = -1,$ $\qquad x = 1$

11. $f(x) = -x^2 + x + 1,$ $\qquad x = 0,$ $\qquad x = 1$

12. $f(x) = 4x^3,$ $\qquad\qquad x = 0,$ $\qquad x = 2$

13. $f(x) = \dfrac{3}{x^2},$ $\qquad\qquad x = 1,$ $\qquad x = 3$

14. $f(x) = x^{1/2},$ $\qquad\qquad x = 0,$ $\qquad x = 4$

15. $f(x) = 3(x + 1)^2,$ $\qquad x = 4,$ $\qquad x = 6$

16. $f(x) = 6 - x^2,$ $\qquad\qquad x = -1,$ $\qquad x = 2$

17. $f(x) = x - x^3,$ $\qquad\qquad x = 0,$ $\qquad x = 1$

18. $f(x) = x + 2,$ $\qquad\qquad x = 2,$ $\qquad x = -2$

19. $f(x) = 2x^2 + 4,$ $\qquad\qquad x = 0,$ $\qquad x = -2$

20. If $f(x) < 0$ for $a < x < b$, show from first principles that
$$A'(x) = y = f(x)$$
is still true.

8.5. More General Areas

In Figure 8.2, we showed the area under consideration in the first quadrant and with y increasing as x increases. This is not essential. In question (1) in the previous exercise, we considered the case where $f(x)$ is decreasing as x increases and with $f(x) > 0$. Question (20) extends this result to the case where $f(x) < 0$.

In general, $A'(x) = y = f(x)$ for any continuous function of x. However, this means that $A'(x)$ is negative when $f(x)$ is negative, and so $A(x) = F(x) + c$ is decreasing as x increases when $f(x)$ is negative. Thus,

$$\text{if } a < b, \quad A(a) > A(b) \quad \text{and} \quad F(b) - F(a) < 0,$$

and if we retain the formula

$$_aA_b = F(b) - F(a)$$

in the case when $y < 0$, then $_aA_b$ is negative. However, the measure of an area is a positive number, and so, for $y < 0$, we must define

$$|_aA_b| = |F(b) - F(a)|$$

to be the measure of the area. In general, if the area lies entirely on one side of the x-axis and is bounded by the graph of $y = f(x)$, the x-axis, and the lines $x = a$ and $x = b$, then its measure is given by $|_aA_b|$ where $_aA_b = F(b) - F(a)$. The following examples illustrate this.

Example 1. Find the area between the graph of $y = x$, the x-axis, and the lines $x = -4$ and $x = 0$.

Solution: The shaded area in the diagram is the area required. For $-4 < x < 0$, y is negative.

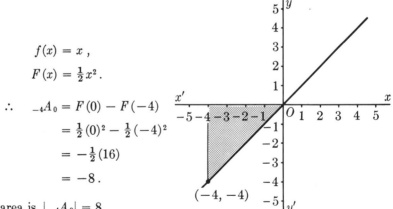

$$f(x) = x \, ,$$

$$F(x) = \tfrac{1}{2}x^2 \, .$$

$$\therefore \quad _{-4}A_0 = F(0) - F(-4)$$

$$= \tfrac{1}{2}(0)^2 - \tfrac{1}{2}(-4)^2$$

$$= -\tfrac{1}{2}(16)$$

$$= -8 \, .$$

Therefore, the area is $|_{-4}A_0| = 8$.

Note that, in this example, we can check our result by simple mensuration. The area required is the area of a triangle: area $= \tfrac{1}{2} \times 4 \times 4 = 8$.

If $f(x)$ is positive for some values of x and negative for other values of x in the domain $a < b$, then the areas above and below the x-axis must be calculated separately and then added together to give the total area.

Example 2.   Find the area between the graph of $y = x^2 - 4$, the x-axis and the lines $x = -1$ and $x = 3$.

Solution: The two shaded areas show the area required.

$$y < 0 \quad \text{for} \quad -2 < x < +2 \;;$$
$$y > 0 \quad \text{for} \quad 2 < x \,.$$

Now

$$f(x) = x^2 - 4 \;;$$

therefore,

$$F(x) = \frac{x^3}{3} - 4x \,.$$

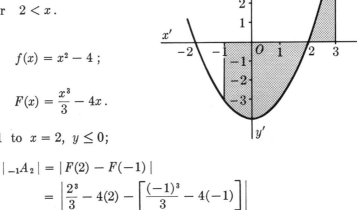

From $x = -1$ to $x = 2$, $y \leq 0$; hence,

$$| _{-1}A_2 | = | F(2) - F(-1) |$$

$$= \left| \frac{2^3}{3} - 4(2) - \left[\frac{(-1)^3}{3} - 4(-1) \right] \right|$$

$$= \left| \frac{8}{3} - 8 - \left[\frac{-1}{3} + 4 \right] \right|$$

$$= \left| \frac{8}{3} - 8 + \frac{1}{3} - 4 \right|$$

$$= 9 \,.$$

From $x = 2$ to $x = 3$, $y \geq 0$; hence,

$$| _2A_3 | = | F(3) - F(2) |$$

$$= \left| \frac{3^3}{3} - 4(3) - \left[\frac{2^3}{3} - 4(2) \right] \right|$$

$$= \left| 9 - 12 - \frac{8}{3} + 8 \right|$$

$$= \frac{7}{3} \,.$$

$$\therefore \quad \text{Area} = | _2A_3 | + | _{-1}A_2 |$$

$$= \frac{7}{3} + 9$$

$$= 11\tfrac{1}{3} \,.$$

Note that $| _{-1}A_3 | = 6\tfrac{2}{3}$ gives the *difference* of the two areas, not the sum.

EXERCISE 8.5

In each of the following, find the area between the graph of $y = f(x)$, the x-axis and the two given lines.

1. $f(x) = x,$ $x = -2,$ $x = 1$

2. $f(x) = x - 2,$ $x = 0,$ $x = 2$

3. $f(x) = 2 - x,$ $x = 0,$ $x = 2$

4. $f(x) = 3x - 1,$ $x = -1,$ $x = 2$

5. $f(x) = 3 - 4x,$ $x = -1,$ $x = 2$

6. $f(x) = x^2 - 4,$ $x = -1,$ $x = 1$

7. $f(x) = x^2 - 1,$ $x = 0,$ $x = 2$

8. $f(x) = (2 - x)^2,$ $x = 0,$ $x = 3$

9. $f(x) = x^2 - 1,$ $x = -2,$ $x = 2$

10. $f(x) = 9 - x^2,$ $x = 0,$ $x = 4$

11. $f(x) = x - x^2,$ $x = 0,$ $x = 2$

12. $f(x) = x^3,$ $x = -2,$ $x = 2$

13. $f(x) = x^3 - 4,$ $x = 0,$ $x = 2$

14. $f(x) = (x + 1)^{1/2},$ $x = 0,$ $x = 3$

15. $f(x) = x^{-2},$ $x = -4,$ $x = -1$

16. $f(x) = (x + 2)^{-2},$ $x = -1,$ $x = 2$

17. $f(x) = x^2 - x^{-2},$ $x = \frac{1}{2},$ $x = 2$

18. $f(x) = -2x^{-3},$ $x = 1,$ $x = 2$

19. $f(x) = x^2 - x - 6,$ $x = -2,$ $x = 1$

20. $f(x) = x^2 + x - 6,$ $x = -2,$ $x = 1$

Chapter Summary

The general solution of $D_x y = F'(x) = f(x)$ is $y = F(x) + c$ where c is an arbitrary real number.

The function $F : x \rightarrow F(x) + c,$ where $F'(x) = f(x),$ is the general primitive of $f : x \rightarrow f(x).$

The graphs determined by $y = F(x) + c,$ the general solution of $D_x y = F'(x) = f(x),$ are a family of curves.

One particular member of the family is determined if one point on the curve is known.

The velocity is a primitive of the acceleration.

The distance is a primitive of the velocity.

The primitive as an area · Areas under graphs · Areas between two graphs

The area bounded by $y = f(x)$, the x-axis, $x = a$ and $x = b$ is given by

$$| {}_aA_b | = | F(b) - F(a) |$$

where $F'(x) = f(x)$.

REVIEW EXERCISE 8

Find the general solution of each of the following.

1. $D_x y = x^4$
2. $D_x y = x^2 - 2x$
3. $D_x y = (x + 1)^2$
4. $D_x y = x^{1/2} - x^{-1/2}$
5. $D_x y = (x + 2)^{1/2}$
6. $D_x y = (x - 1)^{-3}$
7. $D_x y = (2x + 1)^3$
8. $D_x y = (2 - x)^2$
9. $D_x y = x(1 - x^2)^{1/2}$
10. $D_x y = x(2x^2 + 1)^{-1/2}$

Find the general primitive of each of the following.

11. $f : x \rightarrow x^{-1/2}$
12. $f : x \rightarrow x^{3/2}$
13. $f : x \rightarrow 1 - x^2$
14. $f : x \rightarrow 2 - 3x + x^2$
15. $f : x \rightarrow (x - 1)^3$
16. $f : x \rightarrow (1 - 2x)^2$
17. $f : x \rightarrow \dfrac{1}{(x + 2)^2}$
18. $f : x \rightarrow \dfrac{2}{(1 - x)^3}$
19. $f : x \rightarrow \dfrac{x}{(x^2 + 1)^{1/2}}$
20. $f : x \rightarrow \dfrac{x}{(1 - x^2)^2}$

In each of the following, find the area between the graph of $y = f(x)$, the x-axis and the two given lines.

21. $y = 2x + 3$, $x = 1$, $x = 5$
22. $y = x^3$, $x = -4$, $x = 1$
23. $y = x - x^3$, $x = -1$, $x = 1$
24. $y = \dfrac{1}{x^3}$, $x = 1$, $x = 3$

25. $y = \sqrt{x}$, $x = 0$, $x = 6$

26. $y = \dfrac{1}{(2x + 3)^2}$, $x = -1$, $x = 4$

27. $y = (x + 4)^{1/2}$, $x = -3$, $x = 5$

28. $y = x(x^2 + 1)$, $x = 1$, $x = 4$

29. $y = 6 + 3x - 3x^2$, $x = -2$, $x = 2$

30. $y = \dfrac{2x}{(x^2 + 1)^2}$, $x = 0$, $x = 2$

31. Find the equation of the curve that has a slope of x^3 and passes through the origin.

32. Find the equation of the curve that has a slope of $(x + 2)^{-2}$ and passes through the point $(-1, 1)$.

33. Find the equation of the curve that has a slope of $x^2 + 2x - 3$ and passes through the point $(1, 4)$.

34. Find the equation of the curve that has a slope of $x(x^2 + 1)^{-1/2}$ and passes through $(2, -1)$.

35. Find the equation of the curve which has a slope of $x - 1/x^3$ and passes through $(1, 1)$.

36. The acceleration of a body under gravity is 32 ft/sec² downwards. Find the velocity of a body at any time t if it is thrown upwards at $t = 0$ with velocity 192 ft/sec.

37. A moving body accelerates at a rate given by
$$a = 100 + 5t$$
in suitable units. Find the velocity v and distance s at any time t if $v = 0$ and $s = 0$ when $t = 0$.

38. The acceleration provided for a particular rocket is given approximately by
$$a = 64t(20 - t) \quad \text{for} \quad 0 < t < 20.$$
If the rocket starts with zero velocity, find
(a) its velocity at any time t,
(b) its velocity at $t = 20$,
(c) the distance travelled at any time t,
(d) the distance travelled by time $t = 20$.
(All measurements are in the feet-seconds system.)

9

INTEGRATION

9.1. Area by Summation

Let us look at the problem of calculating the area under a curve in a slightly different way. Figures 9.1 and 9.2 show two different ways to find approximate values for the area under a curve by using sets of rectangles.

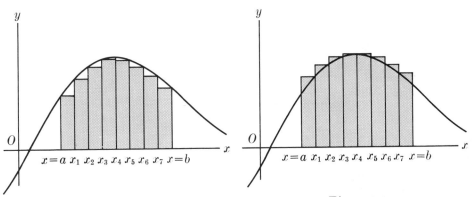

Figure 9.1	*Figure 9.2*

The area of the colored region in Figure 9.1 is given by

$$A_{\mathrm{L}} = f(a)(x_1 - a) + f(x_1)(x_2 - x_1) + \cdots + f(x_7)(x_7 - x_6) + f(b)(b - x_7).$$

The area of the colored region in Figure 9.2 is given by

$$A_{\mathrm{U}} = f(x_1)(x_1 - a) + f(x_2)(x_2 - x_1) + \cdots + f(x_6)(x_7 - x_6) + f(x_7)(b - x_7).$$

One gives an estimate less than the true area and the other an estimate greater than the true area. So we can write the following inequality for the true area, A.

$$A_{\mathrm{L}} = f(a)(x_1 - a) + f(x_1)(x_2 - x_1) + \cdots + f(b)(b - x_7) < A$$
$$< f(x_1)(x_1 - a) + f(x_2)(x_2 - x_1) + \cdots + f(x_7)(b - x_7) = A_{\mathrm{U}}$$

159

If we now write $x_1 - a = x_2 - x_1 = \cdots = b - x_7 = \triangle x$

then

$$A_{\mathrm{L}} = f(a)\triangle x + f(x_1)\triangle x + \cdots + f(b)\triangle x < A$$
$$< f(x_1)\triangle x + f(x_2)\triangle x + \cdots + f(x_7)\triangle x = A_{\mathrm{U}}.$$

In the above diagrams we have used only eight rectangles. What happens if we use more but narrower rectangles? We can continue to use more and more narrower and narrower rectangles (i.e., smaller and smaller $\triangle x$) and obtain closer and closer approximations to the true area A. Thus in the limit when $\triangle x \to 0$, we would obtain the value of the true area A, that is

$$\lim_{\triangle x \to 0} [f(a) + \cdots + f(b)]\triangle x = A = \lim_{\triangle x \to 0} [f(x_1) + \cdots + f(x_n)]\triangle x.$$

In general, these two limits do exist and are equal. In fact, all the narrow rectangles do not need to be the same width and we would still obtain the same limit. Also, instead of using the values of the function at either end of each rectangle (e.g., $f(x_1)$ or $f(x_2)$ for the rectangle on the segment $x_1 \leq x \leq x_2$) as the height of the rectangle, we may use the value of $f(x)$ at any point in the segment $x_1 \leq x \leq x_2$ and obtain the same limit.

This limit is called the definite integral of $f(x)$ from $x = a$ to $x = b$, and it is written thus

$$\int_a^b f(x)dx = \lim_{\triangle x_k \to 0} \sum_{x=a}^{x=b} f(\xi_k)\triangle x_k.$$

The symbol $\sum$ is used to indicate the sum of all terms $f(\xi_k)\triangle x_k$, where $\triangle x_k$ is the width of the kth rectangle based on the segment $x_{k-1} < x < x_k$ and $f(\xi_k)$ is the value of the ordinate of $y = f(x)$ at $x = \xi_k$, $x_{k-1} \leq \xi_k \leq x_k$. The sum is taken from $x = a$ to $x = b$.

The symbol $\int$ is an old form of a printed S and is used to remind us that the definite integral is the limit of a sum. $\int_a^b$ indicates that the summation is taken from $x = a$ to $x = b$.

We have arrived at this definition of the definite integral as a sum by considering an area under a curve, but we may now require the definition to hold whether or not we interpret the value of the function, $f(x)$, as the ordinate of a graph; of course, if we do not interpret the value of the function, $f(x)$, as an ordinate then the definite integral will *not* be interpreted as an area.

We must note also that as we found in Section 8.5, for areas below the x-axis, that is for $y = f(x) \leq 0$, the value found for the definite integral will be negative.

Thus, the numerical value of the area will be given by

$$\left| \int_a^b f(x)dx \right|$$

if $b > a$ and $f(x) \leq 0$.

If, for part of the required area $f(x) \leq 0$ and for another part $f(x) \geq 0$, then the area of each part must be evaluated separately, and added to get the total area.

The following three theorems can be proved from the definition of the definite integral.

Integral Theorem 1.

$$\int_a^b [f(x) + g(x)]dx = \int_a^b f(x)dx + \int_a^b g(x)dx.$$

Integral Theorem 2.

$$\int_a^b [f(x) - g(x)]dx = \int_a^b f(x)dx - \int_a^b g(x)dx.$$

Integral Theorem 3.

$$\int_a^b kf(x)dx = k \int_a^b f(x)dx \qquad \text{where } k \text{ is any constant.}$$

Note the similarity of these theorems to the three Derivative Theorems.

EXERCISE 9.1

1. Draw the graph of $y = x$ for $0 \leq x \leq 4$.

   (a) Use two sets of four rectangles as shown to calculate upper and lower approximations to the area between $y = x$, $y = 0$, and $x = 4$.

   (b) Use two sets of sixteen rectangles to find closer upper and lower approximations.

   (c) Compare the two sets of approximations to the true area.

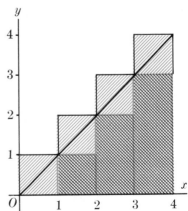

2. Draw the graph of $x^2 + y^2 = 25$ for $y \geq 0$.
   (a) Use two sets of five rectangles to calculate upper and lower approximations to the area between $x^2 + y^2 = 25 (y \geq 0)$ and $y = 0$.
   (b) Use two sets of ten rectangles to calculate upper and lower approximations.
   (c) Compare these approximations with the true area.

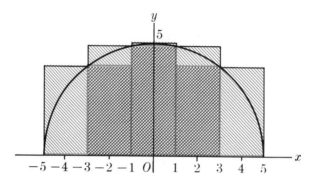

Prove the following from first principles.

3. $\displaystyle\int_a^b [f(x) + g(x)]dx = \int_a^b f(x)dx + \int_a^b g(x)dx.$

4. $\displaystyle\int_a^b kf(x)dx = k\int_a^b f(x)dx$ where k is any constant.

5. $\displaystyle\int_a^b [f(x) - g(x)]dx = \int_a^b f(x)dx - \int_a^b (gx)dx.$

9.2. The Definite Integral

We can evaluate some definite integrals, especially those starting at $x = 0$, by first principles from the definition.

These sums of series will be required (see Vectors, Matrices and Algebraic Structures, Chapter 9):

$$\sum_{k=1}^{n} k = 1 + 2 + 3 + 4 + \cdots + n = \frac{n(n+1)}{2};$$

$$\sum_{k=1}^{n} k^2 = 1^2 + 2^2 + 3^2 + 4^2 + \cdots + n^2 = \frac{n(n+1)(2n+1)}{6};$$

$$\sum_{k=1}^{n} k^3 = 1^3 + 2^3 + 3^3 + 4^3 + \cdots + n^3 = \frac{n^2(n+1)^2}{4};$$

$$\sum_{k=1}^{n} k^4 = 1^4 + 2^4 + 3^4 + 4^4 + \cdots + n^4 = \frac{n(n+1)(2n+1)(3n^2+3n-1)}{30}.$$

Example 1.   Evaluate $\displaystyle\int_0^2 x^2 dx$ by first principles.

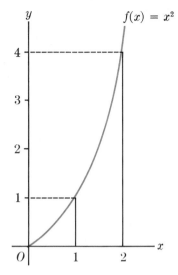

Solution.   Divide the segment $0 \leq x \leq 2$ into n equal intervals, $\triangle x_k$, so that

$$\triangle x_k = \frac{2}{n} \text{ for all } k$$

and $\triangle x_k \to 0$ is equivalent to $n \to \infty$.

Take ξ_k at the right-hand endpoint of the nth interval, so that

$$\xi_k = k \cdot \triangle x_k = \frac{2k}{n}.$$

Then

$$\sum_{x=0}^2 f(\xi_k) \triangle x_k = \sum_{x=0}^2 \xi^2{}_k \cdot \triangle x_k$$

$$= \sum_{k=1}^n \left(\frac{2k}{n}\right)^2 \cdot \frac{2}{n}$$

$$= \sum_{k=1}^n \frac{8k^2}{n^3}$$

$$= \frac{8}{n^3} \sum_{k=1}^n k^2$$

$$= \frac{8}{n^3} \frac{n(n+1)(2n+1)}{6}$$

$$= \frac{4}{3}\left(1 + \frac{1}{n}\right)\left(2 + \frac{1}{n}\right).$$

Therefore,

$$\lim_{\triangle x_k \to 0} \sum_{x=0}^2 \xi^2{}_k \triangle x_k = \frac{4}{3} \lim_{n \to \infty}\left(1 + \frac{1}{n}\right)\left(2 + \frac{1}{n}\right)$$

$$= \tfrac{4}{3} \cdot 1 \cdot 2$$

$$= \tfrac{8}{3}$$

$$= \tfrac{2^3}{3}.$$

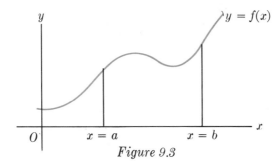

Figure 9.3

If we consider Figure 9.3 and remember the interpretation of the definite integral as the measure of an area, then we see that

$$_aA_b = {}_0A_b - {}_0A_a,$$

so that

$$\sum_{x=a}^{x=b} f(\xi_k)\triangle x_k = \sum_{x=0}^{x=b} f(\xi_k)\triangle x_k - \sum_{x=0}^{x=a} f(\xi_k)\triangle x_k,$$

and, therefore,

$$\int_a^b f(x)dx = \int_0^b f(x)dx - \int_0^a f(x)dx.$$

This property holds for the definite integral in general and can be proved without using its interpretation as an area.

(Note that if $f(x) \leq 0$ for some value of x in $a \leq x \leq b$ and $f(x) \geq 0$ for other values, then the value of the definite integral from a to b is not equal to the area; in such cases the areas of the parts for $f(x) \leq 0$ and $f(x) \geq 0$ have to be evaluated separately.)

Example 2.   Evaluate $\int_1^2 x^2\, dx$.

Solution:

$$\int_0^2 x^2 dx = \tfrac{8}{3} \qquad \text{from Example 1.}$$

$$\int_0^1 x^2 dx = \tfrac{1}{3} \qquad \begin{array}{l}\text{by direct evaluation in the same way as}\\ \text{Example 1.}\end{array}$$

$$\therefore \int_1^2 x^2\, dx = \int_0^2 x^2\, dx - \int_0^1 x^2\, dx$$

$$= \tfrac{8}{3} - \tfrac{1}{3}$$

$$= \tfrac{7}{3}.$$

EXERCISE 9.2

Evaluate the following definite integrals from first principles.

1. $\displaystyle\int_0^3 x\,dx$ 2. $\displaystyle\int_{-2}^0 x\,dx$

3. $\displaystyle\int_0^4 x^3\,dx$ 4. $\displaystyle\int_0^2 (x+x^3)dx$

5. $\displaystyle\int_0^2 (2+x^2)dx$ 6. $\displaystyle\int_0^4 (x^4+x^2)dx$

Evaluate the following definite integrals.

7. $\displaystyle\int_1^3 x\,dx$ 8. $\displaystyle\int_{-2}^{-1} x^2\,dx$

9. $\displaystyle\int_2^4 x^3\,dx$ 10. $\displaystyle\int_{-2}^2 (x+x^3)dx$

11. $\displaystyle\int_{-2}^2 (2+x^2)dx$ 12. $\displaystyle\int_2^4 (x^4+x^2)dx$

9.3. The Integral and the Primitive

In the previous chapter we evaluated the area as shown in Figure 9.4 between the graph of $y = f(x)$, the lines $x = a$, $x = b$, and the x-axis in terms of the primitive $F(x)$ and found that

$$_aA_b = F(b) - F(a).$$

In the last sections we have seen that

$$_aA_b = \int_a^b f(x)dx.$$

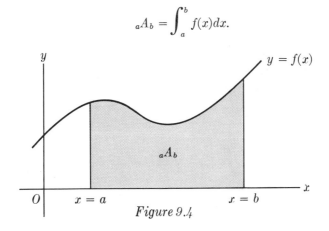

Figure 9.4

Thus,

$$\int_a^b f(x)dx = F(b) - F(a)$$

and again the result is true independent of the interpretation in terms of area. It is usual to use the notation $\left[F(x) \right]_a^b$ for $F(b) - F(a)$, so that

$$\int_a^b f(x)dx = \left[F(x) \right]_a^b$$

$$= F(b) - F(a).$$

So far we have used two given constant values of x, a and b, as the endpoints for the definite integral. We may, of course, consider what happens if we label the upper endpoint x and consider it to be any point; we get

$$\int_a^x f(x)dx = F(x) - F(a).$$

This last form is then generally referred to as the indefinite integral.

As x already appears in the symbolism even without putting it explicitly as the upper endpoint and as a can be taken as any other fixed point so that $-F(a)$ is also just a constant, it is usual to rewrite the last form as

$$\int f(x)dx = F(x) + c,$$

where $F(x)$ is the primitive of $f(x)$, so that

$$F'(x) = f(x),$$

and c is called the constant of integration.

We usually refer to this last written form as the integral without any qualifying adjective. In our further work we will most frequently use this integral notation and language rather than using the notation and language of the primitive.

Naturally, because of the equivalence implied in the defining equation

$$\int f(x)dx = F(x) + c,$$

the process for finding the integral of f is the same as that for finding the complete primitive of f.

Example 1.   Find the integral of $3x^2 + 2x + 1$.

Solution:

We know that

$$3x^2 = D_x(x^3);$$
$$2x = D_x(x^2);$$
$$1 = D_x(x).$$
$$\therefore \quad 3x^2 + 2x + 1 = D_x(x^3 + x^2 + x).$$

Therefore,

$$\int (3x^2 + 2x + 1)dx = x^3 + x^2 + x + c.$$

It is useful to recall the general result that

$$D_x\left(\frac{x^{n+1}}{n+1}\right) = x^n \text{ if } n \neq -1$$

and so remember that

$$\int x^n dx = \frac{x^{n+1}}{n+1} + c \text{ if } n \neq -1.$$

Example 2.   Evaluate $\int_1^4 (2x+1)^2 dx$.

Solution:

$$D_x(2x+1)^3 = 3(2x+1)^2 D_x(2x+1)$$
$$= 3(2x+1)^2 \cdot 2$$
$$= 6(2x+1)^2.$$

$$\therefore \quad \int_1^4 (2x+1)^2 dx = \frac{1}{6}\left[(2x+1)^3\right]_1^4$$

$$= \tfrac{1}{6}\left[(2\cdot 4+1)^3 - (2\cdot 2+1)^3\right]$$
$$= \tfrac{1}{6}\left[(8+1)^3 - (2+1)^3\right]$$
$$= \tfrac{1}{6}\left[9^3 - 3^3\right]$$
$$= \tfrac{1}{6}\left[729 - 81\right]$$
$$= \tfrac{1}{6}\left[648\right]$$
$$= 108.$$

Example 3. Find the area bounded by the graph of $y = 3x^2 + 1$, the x-axis, and lines $x = 1$ and $x = 3$.

Solution:

$$D_x(x^3 + x) = 3x^2 + 1.$$

$$\therefore \quad \text{Area} = \int_1^3 (3x^2 + 1)dx$$

$$= \left[x^3 + x \right]_1^3$$
$$= (3^3 + 3) - (1^3 + 1)$$
$$= (27 + 3) - (1 + 1)$$
$$= 30 - 2$$
$$= 28.$$

EXERCISE 9.3

Integrate these:

1. $\int x^5 dx$

2. $\int x^{-4} dx$

3. $\int x^{3/2} dx$

4. $\int x^{1/2} dx$

5. $\int x^{-1/2} dx$

6. $\int x^{-5/2} dx$

7. $\int 3x^2 dx$

8. $\int -4x^{-5} dx$

9. $\int \frac{5}{4} x^{1/4} dx$

10. $\int -\frac{3}{4} x^{-7/4} dx$

11. $\int (2x + 4x^3) dx$

12. $\int \left(x - \frac{1}{x^2} \right) dx$

13. $\int (x - 2)^2 dx$

14. $\int (2x + 3)^3 dx$

15. $\int (x - 2)^{-2} dx$

16. $\int (1 + t^{1/2})^2 dt$

17. $\int \frac{2}{3}(t + 1)^{1/2} dt$

18. $\int (t - 1)^{-1/2} dt$

19. $\int 4(2t + 2)^{1/2} dt$

20. $\int \frac{3}{2}(1 - 3t)^{-1/2} dt$

21. $\int 2x(x^2 + 1) dx$

22. $\int 3x^2(x^3 - 1) dx$

23. $\int \frac{2x}{(x^2 + 1)^2} dx$

24. $\int \frac{3x^2}{(x^3 - 1)^2} dx$

25. $\int 8x(x^2 - 1)^3 dx$

26. $\int 8x^3(x^4 - 1) dx$

27. $\int 2x(x^2 + 1)^{-1/2} dx$

28. $\int 3x(1 - x^2)^{1/2} dx$

29. $\int x(x^2 - 4)^{1/2} dx$

30. $\int x(4 - x^2)^{1/2} dx$

9.4. The Area Between Two Curves

To find the area between two curves and two lines $x = a$ and $x = b$ that together form a closed figure, or between two curves that form a closed figure, we can calculate the value of the area between each curve, the x-axis, and the given lines $x = a$ and $x = b$, or the lines $x = x_1$ and $x = x_2$ where x_1 and x_2 are the abscissae of the points of intersection of the two curves, and then combine these values to find the area required.   A sketch diagram is essential in such problems.

Example 1.   Find the area between the graphs of $y = x$, $y = 2x$, and the line $x = 2$.

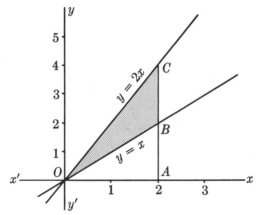

Solution: The graphs intersect where $y = x = 2x$, that is, where $x = 0$.   The area required is the shaded area OBC.

For area OAB: $$f(x) = x,$$

$$\therefore \quad \text{Area } OAB = \int_0^2 x \, dx$$

$$= \left[\frac{x^2}{2} \right]_0^2$$

$$= [\tfrac{4}{2} - \tfrac{0}{2}]$$

$$= 2.$$

For area OAC: $$f(x) = 2x,$$

$$\therefore \quad \text{Area } OAC = \int_0^2 2x \, dx$$

$$= \left[x^2 \right]_0^2$$
$$= [4 - 0]$$
$$= 4.$$

$$\text{Area } OBC = \text{Area } OAC - \text{Area } OAB$$
$$= \left| 4 - 2 \right|$$
$$= 2.$$

In this example, we can verify the result by the usual mensuration results:

$$\text{Area of } \triangle OCA = \tfrac{1}{2}(2 \times 4) = 4,$$
$$\text{Area of } \triangle OBA = \tfrac{1}{2}(2 \times 2) = 2,$$

and therefore

$$\text{Area of } \triangle OCB = 2.$$

Example 2. Find the area between the graphs of $y = x^2 + 1$, $y = x$, and the lines $x = 0$ and $x = 1$.

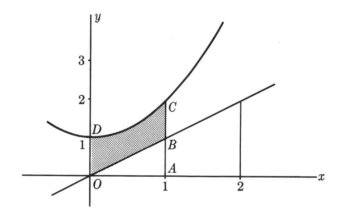

Solution: The area required is the shaded area $OBCD$.

$$\text{Area } OBCD = \text{Area } OACD - \text{Area } OAB.$$

For area OAB:
$$f(x) = x,$$

$$\text{Area } OAB = \int_0^1 x \, dx$$
$$= \left[\frac{x^2}{2} \right]_0^1$$
$$= [\tfrac{1}{2} - 0]$$
$$= \tfrac{1}{2}.$$

For area $OACD$:
$$f(x) = x^2 + 1;$$

$$\text{Area } OACD = \int_0^1 (x^2 + 1)dx$$

$$= \left[\frac{x^3}{3} + x \right]_0^1$$

$$= (\tfrac{1}{3} + 1) - (\tfrac{0}{3} + 0)$$

$$= 1\tfrac{1}{3}.$$

$$\text{Area } OBCD = \left| 1\tfrac{1}{3} - \tfrac{1}{2} \right|$$

$$= \tfrac{5}{6}.$$

Example 3.   Find the area between the y-axis, the curve $y = 4x^3$, and the line $y = 32$.

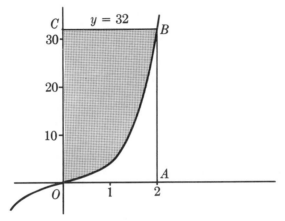

Solution: The curve and the line intersect where $y = 4x^3 = 32$, that is, where $x = 2$. The y-axis is the line $x = 0$. The shaded area OBC is the area required.

$$\text{Area } OBC = \text{Area } OABC - \text{Area } OAB ,$$

$$\text{Area } OABC = 2 \times 32$$

$$= 64 .$$

$$\text{Area } OAB = \int_0^2 4x^3 \, dx$$

$$= \left[x^4 \right]_0^2$$

$$= [2^4 - 0]$$

$$= 16.$$

$$\text{Area } OBC = \left| 64 - 16 \right|$$

$$= 48.$$

Example 4.   Find the area between the graphs of $y = x^2$ and $y = 2x$.

Solution:

$$y = x^2 \quad \text{and} \quad y = 2x$$

intersect when

$$x^2 = 2x \,,$$

that is, when

$$x(x - 2) = 0 \,,$$

$$x = 0 \quad \text{or} \quad 2 \,.$$

Hence, the points of intersection are $O(0,0)$ and $B(2,4)$.

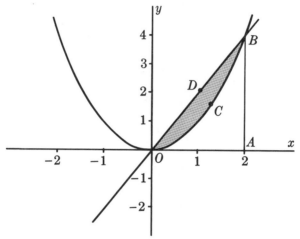

The shaded area $OCBD$ is the area required.

$$\text{Area } OABC = \int_0^2 x^2 \, dx$$

$$= \left[\frac{x^3}{3} \right]_0^2$$

$$= \frac{2^3}{3} - \frac{0^3}{3}$$

$$= 2\tfrac{2}{3}.$$

$$\text{Area } OABD = \int_0^2 x^2 \, dx$$

$$= \left[x^2 \right]_0^2$$

$$= 2^2 - 0^2$$

$$= 4.$$

$$\text{Area } OCBD = \text{Area } OABD - \text{Area } OABC$$
$$= 4 - 2\tfrac{2}{3}$$
$$= 1\tfrac{1}{3}.$$

Note that area $OABD$ is a triangle of base 2 and height 4 so that we could have found the area by direct computation: area of $\triangle OAB = \tfrac{1}{2}(2)(4) = 4$.

Example 5.   Find the area between the graphs of $y = 4 - x^2$ and $y = 2(x^2 - 4)$.

Solution:
$$y = 2x^2 - 8 \quad \text{and} \quad y = 4 - x^2$$

intersect at values of x that are the solution set of the equation

$$2x^2 - 8 = 4 - x^2,$$

that is,
$$3x^2 = 12,$$
$$x^2 = 4,$$
$$x = 2 \quad \text{or} \quad -2.$$

Hence, the points of intersection are $A(2, 0)$ and $C(-2, 0)$.

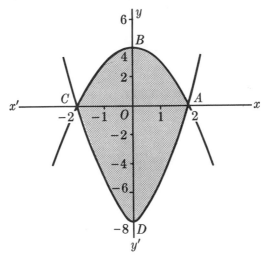

The area required is the shaded area $ABCD$.

$$\text{Area } ABC = \int_{-2}^{2} (4 - x^2)dx$$

$$= \left[4x - \frac{x_3}{3} \right]_{-2}^{2}$$

$$= (4(2) - \tfrac{2}{3}^3) - (4(-2) - (-\tfrac{2}{3})^3)$$
$$= (8 - \tfrac{8}{3}) - (-8 + \tfrac{8}{3})$$
$$= \tfrac{16}{3} - (-\tfrac{16}{3})$$
$$= \tfrac{32}{3}$$
$$= 10\tfrac{2}{3}.$$

Note $f(x) = 2x^2 - 8$ is negative for $-2 < x < 2$.

Therefore,

$$\text{Area } ADC = \left| \int_{-2}^{2} (2x^2 - 8)dx \right|$$
$$= \left| \left[\frac{2x^3}{3} - 8x \right]_{-2}^{2} \right|$$
$$= \left| \left(\frac{2(2^3)}{3} - 8(2) \right) - \left(\frac{2(-2)^3}{3} - 8(-2) \right) \right|$$
$$= \left| \left(\frac{16}{3} - 16 \right) - \left(\frac{-16}{3} + 16 \right) \right|$$
$$= \left| -\tfrac{32}{3} - \tfrac{32}{3} \right|$$
$$= \tfrac{64}{3}$$
$$= 21\tfrac{1}{3}.$$

Therefore,

$$\text{Area } ABCD = \left| 10\tfrac{2}{3} + 21\tfrac{1}{3} \right|$$
$$= 32.$$

When solving problems such as these, the student is advised to draw a sketch graph of the curves involved and to show the area required. This is especially the case if one of the graphs, or both, lies partly above and partly below the x-axis. The student must take great care to identify each of the parts of the composite area and to calculate each part separately from the values of the appropriate primitive.

EXERCISE 9.4

1. Find the area between the graphs of $y = x^2 + 2$ and $y = x$ and the lines $x = 1$ and $x = 4$.

2. Find the area in the first quadrant, between the graphs of $y = x^{-2}$ and $y = x^2$ and the line $x = 2$.

3. Find the area enclosed between the graphs of $y = x$ and $y = x^2$.

4. Find the area enclosed between the x-axis and that part of the graph of $y = 6 - x - x^2$ which is above the x-axis.

5. Find the area enclosed between that part of the graph of $y = x^2 - 5x + 6$ which is below the x-axis and the x-axis itself.

6. Find the area enclosed by the graphs of $y = x^2$ and $y = 4$.

7. Find the area in the first quadrant between the graphs of $y = x^3$ and $y = 4x(1 - x)$.

8. Find the area enclosed between the graphs of $y = x^2$ and $y = x + 6$.

9. Find the area enclosed by the graphs of the parabolas $y = 9 - x^2$ and $y = (x - 1)^2 - 4$.

10. Find the area enclosed by the graphs of $y = -x^2 + 4$ and $y = x$.

11. Find the area enclosed between the graphs of $y = x^2$ and $y = 9$.

12. Find the area enclosed between the graphs of $y = x^2$ and $y = 2x + 8$.

13. Find the area bounded by the graphs of $y = 4\sqrt{x}$ and $y = 2x$.

14. Find the area bounded by the graphs of $y = 8\sqrt{x}$ and $y = x^2$.

15. Find the area in the first quadrant bounded by the graphs of $y = x^{-2}$ and $y = 4\frac{1}{4} - x^2$.

9.5. Volumes of Revolution by Cylindrical Discs

Integration may also be used to evaluate the volume of revolution of a curve about the x-axis. The simplest volume to calculate is the volume bounded by the curve $y = f(x)$ and by the lines $x = a$ and $x = b$ as the curve rotates around the x-axis.

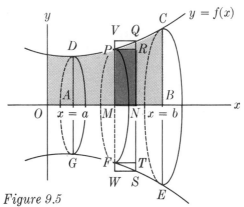

Figure 9.5

Consider first the area bounded above by the curve, to the left by the line $x = a$, below by the x-axis, and to the right by the line PM through $P(x, y)$ and perpendicular to the x-axis as shown in Figure 9.5. If this region is rotated about the x-axis the solid $DGFP$ is generated. Obviously this volume changes as the position of P is changed on the graph. If none of the other boundaries is changed, the volume is uniquely determined by the position of P. The position of P is determined by the value of x at P. The volume bounded on the right by PMF is a function of x and we write $V(x)$ for the volume of $DGFP$.

Now consider the point $Q(x + \triangle x, y + \triangle y)$ close to $P(x, y)$ on the curve. The volume $PFSQ$ is written as $\triangle V$, that is, as the change of the volume $V(x)$ as x changes to $x + \triangle x$. If we construct $PR \perp QS$, $QV \perp PF$, $FT \perp RS$, $SW \perp PF$, then

$$\text{Volume } PFTR \leq \text{Volume } PFSQ \leq \text{Volume } VWSQ.$$

Now

volume of $PFTR$ as the curve rotates about the x-axis is the volume of the cylindrical disc of radius y and altitude $\triangle x$.

Hence,

$$\text{volume } PFTR = \pi y^2 \triangle x.$$

Similarly,

$$\text{volume } VWSQ \leq \pi(y + \triangle y)^2 \triangle x.$$

Hence,

$$\pi y^2 \triangle x \leq \triangle V \leq \pi(y + \triangle y)^2 \triangle x.$$

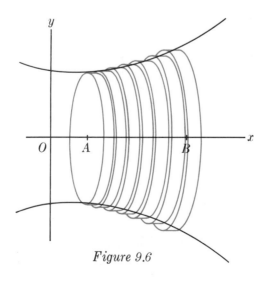

Figure 9.6

We obtain an approximation to the total volume of revolution by summing the volumes of all such cylindrical discs between $x = a$ and $x = b$, as indicated in Figure 9.6.

Therefore,

$$\sum_{x=a}^{x=b} \pi y^2 \triangle x \leq \sum_{x=a}^{x=b} \triangle V \leq \sum_{x=a}^{x=b} \pi\, (y + \triangle y)^2 \triangle x.$$

In the limit as $\triangle x \rightarrow 0$, $\sum_{x=a}^{x=b} \triangle V$ gives exactly the total volume V of the solid of revolution.

Now

$$\lim_{\triangle x \rightarrow 0} \sum_{x=a}^{x=b} \pi y^2 \triangle x = \int_a^b \pi y^2 dx,$$

and also

$$\lim_{\triangle x \rightarrow 0} \sum_{x=a}^{x=b} \pi(y + \triangle y)^2 \triangle x = \int_a^b \pi y^2 dx.$$

Therefore,

$$V = \int_a^b \pi y^2 dx;$$

or

$$V = \pi \int_a^b y^2 dx;$$

or

$$V = \pi \int_a^b [f(x)]^2 dx.$$

In all applications of this result it is most desirable to draw a sketch of the volume of revolution and the elementary cylindrical disc.

Example 1.   Find the volume of the cone generated by revolving the area bounded by $y = x$, $x = 3$, and the x-axis about the x-axis.

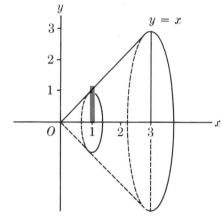

Solution:

$$V = \pi \int_0^3 y^2 dx$$

$$= \pi \int_0^3 x^2 dx$$

$$= \pi \left[\frac{x^3}{3} \right]_0^3$$

$$= \pi \left[\frac{3^3}{3} - \frac{0^3}{3} \right]$$

$$= 9\pi.$$

The same method can be used to find the volume of hollow solids of revolution, as the following example shows.

Example 2.   Find the volume of revolution generated by revolving the area between $y = x^2$ and $y = x^{1/2}$ for x, $y \geq 0$ about the x-axis.

Solution:

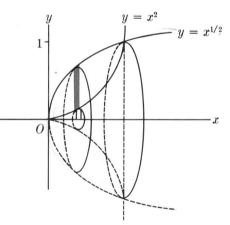

$$y = x^2 \quad \text{and} \quad y = x^{1/2}$$

intersect at

$$(0,0) \quad \text{and} \quad (1,1).$$

Therefore, the limits of integration will be from

$$x = 0 \quad \text{to} \quad x = 1.$$

The volume of revolution, V, generated by the area between $y = x^{1/2}$ and $y = x^2$ is the difference between the volume of revolution, V_1, formed by $y = x^{1/2}$ and the volume of revolution, V_2, formed by $y = x^2$.

$$V_1 = \pi \int_0^1 (x^{1/2})^2 dx \qquad V_2 = \pi \int_0^1 (x^2)^2 dx$$

$$= \pi \int_0^1 x \, dx \qquad\qquad = \pi \int_0^1 x^4 dx$$

$$= \pi \left[\frac{x^2}{2} \right]_0^1$$

$$= \frac{\pi}{2}.$$

$$= \pi \left[\frac{x^5}{5} \right]_0^1$$

$$= \frac{\pi}{5}.$$

$$\therefore \quad V = V_1 - V_2$$

$$= \frac{\pi}{2} - \frac{\pi}{5}$$

$$= \frac{3\pi}{10}.$$

EXERCISE 9.5

Use the method of cylindrical discs to find the volume of revolution about the x-axis generated by each of the following areas bounded by the given curves.

1. $y = x^{1/2}$, $y = 0$, $x = 4$

2. $y = x^2$, $y = 0$, $x = 4$

3. $y = x^3$, $y = 0$, $x = 2$

4. $y = x^{3/2}$, $y = 0$, $x = 3$

5. $x^2 + y^2 = 25$, $y = 0$

6. $\dfrac{x^2}{16} + \dfrac{y^2}{9} = 1$, $y = 0$

7. $\dfrac{x^2}{9} + \dfrac{y^2}{16} = 1$, $y = 0$

8. $y = 4 - x^2$, $y = 0$

9. $y = 4 - x^4$, $y = 0$

10. $y = 4 - |x|^{1/2}$, $y = 0$

11. $y^2 = 4x$, $y = 0$, $x = 1$, $x = 4$

12. $y = x^2$, $y = 0$, $x = 2$, $x = 4$

13. $y^2 = 4x$, $y = x$

14. $y^2 = 4x$, $y = 2x^2$

15. $x^2 + y^2 = 25$, $y = 0$, $x = 0$

16. $x^2 + y^2 = 25$, $y = 0$, $x = 3$

17. $x^2 + y^2 = 25$, $y = 0$, $4y = 3x$

18. $x^2 + y^2 = 25$, $4y = 3x$, $4y = -3x$,

19. Find the volume of a sphere of radius r by integration.

20. Find the volume of a cone of height h and with a base of radius r.

9.6. Volumes of Revolution by Cylindrical Shells

It is often desirable to find the volume of revolution by an alternative method; sometimes because the calculation is easier; often because the use of a second method provides an independent check on the first computation. This alternative method considers the volume of revolution to be built up from thin concentric hollow cylinders or cylindrical shells. Consider the volume of revolution, V, generated by revolving the area ABC about the y-axis as indicated in Figure 9.7. We may consider as an element of that volume the thin cylindrical shell formed by revolving the thin strip $PQRS$ about the y-axis.

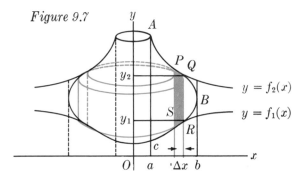

Figure 9.7

The inner radius of the shell is x and the thickness of the shell is $\triangle x$, so that the area of the end is approximately $2\pi x \triangle x$.

The length of the shell is $(y_2 - y_1)$ and, therefore, the volume of the shell is approximately

$$\triangle V = (y_2 - y_1)\, 2\pi x \triangle x = 2\pi(y_2 - y_1)x \triangle x.$$

We obtain an approximation to the total volume of revolution by summing the volumes of all such shells from $x = a$ to $x = b$, as indicated in Figure 9.8.

Therefore,

$$V = \sum_{x=a}^{x=b} \triangle V = 2\pi \sum_{x=a}^{x=b} (y_2 - y_1)x \triangle x.$$

In the limit as $\triangle x \rightarrow 0$, $\sum_{x=a}^{x=b} \triangle V$ gives exactly the total volume of revolution and

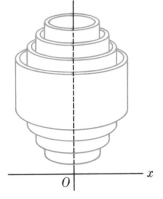

Figure 9.8

$$\lim_{\triangle x \rightarrow 0} \sum_{x=a}^{x=b} (y_2 - y_1)x \triangle x = \int_a^b (y_2 - y_1)x\, dx,$$

so that

$$V = 2\pi \int_a^b (y_2 - y_1)x \, dx.$$

Note that y_2 and y_1 are the values of f_2 and f_1 at the value x where the general element of integration is chosen. It should also be noted that f_1 and f_2 may be two functions which together are equivalent to a relation which can be expressed by a single algebraic equation.

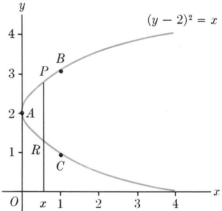

An example is shown in the diagram:

A to P, $y_2 = 2 + \sqrt{x}$;

A to R, $y_1 = 2 - \sqrt{x}$.

So that, in particular

at A, $y_1 = y_2 = 2$;

at B, $y_2 = 3, y_1 = 1$;

at C, $y_2 = 4, y_1 = 0$.

Example 1.   Use cylindrical shells to find the volume of revolution generated by rotating the area between $x = 1$, $(y - 2)^2 = x$, and $x = 4$ about the y-axis.

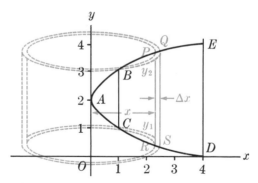

Solution: The area to be revolved about the y-axis is $BCDE$. The limits of x for $BCDE$ are $x = 1$(on BC)   to $x = 4$ (on DE). The element of area $PQSR = (y_2 - y_1)\triangle x$. The element of volume $= 2\pi x(y_2 - y_1)\triangle x$. y_1 and y_2 are lower and upper points on curve $DCABE$.

Therefore,

$$y_2 = 2 + \sqrt{x};$$
$$y_1 = 2 - \sqrt{x};$$

and

$$y_2 - y_1 = 2\sqrt{x}.$$

Hence,

$$V = 2\pi \int_1^4 (y_2 - y_1)x \, dx$$

$$= 2\pi \int_1^4 2\sqrt{x}\, x \, dx$$

$$= 4\pi \int_1^4 x^{3/2} \, dx$$

$$= 4\pi \left[\frac{x^{5/2}}{\frac{5}{2}} \right]_1^4$$

$$= 4\pi \cdot \frac{2}{5} \left[x^{5/2} \right]_1^4$$

$$= \tfrac{8}{5}\pi \, [4^{5/2} - 1^{5/2}]$$
$$= \tfrac{8}{5}\pi \, [32 - 1]$$
$$= \tfrac{8}{5}\pi \, (31)$$
$$= \tfrac{248}{5}\pi.$$

Example 2.   Use cylindrical shells to calculate the volume of revolution generated by revolving about the x-axis the area between $y = x$, $y = -x$, and $y = 2$.

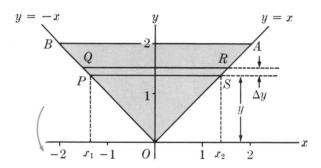

Solution: Note in this case we have a volume of revolution about the x-axis and so using shells we must integrate with respect to y. The area to be revolved about the x-axis is OAB. The limits of y for OAB are:

$$y = 0 \text{ (at 0) to } y = 2 \text{ (on } AB).$$

The element of area $PQRS = (x_2 - x_1)\triangle y$.
The element of volume $= 2\pi y(x_2 - x_1)\triangle y$.
We must express x_2 and x_1 in terms of y which locates the element of area; we have

$$x_2 = y, \; x_1 = -y.$$

Hence,

$$V = 2\pi \int_0^2 y(y - (-y))dy$$

$$= 2\pi \int_0^2 2y^2\, dy$$

$$= 4\pi \int_0^2 y^2\, dy$$

$$= 4\pi \left[\frac{y^3}{3}\right]_0^2$$

$$= 4\pi \left[\tfrac{8}{3} - \tfrac{0}{3}\right]$$

$$= \tfrac{32}{3}\pi.$$

EXERCISE 9.6

Use the method of cylindrical shells to find the volume of revolution about the y-axis generated by each of the following areas bounded by the curves given.

1. $y^2 = x$, $y = 4$, $x = 0$
2. $y = x^2$, $y = 4$, $x = 0$
3. $x^2 + y^2 = 25$, $x = 0$
4. $\dfrac{x^2}{16} + \dfrac{y^2}{9} = 1$, $x = 0$
5. $y = 4 - x^2$, $y = 0$
6. $y = x$, $y = 4$, $x = 0$
7. $y = x$, $y = 4 - x$, $x = 0$
8. $y = x^2$, $y = x$
9. $y^2 = x$, $y = x$
10. $y = 2x^2$, $y^2 = 4x$

Use any method, or two different methods if possible, to find the volumes of revolution generated as follows.

11. $y = x$, $y = 2(x - 1)$, $y = 0$ about the x-axis
12. $y = x$, $y = 2(x - 1)$, $y = 0$ about the y-axis
13. $y = x^2$, $y = 4x$ about the x-axis
14. $y = x^2$, $y = 4x$ about the y-axis
15. $y^2 = x$, $y = \tfrac{1}{4}x$ about the x-axis

9.7. The Trapezoidal Rule and Simpson's Rule

It is often necessary to compute the numerical value of a definite integral and sometimes the function for a graph is not known or the function cannot be integrated analytically. In such cases we resort to numerical integration. We could, of course, use the sets of rectangles in terms of which we defined the definite integral, but as we have seen, such approximations may not be very accurate unless a very large number of rectangles is used. We will discuss here two of the simplest methods which give better approximations.

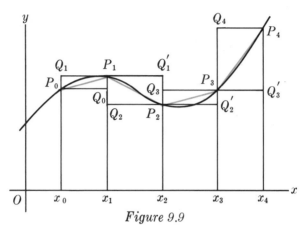

Figure 9.9

The diagram shows two sets of rectangles which give lower and upper approximations to the definite integral. Obviously a better approximation will be given if we use the average of these two approximations. We see from the diagram that this is equivalent to replacing typical rectangles (e.g., $x_2 x_3 Q_2' P_2$ or $x_2 x_3 P_3 Q_3$) by the typical trapezoid on the same base (e.g., $x_2 x_3 P_3 P_2$).

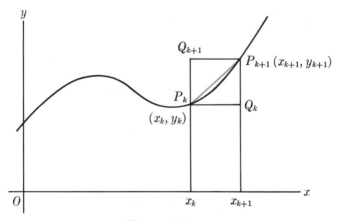

Figure 9.10

Let us divide the interval of integration $a \le x \le b$ into n equal subintervals so that

$$x_{k+1} - x_k = h.$$

Then,

$$\text{Area of } x_k x_{k+1} Q_k P_k = h y_k = h f(x_k);$$

$$\text{Area of } x_k x_{k+1} P_{k+1} Q_{k+1} = h y_{k+1}$$

$$= h f(x_{k+1});$$

and so

$$\text{Area of } x_k x_{k+1} P_{k+1} P_k = \frac{h}{2}(y_k + y_{k+1})$$

$$= \frac{h}{2}[f(x_k) + f(x_{k+1})].$$

Therefore, the approximate value of the definite integral from $x_0 = a$ to $x_n = b$ is given by

$$\int_a^b f(x)dx \simeq \frac{h}{2}[f(x_0) + f(x_1)] + \frac{h}{2}[f(x_1) + f(x_2)] + \frac{h}{2}[f(x_2) + f(x_3)] + \cdots$$

$$+ \frac{h}{2}[f(x_{n-2}) + f(x_{n-1})] + \frac{h}{2}[f(x_{n-1}) + f(x_n)].$$

$$\therefore \quad \int_a^b f(x)dx \simeq h[\tfrac{1}{2} f(x_0) + f(x_1) + f(x_2) + \cdots + f(x_{n-1}) + \tfrac{1}{2} f(x_n)].$$

This formula is known as the Trapezoidal Rule.

In effect when we use the trapezoidal rule we are approximating to the curve of the graph of $y = f(x)$ by a polygon which is a sequence of line segments. A much better approximation can be obtained if we use a sequence of parabolic arcs to approximate the graph. However, we can only use this method of approximation if we know the area under a parabolic arc, and if it is a simple expression; fortunately, we can easily integrate to find the area under a parabolic arc and obtain a simple expression.

Consider the area under the parabola through these three adjacent points on the graph of $y = f(x)$;

$$P_{n-1}(x_n - h, f(x_{n-1})), \ P_n(x_n, f(x_n)), \ P_{n+1}(x_n + h, f(x_{n+1})).$$

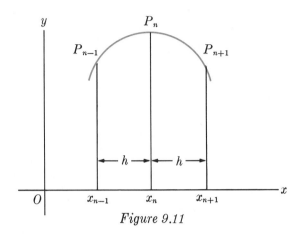

Figure 9.11

If $y = Ax^2 + Bx + C$ is the equation of the parabola,

then

$$f(x_{n-1}) = A(x_n - h)^2 + B(x_n - h) + C; \quad 1$$

$$f(x_n) \quad = A \, x_n{}^2 \qquad + B \, x_n \qquad + C; \quad 2$$

and

$$f(x_{n+1}) = A(x_n + h)^2 + B(x_n + h) + C \quad 3$$

are three simultaneous equations which would determine the values of A, B, and C.

Let us first calculate the value of the definite integral for the area under the arc $P_{n-1}P_nP_{n+1}$ and we will find that we do not need to find A, B, and C separately.

$$\int_{x_n-h}^{x_n+h} (Ax^2 + Bx + C)dx = \left[A\frac{x^3}{3} + B\frac{x^2}{2} + Cx \right]_{x_n-h}^{x_n+h}$$

$$= A\left[\frac{(x_n + h)^3 - (x_n - h)^3}{3} \right] + B\left[\frac{(x_n + h)^2 - (x_n - h)^2}{2} \right]$$

$$+ C[(x_n + h) - (x_n - h)]$$

$$= A\frac{6x_n{}^2 h + 2h^3}{3} + B\frac{4x_n h}{2} + C(2h)$$

$$= \frac{h}{3}[6Ax_n^2 + 2Ah^2 + 6Bx_n + 6C]$$

$$= \frac{h}{3}[2\{A(x_n^2 + h^2) + 2Bx_n + 2C\} + 4\{Ax_n^2 + Bx_n + C\}]$$

Now, from equations 1 and 3

$$f(x_{n-1}) + f(x_{n+1}) = 2A(x_n^2 + h^2) + 2Bx_n + 2C$$

and equation 2 is

$$f(x_n) = Ax_n^2 + Bx_n + C.$$

$$\therefore \int_{x_n-h}^{x_n+h} (Ax^2 + Bx + C)dx = \frac{h}{3}[f(x_{n-1}) + 4f(x_n) + f(x_{n+1})].$$

Let us now divide the interval of integration $a \leq x \leq b$ into $2n$ equal intervals each of length h. Then apply the above result for the area under a parabolic arc for each pair of intervals in succession.

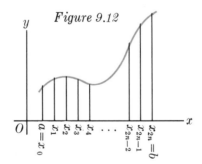

Figure 9.12

$$\int_{a=x_0}^{x_2} f(x)dx \simeq \frac{h}{3}[f(x_0) + 4f(x_1) + f(x_2)];$$

$$\int_{x_2}^{x_4} f(x)dx \simeq \frac{h}{3}[f(x_2) + 4f(x_3) + f(x_4)];$$

$$\vdots$$

$$\int_{x_{2n-2}}^{x_{2n}=b} f(x)dx \simeq \frac{h}{3}[f(x_{2n-2}) + 4f(x_{2n-1}) + f(x_{2n})].$$

By adding

$$\int_a^b f(x)dx = \frac{h}{3}[f(x_0) + 4f(x_1) + 2f(x_2) + 4f(x_3) + 2f(x_4) + \cdots$$

$$+ 2f(x_{2n-2}) + 4f(x_{2n-1}) + f(x_{2n})].$$

This formula is known as Simpson's Rule.

Example. Evaluate $\displaystyle\int_0^8 (x^3 + x)dx$

(a) exactly;

(b) using the trapezoidal rule with division points at $x = 2, 4, 6$;

(c) using the trapezoidal rule with division points at $x = 1, 2, 3, 4, 5, 6, 7$;

(d) using Simpson's rule with division points at $x = 2, 4, 6$.

Solution:

(a)
$$\int_0^8 (x^3 + x)dx = \left[\frac{x^4}{4} + \frac{x^2}{2}\right]_0^8$$

$$= [\tfrac{8^4}{4} + \tfrac{8^2}{2}]$$

$$= 1024 + 32$$

$$= 1056.$$

(b) $h = 2$

x	0	2	4	6	8
$f(x)$	$0 + 0$	$2^3 + 2$	$4^3 + 4$	$6^3 + 6$	$8^3 + 8$
	0	10	68	222	520

$$\therefore \int_0^8 (x^3 + x)dx \simeq 2[\tfrac{1}{2} \cdot 0 + 10 + 68 + 222 + \tfrac{1}{2} \cdot 520]$$

$$= 2[300 + 260]$$
$$= 2 \cdot 560$$
$$= 1120.$$

(c) $h = 1$

x	0	1	2	3	4	5	6	7	8
$f(x)$	0	2	10	30	68	130	222	350	520

$$\int_0^8 (x^3 + x)dx = 1[\tfrac{1}{2}(0) + 2 + 10 + 30 + 68 + 130 + 222 + 350 + \tfrac{1}{2}(520)]$$

$$= 1072.$$

(d) $h = 2$

x	0	2	4	6	8
$f(x)$	0	10	68	222	520

$$\int_0^8 (x^3 + x)dx = \tfrac{2}{3}[0 + 4\cdot 10 + 2\cdot 68 + 4\cdot 222 + 520]$$

$$= \tfrac{2}{3}[40 + 136 + 888 + 520]$$

$$= 1056.$$

The great improvement obtained by using the more complex Simpson's rule is obvious here; note that the result is more accurate than even a trapezoidal rule with twice the number of division points.   In fact, in this particular case, Simpson's rule gives the *exact* value of the integral; this occurs whenever Simpson's rule is used for any cubic function.

EXERCISE 9.7

Estimate each of the following integrals

(a) using the trapezoidal rule with three interval division points;

(b) using the trapezoidal rule with five interval division points;

(c) using Simpson's rule with three interval division points.

Where possible, evaluate the integral exactly for comparison.

1. $\displaystyle\int_0^4 x^3 dx$

2. $\displaystyle\int_0^4 x^4 dx$

3. $\displaystyle\int_1^9 \frac{100}{x^2}\, dx$

4. $\displaystyle\int_1^9 \left(x^2 - \frac{1}{x^2}\right) dx$

5. $\displaystyle\int_0^4 (x^4 - 2x^2 + 1)dx$

6. $\displaystyle\int_1^5 (x^3 - 1)dx$

7. $\displaystyle\int_1^9 \frac{10}{x}\, dx$

8. $\displaystyle\int_0^\pi 4\sin x\, dx$

9. $\displaystyle\int_0^8 e^x dx$

10. $\displaystyle\int_2^{10} \ln x\, dx$

Chapter Summary

Area as a sum · The definite integral as the limit of a sum

The integral and the primitive $\int f(x)dx = F(x) + c$

The area between two curves · Volumes of revolution

The trapezoidal rule for numerical integration

Simpson's rule for numerical integration

REVIEW EXERCISE 9

Integrate these.

1. $\int (x^4 + 4x^2 + 4)dx$ 2. $\int (x^3 + x^{-2})dx$ 3. $\int (x^{1/2} - x^{-1/2})dx$

4. $\int (x + 1)^2 dx$ 5. $\int (1 - x)^3 dx$ 6. $\int (4 - x)^{-2} dx$

7. $\int x(x^2 + 1)dx$ 8. $\int x(x^2 + 4)^{-2}dx$ 9. $\int x(x^2 + 16)^{1/2}dx$

10. $\int x(x^2 - 1)^{-1/2}dx$

Find the areas enclosed between the graphs of the following equations.

11. $y = (x - 1)(x - 4)$ and $y = 0$
12. $y = 3x^2 - x - 3$ and $y = -2x^2 + 4x + 7$
13. $y = x^2 - 7x + 11$ and $y = 5 - 2x$
14. $y = (9 - x^2)^2$ and $y = 4$
15. $y = \dfrac{4}{x^2}$ and $y = 5 - x^2$

Compute the volume of revolution generated by each of the areas revolved about the axis stated; use two different methods to check your results whenever possible.

16. $y = x^2 + 1$, $y = 0$, $x = 0$, $x = 2$ about the x-axis
17. $y^2 = x - 1$, $y = 0$, $x = 5$ about the x-axis
18. $xy = 4$, $y = 0$, $x = 1$, $x = 4$ about the x-axis
19. $xy = 4$, $y = 1$, $x = 0$, $y = 4$ about the y-axis
20. $y = x^2 + 1$, $y = 0$, $x = 0$, $x = 2$ about the y-axis
21. $y^2 = x - 1$, $y = 0$, $x = 5$ about the y-axis

Evaluate each of the following integrals
    (a) using the trapezoidal rule with nine interval division points;
    (b) using Simpson's rule with five interval division points.

Check by exact evaluation where possible.

22. $\int_{1}^{2} (x^3 + 1)dx$ 23. $\int_{0}^{100} (1 + x^{1/2})dx$ 24. $\int_{0}^{\pi/3} \tan x \, dx$ 25. $\int_{-5}^{5} e^{-x}dx$

Chapter 10

TRIGONOMETRIC FUNCTIONS

10.1. Some Limits for Trigonometric Functions

A limit of fundamental importance in the study of the derivatives of the trigonometric functions is

$$\lim_{\theta \to 0} \frac{\sin \theta}{\theta}.$$

(Note that the value of $\frac{\sin \theta}{\theta}$ at $\theta = 0$ does not exist.) Before we give a proof that establishes the value of this limit, we shall examine the values of $\frac{\sin \theta}{\theta}$ for small values of θ, bearing in mind that θ must be measured in radians.

In the following table, the values of $\sin \theta$ are given correctly to five decimal places.

θ	.2	.1	.05	.02	.01
$\sin \theta$	.19867	.09983	.04998	.02000	.01000
$\dfrac{\sin \theta}{\theta}$	.9934	.9983	1.000	1.000	1.000

The trend of the values of $\frac{\sin \theta}{\theta}$ in the table certainly suggests that

$$\lim_{\theta \to 0} \frac{\sin \theta}{\theta} = 1.$$

In fact, $\frac{\sin \theta}{\theta} \simeq 1$ for relatively large values of θ. For example, even for

$$\theta = .5,$$
$$\sin \theta \simeq .47943,$$

and so

$$\frac{\sin \theta}{\theta} \simeq .95886.$$

The limit as $\theta \to 0$ is in fact 1, and we present a geometrical proof. Note that, in this case, we cannot divide $\sin \theta$ by θ and then let $\theta \to 0$ in the resulting quotient in the way that we did in many cases for the limits of rational algebraic functions.

Proof: Arc AD is part of a unit circle, centre O, and $\angle AOB = \theta$ measured in radians. AC is perpendicular to OB, and BA is perpendicular to OA. From the diagram,

$$0 < \theta < \frac{\pi}{2},$$

and

$$\text{Area } OAC \leq \text{Area } OAD \leq \text{Area } OAB.$$

$$AC = \sin \theta, \quad OC = \cos \theta, \quad AB = \tan \theta,$$

$$\therefore \quad \frac{1}{2} \sin \theta \cos \theta \leq \frac{1}{2} \theta \leq \frac{1}{2} \tan \theta.$$

Now

$$\sin \theta > 0 ;$$

$$\therefore \quad \cos \theta \leq \frac{\theta}{\sin \theta} \leq \frac{1}{\cos \theta}.$$

As $\theta \to 0$, $\cos \theta \to 1$; therefore,

$$1 \leq \lim_{\theta \to 0} \frac{\theta}{\sin \theta} \leq 1 ;$$

hence,

$$\lim_{\theta \to 0} \frac{\theta}{\sin \theta} = 1$$

and

$$\lim_{\theta \to 0} \frac{\sin \theta}{\theta} = 1 .$$

This new result can be used to establish many other limits for trigonometric functions.

Example.   Find the limit of $\dfrac{1 - \cos \theta}{\theta}$ as θ approaches 0.

Solution:

$$\lim_{\theta \to 0} \frac{1 - \cos \theta}{\theta} = \lim_{\theta \to 0} \frac{(1 - \cos \theta)(1 + \cos \theta)}{\theta(1 + \cos \theta)}$$

$$= \lim_{\theta \to 0} \frac{\sin^2 \theta}{\theta(1 + \cos \theta)}$$

$$= \left(\lim_{\theta \to 0} \frac{\sin \theta}{\theta} \right) \left(\lim_{\theta \to 0} \frac{\sin \theta}{1 + \cos \theta} \right)$$

$$= (1)(0) = 0 .$$

EXERCISE 10.1

1. Tabulate the values of $\dfrac{1 - \cos \theta}{\theta}$ for $\theta = .5236, .2094, .1047, .0524, .0175$.

2. Tabulate the values of $\dfrac{\tan \theta}{\theta}$ for $\theta = .5236, .2094, .1047, .0524, .0175$.

Evaluate the following limits (if they exist).

3. $\lim\limits_{\theta \to 0} \dfrac{\tan \theta}{\theta}$

4. $\lim\limits_{\theta \to 0} \dfrac{\sin \theta}{\theta^2}$

5. $\lim\limits_{x \to 0} \dfrac{1 - \cos x}{x^2}$

6. $\lim\limits_{x \to 0} \dfrac{1 - \cos x}{\sin x}$

7. $\lim\limits_{x \to 0} \dfrac{\sin 2x}{x}$

8. $\lim\limits_{x \to 0} \dfrac{\sin 4x}{3x}$

9. $\lim\limits_{x \to \pi/2} \dfrac{\cot x}{\dfrac{\pi}{2} - x}$

10. $\lim\limits_{x \to \pi} \dfrac{\sin x}{(\pi - x)}$

10.2. The Derivatives of the Sine and Cosine Functions

To find the derivative of the sine and cosine functions, we proceed from first principles.   We make frequent use of the trigonometric formulae for the sine and cosine of sums and multiples of angles.

The Derivative of sin x

Let $y = \sin x$; then

$$y + \triangle y = \sin (x + \triangle x) ,$$

and

$$\triangle y = \sin (x + \triangle x) - \sin x$$
$$= 2 \cos \left(x + \frac{\triangle x}{2} \right) \sin \left(\frac{\triangle x}{2} \right) .$$

Therefore,

$$\frac{\triangle y}{\triangle x} = 2 \cos \left(x + \frac{\triangle x}{2} \right) \frac{\sin \left(\dfrac{\triangle x}{2} \right)}{\triangle x}$$

$$= \cos \left(x + \frac{\triangle x}{2} \right) \frac{\sin \left(\dfrac{\triangle x}{2} \right)}{\left(\dfrac{\triangle x}{2} \right)} .$$

$$D_x y = \lim_{\triangle x \to 0} \frac{\triangle y}{\triangle x}$$

$$= \left[\lim_{\triangle x \to 0} \cos \left(x + \frac{\triangle x}{2} \right) \right] \left[\lim_{\triangle x \to 0} \frac{\sin \left(\frac{\triangle x}{2} \right)}{\left(\frac{\triangle x}{2} \right)} \right]$$

$$= [\cos x] [1]$$

$$= \cos x \; ;$$

that is,

$$D_x (\sin x) = \cos x \, .$$

The Derivative of cos x

The value of the derivative of cos x can be found from first principles in a way similar to that used in finding the value of the derivative of sin x (see (1) Exercise 10.2 on opposite page).   Alternatively,

$$D_x (\cos x) = D_x \left[\sin \left(\frac{\pi}{2} - x \right) \right].$$

If we write $u = \pi/2 - x$, then

$$D_x(\cos x) = D_u [\sin u] \cdot D_x u$$
$$= (\cos u)(-1)$$
$$= -\cos \left(\frac{\pi}{2} - x \right).$$

Therefore,

$$D_x(\cos x) = -\sin x \, .$$

Example 1.   Find $D_x (\sin 3x)$.

Solution: If we write $u = 3x$, then

$$D_x (\sin 3x) = D_u (\sin u) \cdot D_x (3x)$$
$$= (\cos u)(3)$$
$$= 3 \cos 3x \, .$$

Example 2.   Find $D_x (\tan x)$.

Solution:

$$D_x (\tan x) = D_x \left(\frac{\sin x}{\cos x} \right)$$

$$= \frac{\cos x \cdot D_x (\sin x) - \sin x \cdot D_x (\cos x)}{\cos^2 x}$$

$$= \frac{\cos x (\cos x) - \sin x (-\sin x)}{\cos^2 x}$$

$$= \frac{\cos^2 x + \sin^2 x}{\cos^2 x}$$

$$= \frac{1}{\cos^2 x}$$

$$= \sec^2 x .$$

Example 3.   Find $D_x[\cos(x^2 + 4)]$.

Solution: If we write $u = x^2 + 4$, then

$$D_x[\cos(x^2 + 4)] = D_u(\cos u) \cdot D_x(x^2 + 4)$$
$$= (-\sin u)\,(2x)$$
$$= -2x \sin(x^2 + 4) .$$

EXERCISE 10.2

1. Prove from first principles that

$$D_x(\cos x) = -\sin x .$$

For each of the following, find the value of the derivative with respect to the appropriate variable.

2. $\sin \dfrac{x}{2}$ 3. $\sin 5\theta$

4. $\cos 3x$ 5. $\cos \dfrac{\theta}{4}$

6. $\sin(2x + 4)$ 7. $\sin \left(\dfrac{t + 2}{3} \right)$

8. $\cos(3x - 2)$ 9. $\cos \left(\dfrac{2t + 1}{4} \right)$

10. $\sin 2x + \sin x$ 11. $\cos 3x + \cos 5x$

12. $\dfrac{1}{\sin x}$ $(= \operatorname{cosec} x)$ 13. $\dfrac{1}{\cos x}$ $(= \sec x)$

14. $\sin^2 x$ 15. $\cos^2 x$

16. $\sin^3 u$ 17. $\cos^4 v$

18. $\sin^3 2x$ 19. $\cos^2 3x$

20. $\tan 2x$ 21. $\cot x$

22. $\sin (x^2)$ 23. $\cos (x^3)$

24. $\sin (x^2 + 1)$ 25. $\sin (x^{-1})$

26. $\cos(2t^2 + 1)$

27. $\cos[(s+1)^2]$

28. $\sin(x^2 + 2x + 3)$

29. $\cos(2x^2 - x)$

30. $x \sin x$

31. $x \cos x$

32. $t^2 \sin t$

33. $\theta^2 \cos \theta$

34. $\theta \sin(\theta + 1)$

35. $s \cos(2s + 3)$

36. $(2x + 1) \sin(x + 1)$

37. $(3x + 4) \sin(2x - 1)$

38. $(x + 3) \cos(2x + 1)$

39. $(\theta - 2) \cos(3\theta - 2)$

40. $(x^2 + 1) \sin(x^2 + 1)$

41. $(x + 1)^2 \sin(x^2 + 2x)$

42. $(x + 1) \sin(1 - x)$

43. $(1 - x) \sin(x + 1)$

44. $(x + 2) \cos(2 - 3x)$

45. $(x - 1) \cos(1 - 2x)$

46. $\dfrac{\sin t}{t + 1}$

47. $\dfrac{\sin(2s + 1)}{s + 3}$

48. $\dfrac{\cos(x - 3)}{x}$

49. $\dfrac{\cos(2x - 1)}{(2x - 1)}$

50. $\dfrac{\cos 2\theta}{\sin \theta}$

51. $\dfrac{\sin 2x}{\cos x}$

52. $\dfrac{\cos(x + 1)}{\sin 2x}$

53. $\dfrac{\sin(1 - t)}{\sin t}$

54. $\sin(x^{1/2} + 2)$

55. $\cos(x^{-1/2} + 1)$

10.3. Maxima and Minima

The simplest exercise in maxima and minima involving sine and cosine functions is to use the derivative to find the positions of the maxima and minima of the graph of $y = \sin x$ itself.

Example. Find the maxima and minima of $y = \sin x$.

Solution: If
$$y = \sin x,$$

then
$$D_x y = \cos x.$$

At a maximum or minimum,
$$D_x y = 0;$$

therefore, at a maximum or minimum,
$$\cos x = 0.$$

This equation has the solution set

$$\left\{ \cdots, \ -\frac{5\pi}{2}, \ -\frac{3\pi}{2}, \ -\frac{\pi}{2}, \ \frac{\pi}{2}, \ \frac{3\pi}{2}, \ \frac{5\pi}{2}, \ \cdots \right\}.$$

This solution set may be written more concisely as

$$\left\{ \left(\frac{2n+1}{2} \right) \pi \ \middle|\ n \in I \right\}.$$

Considering the values for x from this solution set, we see that,

$$\text{when} \quad x = \frac{\pi}{2}, \quad \sin x = 1 \ ;$$

$$\text{when} \quad x = \frac{3\pi}{2}, \quad \sin x = -1 \ ;$$

$$\text{when} \quad x = \frac{5\pi}{2}, \quad \sin x = 1 \ ;$$

$$\text{when} \quad x = \frac{7\pi}{2}, \quad \sin x = -1 \ ;$$

. . . .

It appears obvious (and we know from our previous studies of the graph of $y = \sin x$) that the set of values $\{ \ \cdots, \ \frac{1}{2}\pi, \ \frac{5}{2}\pi, \ \cdots \ \}$ for x give a set of maxima for $\sin x$. Similarly, the set of values $\{ \ \cdots, \ -\frac{1}{2}\pi, \ \frac{3}{2}\pi, \ \frac{7}{2}\pi, \ \cdots \ \}$ for x give a set of minima for $\sin x$. It is interesting to confirm this by evaluating the second derivative:

$$D_x(\sin x) = \cos x \ ;$$

$$\therefore \quad D_x^2(\sin x) = D_x(\cos x)$$

$$= -\sin x \ . \tag{1}$$

Thus, at $x = \frac{1}{2}\pi$, when $\sin x = 1$,

$$D_x^2(\sin x) = -1 \ ;$$

that is, $D_x^2(\sin x)$ is negative, and so $x = \frac{1}{2}\pi$ gives a maximum value of 1 for $\sin x$. All the other values can be tested in the same way.

Notice that, if we write y for $\sin x$, equation (1) may be written

$$D_x^2 y = -y \ , \quad \text{or} \quad D_x^2 y + y = 0 \ .$$

This is a very important equation in physics and is known as the equation for *simple harmonic motion*. Obviously, one set of values of y that satisfies this equation is given by $y = \sin x$. Another solution is $y = \cos x$.

We can solve many applied problems in maxima and minima by using sine and cosine functions and their derivatives.

Example 1.   The hypotenuse of a right-angled triangle is 12 inches.   What are the acute angles in the triangle with maximum perimeter?

Solution: Let AC be the hypotenuse of $\triangle ABC$, $\angle ABC = \pi/2$.   Let $\angle CAB = \theta$, and let the length in inches of the perimeter be p.

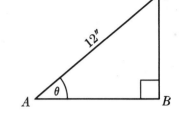

Length of CA in inches is 12.
Length of AB in inches is 12 cos θ.
Length of BC in inches is 12 sin θ.

$$\therefore \quad p = 12 + 12 \cos\theta + 12 \sin\theta.$$

$$\therefore \quad D_\theta p = -12 \sin\theta + 12 \cos\theta.$$

At the maximum value of p, $D_\theta p = 0$; that is,

$$-12 \sin\theta + 12 \cos\theta = 0 \; ;$$

$$\therefore \quad \sin\theta = \cos\theta \; ;$$

$$\therefore \quad \tan\theta = 1 \quad \text{if} \quad \cos\theta \neq 0.$$

Now θ is an acute angle; therefore $\theta = \dfrac{\pi}{4}$, and

$$\angle CAB = \frac{\pi}{4} \quad \text{and} \quad \angle BCA = \frac{\pi}{4}.$$

Example 2.   A cone is inscribed in a sphere of radius a.   Find the maximum possible volume of the cone.

Solution: The diagram shows a cross section of the sphere and cone.   Let θ be the angle shown. Then the radius of the base of the cone is

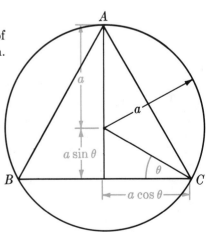

$$a \cos\theta,$$

and the height of the cone is

$$a + a \sin\theta.$$

Therefore, the volume of the cone is

$$V = \frac{\pi}{3}(a \cos\theta)^2 (a + a \sin\theta)$$

$$= \frac{\pi a^3}{3} \cos^2\theta (1 + \sin\theta).$$

$$D_\theta V = \frac{\pi a^3}{3}[-2 \sin \theta \cos \theta(1 + \sin \theta) + \cos^2\theta \cos \theta]$$

$$= \frac{\pi a^3}{3}[-2 \sin \theta \cos \theta (1 + \sin \theta) + \cos \theta (1 - \sin^2\theta)]$$

$$= \frac{\pi a^3}{3} \cos \theta (1 + \sin \theta)(1 - 3 \sin \theta) .$$

When V is a maximum, $D_\theta V = 0$; hence

$$\cos \theta(1 + \sin \theta) (1 - 3 \sin \theta) = 0 .$$

$$\therefore \quad \cos \theta = 0, \quad \sin \theta = -1, \quad \text{or} \quad 3 \sin \theta = 1 .$$

When $\cos \theta = 0$,

$$V = 0, \quad \text{which is obviously not a maximum.}$$

When $\sin \theta = -1$,

$$V = 0, \quad \text{which is obviously not a maximum.}$$

When $\sin \theta = \frac{1}{3}$,

$$V = \frac{\pi a^3}{3}\left(1 - \frac{1}{3^2}\right)\left(1 + \frac{1}{3}\right)$$

$$= \frac{\pi a^3}{3} \cdot \frac{8}{9} \cdot \frac{4}{3}$$

$$= \frac{32\pi a^3}{81} .$$

The maximum volume is $V = \frac{32\pi a^3}{81}$.

EXERCISE 10.3

1. The voltage fed to an electrical circuit is given by
$$V = 100 \sin 50t + 50 \sin 100t .$$
Find the maximum and minimum values of V.

2. A triangle is inscribed in a semicircle, with the diameter of the semicircle as its hypotenuse. Determine the value of θ so that the triangle has a maximum area.

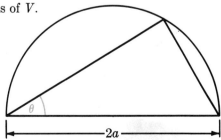

3. An isosceles triangle is drawn in a semi-circle, with its apex at the centre of the circle. Find the area of the isosceles triangle of maximum area.

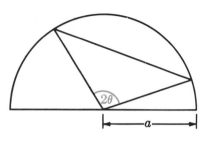

4. An isosceles triangle with an apex angle of 2θ is inscribed in a circle of radius 5 inches. Find the value of θ when the triangle has maximum area, and show that the maximum area is $\dfrac{75\sqrt{3}}{4}$.

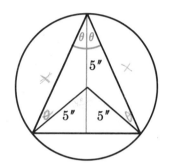

5. An isosceles triangle ABC is circumscribed about a circle of radius 3 inches. Find the minimum possible area of the triangle.

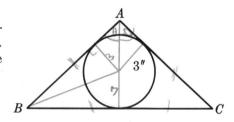

6. In question (5), find the minimum possible perimeter of the triangle.

7. The range R in feet of a projectile fired with a velocity v ft/sec at an angle θ to the horizontal is given by

$$R = \frac{2v^2}{g} \sin \theta \cos \theta .$$

Find the angle of projection θ so that the range is a maximum.

8. The slant height of a right circular cone is 1 metre. Show that the maximum volume possible for the cone is $\dfrac{2\pi\sqrt{3}}{27}$ cubic metres.

9. One corner of a rectangular sheet of note
    paper $ABCD$ is folded over so that the
    corner D moves to R on AB as shown
    in the figure below.   Find the minimum
    length of the crease PQ.

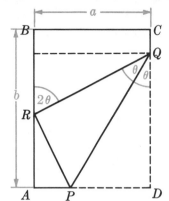

10. A line segment AB intercepted by the
    axes Ox and Oy passes through the
    fixed point $P(a, b)$.   Find the minimum
    possible length of AB.

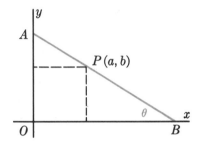

10.4. Primitives and Integrals of sin x and cos x

In the same way that

$$F' : x \to x^2 \quad \text{implies} \quad F : x \to \tfrac{1}{3}x^3 + c,$$

so

$$F' : x \to \cos x \quad \text{implies} \quad F : x \to \sin x + c,$$

as we easily see by differentiating $F(x) = \sin x$ with respect to x.   The function

$$F : x \to \sin x + c$$

is the general primitive (or anti-derivative) of

$$f : x \to \cos x \; ;$$

the general solution of the equation

$$D_x y = \cos x$$

is

$$y = \int \cos x \, dx = \sin x + c.$$

Similarly, the general solution of

$$D_x y = \sin x$$

is

$$y = \int \sin x \, dx = -\cos x + c.$$

(Check this result by differentiating y with respect to x.)

We shall find a tabulation of the general primitives of the sine and cosine functions helpful as a reference in working the examples and exercises that follow. (Check the last two results listed in the table by differentiating y with respect to x.)

$f(x) = F'(x)$	$F(x) = \int f(x)dx$
$\cos x$	$\sin x + c$
$\sin x$	$-\cos x + c$
$\cos bx$	$\dfrac{1}{b} \sin bx + c$
$\sin bx$	$-\dfrac{1}{b} \cos bx + c$

Example 1.   Find the general solution of $D_x y = 4 \sin 2x$.

Solution:

$$D_x(\cos 2x) = -2 \sin 2x$$

and

$$D_x(-2 \cos 2x) = 4 \sin 2x .$$

Therefore,

$$y = \int 4 \sin 2x \, dx = -2 \cos 2x + c$$

is the general solution of $D_x y = 4 \sin 2x$.

Example 2.   Find the integral of $f : x \rightarrow \cos x \, \sin^2 x$.

Solution:

$$D_x (\sin x) = \cos x ,$$

and if we write $u = \sin x$, then

$$D_x (\sin^3 x) = D_u (u^3) \cdot D_x u$$
$$= 3u^2 \cos x$$
$$= 3 \sin^2 x \cos x .$$
$$\therefore \quad D_x (\tfrac{1}{3} \sin^3 x) = \sin^2 x \cos x .$$

Therefore, the integral is

$$\int \cos x \, \sin^2 x \, dx = \tfrac{1}{3} \sin^3 x + c.$$

Example 3.   Solve $D_x y = 3x \cos(x^2)$.

Solution: If we write $u = x^2$, then

$$D_x[\sin(x^2)] = D_u(\sin u) \cdot D_x(u)$$
$$= (\cos u)(2x)$$
$$= 2x \cos(x^2) .$$

$$\therefore \quad D_x[\tfrac{3}{2}\sin(x^2)] = 3x \cos(x^2) .$$

Hence,

$$y = \int 3x \cos(x^2) dx = \tfrac{3}{2}\sin(x^2) + c$$

is the general solution of $D_x y = 3x \cos(x^2)$.

EXERCISE 10.4

Find the general solution of each of the following equations.

1. $D_x y = \sin 3x$

2. $D_x y = \cos 4x$

3. $D_x y = 6 \sin 2x$

4. $D_x y = 5 \cos 5x$

5. $D_x y = 2 \sin x \cos x$

6. $D_x y = 2 \cos^2 x - 1$

7. $D_x y = \cos^2 x \sin x$

8. $D_x y = \sin^4 x \cos x$

9. $D_x y = (\sin x)^{1/2} \cos x$

10. $D_x y = (\cos x)^{3/2} \sin x$

Find the general primitive of each of the following.

11. $\sin(x + 1)$

12. $\cos(2x - 3)$

13. $\cos(\tfrac{1}{2}x + 1)$

14. $\sin(\tfrac{2}{3}x + \tfrac{1}{3})$

15. $x \sin(x^2)$

16. $x \cos(x^2 + 2)$

17. $2(x + 1)\cos(x + 1)^2$

18. $(2x + 3) \sin(x^2 + 3x)$

19. $(2x - 1) \sin(x^2 - x + 6)$

20. $x^2 \cos(x^3 + 1)$

Solve each of the following equations.

21. $D_x y = \sin^2 x \cos x$

22. $D_x y = \sin x(1 - \sin^2 x)$

23. $D_x y = \dfrac{\sin x}{\cos^3 x}$

24. $D_x y = \dfrac{\cos x}{\sin^2 x}$

25. $D_x y = \sec^2 x$

26. $D_x y = \sin^3 x$

27. $D_x y = \dfrac{\sin x}{(1 + \cos x)^2}$

28. $D_x y = \dfrac{\cos x}{(1 - \sin x)^2}$

29. $D_x y = \sin^2 x \cos x + \cos^3 x$

30. $D_x y = \sin x + \sin 2x$

10.5. Applications

The trigonometric functions are of particular importance in science, as they are the simplest periodic functions. In fact, most periodic or repetitive phenomena occurring in science are studied mathematically in terms of sine and cosine functions.

Example 1. The angle θ (in radians) that a pendulum makes with the vertical as it swings is given in terms of the time t (in seconds) by

$$\theta = \frac{1}{5} \sin \pi t \,.$$

(a) What is the period of the pendulum?

(b) Find the angular velocity $D_t\theta$.

(c) Find the angular acceleration $D_t^2\theta$.

Solution:

(a) One *period* in time is that value of t which makes the argument of the sine function, πt, change by 2π, the period of the sine function itself. If T is this period, then

$$\pi T = 2\pi \,,$$
$$T = 2 \,.$$

(This is called a "seconds" pendulum; it has a period of 2 seconds, so that the time between extreme positions is 1 second.)

(b) $$\theta = \frac{1}{5} \sin \pi t \,;$$

$$\therefore \quad D_t\theta = \frac{\pi}{5} \cos \pi t \,.$$

(c) $$D_t^2\theta = -\frac{\pi^2}{5} \sin \pi t \,.$$

Note that, in this example,

$$D_t^2\theta + \pi^2\theta = 0 \,,$$

which is a form of the simple harmonic motion equation (see page 197).

Example 2. The velocity v (in cm/sec) of the piston in an engine is given by

$$v = 80\pi \sin 10\pi t \,,$$

where time t is in seconds.

(a) Find a formula for the position s (in centimetres) of the piston at any time t if $s = 0$ when $t = 0$.

(b) What is the maximum value of s?

Solution:

(a)
$$v = D_t s \; ;$$
$$\therefore \quad D_t s = 80\pi \sin 10\pi t \; ;$$
$$\therefore \quad s = -8 \cos 10\pi t + c \; .$$

When $t = 0$, $s = 0$; therefore,
$$0 = -8 + c \; ,$$
$$c = 8 \; .$$
$$\therefore \quad s = 8(1 - \cos 10\pi t) \; .$$

(b) At a maximum or minimum of s, $D_t s = 0$. Therefore,
$$\sin 10\pi t = 0 \; ;$$

that is,
$$10\pi t = n\pi \; , \quad n \in I \; ,$$
$$t = \frac{n}{10} \; , \quad n \in I \; .$$

For this value of t,
$$\cos 10\pi t = \cos n\pi$$
$$= +1 \quad \text{or} \quad -1 \; .$$

When $\cos 10\pi t = +1$,
$$s = 0 \; .$$

When $\cos 10\pi t = -1$,
$$s = 16 \; .$$

Therefore, $s = 16$ is the maximum value of s.

Note that we can find the maximum value of s without the use of differentiation: since $-1 \leq \cos \theta \leq +1$, we can immediately see that the maximum value of s must be
$$8[1 - (-1)] = 16 \; .$$

EXERCISE 10.5

1. The position y (in feet) of a weight of 1 pound that is suspended by a spring from a fixed point is given by
$$y = \tfrac{1}{6} \sin 30t \; ,$$
where t is measured in seconds. Find the velocity and acceleration at any time, and show that
$$D_t^2 y + 900y = 0 \; .$$

2. The displacement s (in inches) of the midpoint of a vibrating violin string at any time is given by

$$s = .05 \sin 512\pi t\,,$$

where t is measured in seconds. Find the velocity and acceleration at any time, and show that at time $t = 0$ the velocity has a maximum value. Show also that, when the velocity is zero, both the displacement and acceleration have maximum or minimum values.

3. The current i in an electrical circuit is given by the rate of change of the charge q with respect to time t; that is,

$$i = D_t q\,.$$

If the charge on an electrical condenser is given by

$$q = 10^{-4} \cos 10^3 t\,,$$

find the current at any time.

4. The current i flowing into or out of an electrical condenser at any time t is given by

$$i = 5 \times 10^{-2} \sin 10^4 t\,.$$

Find the charge q on the condenser at any time t if the charge is zero when $t = 0$.

5. The angular velocity $D_t \theta$ of a pendulum is given by

$$D_t \theta = \frac{\pi}{10} \cos \pi t\,.$$

Find the angle of displacement θ from the vertical at any time t if the angle is zero when t is zero. What is the maximum angle?

6. A piston is limited to a maximum acceleration of 320 ft/sec² and executes a simple harmonic motion at 5 cycles per second; therefore, its velocity is given by

$$D_t y = 320 \cos 10\pi t\,,$$

where t is the time (in seconds) and y is the displacement (in feet) of the piston. Find the acceleration and displacement at any time if the displacement is zero when $t = 0$. What are the maximum velocity and the maximum displacement?

10.6. Areas and Volumes of Revolution

In Chapter 8, we showed that the value of the area that lies entirely on one side of the x-axis and is bounded by the graph of $y = f(x)$, the x-axis, and the lines $x = a$ and $x = b$ is given by

$$\left|\,{}_a A_b\,\right| = \int_a^b f(x)dx = \left|\left[F(x)\right]_a^b\right| = \left|F(b) - F(a)\right|$$

where F is any primitive of f. This result applies to all functions f that have primitives, not just to the rational algebraic functions used in the previous chapter.

Example 1.   Find the area between the graph of $y = 4 \sin 2x$, the x-axis, and the lines $x = 0$ and $x = \pi/4$.

Solution: If F is a primitive of $4 \sin 2x$, then

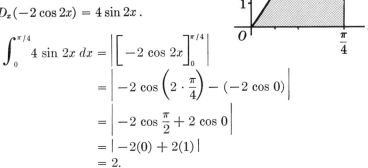

$$F'(x) = f(x) = 4 \sin 2x .$$

Now

$$D_x(\cos 2x) = -2 \sin 2x ,$$

and so

$$D_x(-2 \cos 2x) = 4 \sin 2x .$$

Therefore,

$$\int_0^{\pi/4} 4 \sin 2x \, dx = \left| \left[-2 \cos 2x \right]_0^{\pi/4} \right|$$

$$= \left| -2 \cos \left(2 \cdot \frac{\pi}{4} \right) - (-2 \cos 0) \right|$$

$$= \left| -2 \cos \frac{\pi}{2} + 2 \cos 0 \right|$$

$$= \left| -2(0) + 2(1) \right|$$

$$= 2.$$

We must note that the trigonometric functions have both positive and negative values.   As a consequence, the values found for the difference between the values of a primitive at the two bounding lines $x = a$ and $x = b$ will not always be the total area bounded by the graph, the x-axis, and the given lines.   For instance, if the lines given in Example 1 were $x = 0$ and $x = \pi$, we would obtain

$$\int 4 \sin 2x \, dx = 2 \cos 2\pi + 2 \cos 0 = 0.$$

(Check this result.)   This is the correct algebraic value of the difference of the values of the primitives, but the area between the graph of $y = 4 \sin 2x$ and the x-axis is equal to 8, that is,

$$\left| {}_0A_{\pi/2} \right| + \left| {}_{\pi/2}A_\pi \right| = 8 .$$

If we draw the graph (Figure 10.5) to include the required values, we can see by symmetry considerations that the area between the graph and the x-axis from $x = 0$ to $x = \pi$ is also equal to

$$2 \, {}_0A_{\pi/2} \quad \text{or} \quad 4 \, {}_0A_{\pi/4} .$$

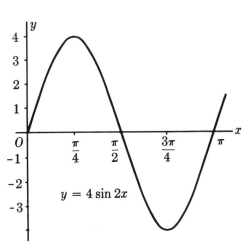

Figure 10.5

Example 2. Find the area bounded by the graph of $y = \cos x$, the x-axis, and the lines $x = \frac{1}{4}\pi$ and $x = \frac{3}{4}\pi$.

Solution: The part of the required area from $x = \frac{1}{4}\pi$ to $x = \frac{1}{2}\pi$ lies above the x-axis, and that from $x = \frac{1}{2}\pi$ to $x = \frac{3}{4}\pi$ lies below the x-axis.

$$\text{Area} = \left|\, _{\pi/4}A_{\pi/2}\right| + \left|\, _{\pi/2}A_{3\pi/4}\right|$$

$$= \left|F\left(\frac{\pi}{2}\right) - F\left(\frac{\pi}{4}\right)\right| + \left|F\left(\frac{3\pi}{4}\right) - F\left(\frac{\pi}{2}\right)\right|.$$

Now

$$f(x) = \cos x\,;$$

$$\therefore \quad F(x) = \int \cos x\, dx = \sin x.$$

Hence,

$$_{\pi/4}A_{3\pi/4} = \left|\sin\frac{\pi}{2} - \sin\frac{\pi}{4}\right| + \left|\sin\frac{3\pi}{4} - \sin\frac{\pi}{2}\right|$$

$$= \left|1 - \frac{1}{\sqrt{2}}\right| + \left|\frac{1}{\sqrt{2}} - 1\right|$$

$$= 2\left(1 - \frac{1}{\sqrt{2}}\right).$$

Note that we have an alternative method of finding this area. By symmetry, the magnitude of the area between the lines $x = \frac{1}{4}\pi$ and $x = \frac{1}{2}\pi$ is equal to the magnitude of the area between the lines $x = \frac{1}{2}\pi$ and $x = \frac{3}{4}\pi$. Hence,

$$_{\pi/4}A_{3\pi/4} = 2\,_{\pi/4}A_{\pi/2}$$

$$= 2\left(\sin\frac{\pi}{2} - \sin\frac{\pi}{4}\right)$$

$$= 2\left(1 - \frac{1}{\sqrt{2}}\right).$$

Example 3. Find the volume generated when the area enclosed by $y = 4\sin\frac{x}{2}$, $(0 \le x \le 2\pi)$ and $y = 0$ is revolved about the x-axis.

Solution:

$$\text{Element of volume} = \pi y^2 \, \triangle x$$

$$= 4\pi \sin^2\frac{x}{2} \, \triangle x.$$

$$\therefore \quad \text{Volume of revolution} = 4\pi \int_0^\pi \sin^2\frac{x}{2} \, dx$$

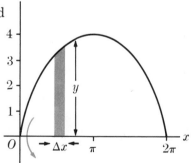

$$= 2\pi \int_0^\pi (1 - \cos x)\, dx$$

$$= 2\pi \left[x - \sin x \right]_0^\pi$$

$$= 2\pi[\pi - 0 - (0 - 0)]$$

$$= 4\pi^2.$$

EXERCISE 10.6

1. Find the area between the graph of $y = \sin x$ and the x-axis from $x = 0$ to $x = \pi$.

2. Find the area between the graph of $y = \sin 2x$ and the x-axis from $x = 0$ to $x = \pi$.

3. Find the area between the graphs of $y = \cos x$ and $y = -1$ from $x = -\pi$ to $x = \pi$.

4. Find the area between the graphs of $y = \sin x$. and $y = \frac{1}{2}$ from $x = \frac{1}{6}\pi$ to $x = \frac{5}{6}\pi$.

5. Find the area between $y = 2 \cos x - \sin 2x$ and the x-axis from $x = -\frac{1}{2}\pi$ to $x = 0$. Sketch the curve $y = 2 \cos x - \sin 2x$ for $-\frac{1}{2}\pi \le x \le 0$.

6. Find the area between $y = 2 \cos x - \sin 2x$ and the x-axis from $x = -\frac{1}{2}\pi$ to $x = \frac{1}{2}\pi$. Sketch the curve $y = 2 \cos x - \sin 2x$ for $-\frac{1}{2}\pi < x < \frac{1}{2}\pi$.

7. Find the area between the graphs of $y = 2 \sin \frac{1}{2}x$ and $y = \sin x$ from $x = 0$ to $x = 2\pi$.

8. Find the area between the graphs of $y = \cos x$ and $y = \sin x$ from $x = -\frac{1}{4}\pi$ to $x = +\frac{1}{4}\pi$.

9. Find the area between the graphs of $y = \sin x$ and $y = \cos 2x$ between $x = \frac{1}{6}\pi$ and $x = \frac{5}{6}\pi$.

10. Find the area between the graphs of $y = 3 \sin x$ and $y = \sin 3x$ from $x = 0$ to $x = \pi$.

Find the volume generated when each of the areas bounded by the given graphs is revolved about the given axis.

11. $y = \cos 2x$ for $\left(0 \le x \le \dfrac{\pi}{4}\right)$, $x = 0$ and $y = 0$ about $y = 0$

12. $y = \sin^{1/2} x$ for $(0 \le x \le \pi)$, $y = 0$ about $y = 0$

13. $y = \sin(x^2)$ for $(0 \le x \le \sqrt{\pi})$, $y = 0$ about $x = 0$

14. $y = \sin x + \cos x$, $x = 0$, $y = 0$, $x = \dfrac{\pi}{2}$ about $y = 0$

15. $y = \sec x$, $x = 0$, $y = 0$, $x = \dfrac{\pi}{3}$ about $y = 0$

Chapter Summary

$$\lim_{\theta \to 0} \frac{\sin \theta}{\theta} = 1 \qquad\qquad D_x(\sin x) = \cos x \qquad\qquad D_x(\cos x) = -\sin x$$

$$D_x(\tan x) = \sec^2 x \qquad\qquad \int \cos x \, dx = \sin x + c \qquad\qquad \int \sin x \, dx = -\cos x + c$$

Maxima and minima · Kinematics · Areas

REVIEW EXERCISE 10

Evaluate the following limits.

1. $\lim\limits_{\theta \to 0} \dfrac{\sin 2\theta}{\theta}$

2. $\lim\limits_{\theta \to 0} \dfrac{\sin^2 \theta}{\theta}$

3. $\lim\limits_{\theta \to 0} \dfrac{1 - \cos 2\theta}{\theta^2}$

4. $\lim\limits_{\theta \to 0} \dfrac{\tan \theta}{\sin \theta}$

Differentiate each of the following.

5. $\sin 4x$

6. $\cos 5x$

7. $\cos .25x$

8. $\sin \pi x$

9. $\sin 2(x + \pi)$

10. $\cos \pi (x + 2)$

11. $\sin^4 x$

12. $\cos^3 x$

13. $\cos^2 3x$

14. $\sin^3 2x$

15. $\sin x \cos 2x$

16. $\cos x \sin 3x$

17. $\tan 3x$

18. $\cot 2x$

19. $x^2 \sin 2x$

20. $x^5 \cos x$

21. $\cos x^{-2}$

22. $\sin (x^2 + 1)$

23. $\dfrac{\cos 2x}{x^2}$

24. $\dfrac{\sin 3x}{x + 1}$

25. $\sin (2x^2 + 1)$

26. $\cos (x^2 - 4)$

27. $\dfrac{\sin x}{\sin (x + 2)}$

28. $\dfrac{\cos (2x + 1)}{\cos (2x - 1)}$

29. $\sin \sqrt{x^2 + 1}$

30. $\cos \sqrt{x^2 - 1}$

31. The range R (in feet) of a projectile fired with a velocity v (in feet per second) at an angle θ to the horizontal up a sloping surface inclined at an angle α to the horizontal is given by

$$R = \frac{2v^2}{g} \cdot \frac{\sin(\theta - \alpha)\cos\theta}{\cos^2\alpha}.$$

Find the value of θ for which the range is a maximum.

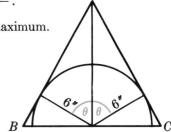

32. An isosceles triangle has its base on a diameter of a semicircle and the sides are tangent to the semicircle. If the radius of the circle is 6 inches, what is the minimum area of the triangle?

33. The displacement s of a weight hanging on the end of a spring is given by

$$s = 4\sin 120\pi t.$$

Find the velocity and acceleration at any time t, and hence show that

$$D_t^2 s + (120\pi)^2 s = 0.$$

34. If the displacement s of a vibrating particle is given by

$$s = 10\cos 6t + 20\cos 3t,$$

find the values of any maximum and minimum displacements at which the velocity is zero.

Integrate each of the following.

35. $6\sin 3x$

36. $3\sin^2 x \cos x$

37. $x\cos(x^2)$

38. $x^2\sin(x^3 + 1)$

39. $(1 + 2\sin x)^2 \cos x$

40. $(1 + \sin x)^{-2}\cos x$

41. $(x + 2)\sin(x^2 + 4x)$

42. $\sec x \tan x$

43. $\sin 2x \cos x$

44. $\cos^3 x$

45. Find the area between the graph of $y = 4\cos 3x$ and the x-axis in the domain $-\frac{1}{6}\pi < x < \frac{1}{6}\pi$.

46. Find the area bounded by the graph of $y = 5\sin \frac{1}{2}x$, the x-axis, and the lines $x = \frac{1}{2}\pi$ and $x = \frac{3}{2}\pi$.

47. Find the area between the graphs of $y = \cos x$ and $y = -1$ in the domain $-\pi < x < \pi$.

48. Find the area between the graph of $y = 1 + \sin x$ and the x-axis from $x = -\frac{1}{2}\pi$ to $x = \frac{3}{2}\pi$.

49. Find the area between the graphs of $y = \sin x$ and $y = 1 - \sin x$ from $x = \frac{1}{6}\pi$ to $x = \frac{5}{6}\pi$.

50. Find the area between the graphs of $y = 2 \cos x$ and $y = \sin 2x$ from $x = -\frac{1}{2}\pi$ to $x = \frac{1}{2}\pi$.

Find the volumes of revolution generated when each of the following areas is revolved about the given axis.

51. $y = \sqrt{\sin x}$ for $(0 \leq x \leq \pi)$, $y = 0$ about $y = 0$

52. $y = \cos(x^2)$ for $\left(0 \leq x \leq \sqrt{\dfrac{\pi}{2}}\right)$, $y = 0$ about $x = 0$

Using (a)   the trapezoidal rule and
      (b)   Simpson's rule
each with three interval division points, evaluate the following definite integrals.

53. $\displaystyle\int_0^\pi \sin x \, dx$

54. $\displaystyle\int_{-\pi/3}^{\pi/3} \sec x \, dx$

55. $\displaystyle\int_0^\pi (\sin x + \frac{1}{3} \sin 3x) \, dx$

Chapter 11

EXPONENTIAL AND LOGARITHMIC FUNCTIONS

11.1. Exponential and Logarithmic Functions

We recall that the concept of a power can be generalized from the simple forms in which the exponents are integers (for example, 2^2, 10^3, 5^{-4}, $(-3)^5$, $(-5)^{-1}$, etc.) to forms in which the exponents are rational numbers (for example, $2^{1/2} = \sqrt{2}$, $(1.35)^{5/2} = \sqrt{(1.35)^5}$, $\pi^{3/5} = \sqrt[5]{\pi^3}$) and even to forms in which the exponents are real numbers (for example, $\pi^{\sqrt{2}}$, 3^π). Note that, if the exponent is *not* an integer and the base is *not* a *positive* real number, the power may not be a real number; thus $(-8)^{2/3} = 4$, but $(-4)^{1/2}$ is *not* a real number.

In general, we can choose any positive real number a as a base, and the exponent may be any real number x. For each value of x, a^x has a unique value, and so we determine an exponential function to a chosen fixed base a $(a \in Re^+)$:

$$f : x \to a^x, \quad x \in Re.$$

The range of the exponential function is Re^+. The graph of $y = a^x$ for $a = 1.5$ is shown in Figure 11.1.

x	1.5^x
-2	.45
-1	.66
0	1.00
1	1.50
2	2.25
3	3.38
4	5.06
5	7.59

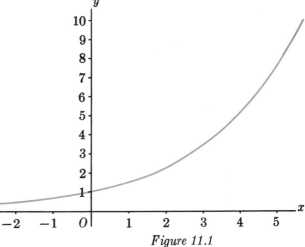

Figure 11.1

213

The logarithmic function to base a is the inverse function of the exponential function to base a. **Thus,**

$$\text{if } y = a^x, \quad \text{then} \quad x = \log_a y,$$

and the domain of the logarithmic function is Re^+.

The graph of $y = \log_a x$ for $a = 2$ is shown in Figure 11.2; for comparison, the graph of $y = 2^x$ is also shown.

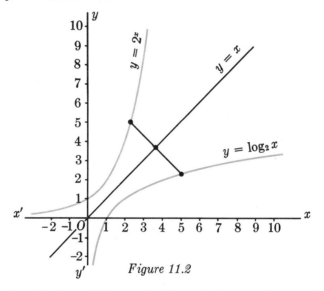

Figure 11.2

We note that the slope of the graph of $y = 2^x$ is everywhere positive and that the values of y and of the slope $D_x y$ increase steadily as x increases. For the graph of $y = \log_2 x$, the slope is again positive everywhere, and y increases steadily as x increases; but the slope, $D_x y$, although it remains positive, decreases steadily.

EXERCISE 11.1

1. Sketch the graphs of
$$y = 3^x, \quad y = 1.5^x, \quad \text{and} \quad y = 5^x$$
for $.25 < x < 3$. Give an estimate of the slopes at $x = \frac{1}{2}$, $x = 1$, and $x = 2$ in each case.

2. Sketch the graphs of
$$y = \log_3 x, \quad y = \log_5 x \quad \text{and} \quad y = \log_{10} x$$
for $.1 < x < 100$. Give an estimate of the slopes at $x = .3$, $x = 1$, and $x = 10$ in each case.

3. Show that

   (a) $a^x = 10^{x \log_{10} a}$.   (b) $\log_a x = \dfrac{\log_{10} x}{\log_{10} a}$.

4. Use the result of question (3(b)) and the tables of the logarithmic function to base 10 to draw the graph of

$$y = \log_a x$$

for each of the values of $a = 2.5,\ 2.6,\ 2.7,\ 2.8,\ 2.9,\ 3.0$ and for $.1 < x < 10$. Find the slope of the tangent at $x = 1$ in each case. Does it seem possible that a value of a exists for which the slope of $y = \log_a x$ at $x = 1$ is equal to 1?

11.2. The Number $e = \lim\limits_{n \to \infty} \left(1 + \dfrac{1}{n}\right)^n = 2.71828 \cdots$

Although we may choose any base for exponential and logarithmic functions, two bases are particularly useful. As some of the questions in Exercise 11.1 remind us, the base 10 is very useful if we are to use logarithms for computation. However, just as in trigonometry the degree as a unit of angular measurement has some advantages in practical applications whereas the radian is the simpler unit in most mathematical situations, so another base than that of 10 is most useful in the study of exponential and logarithmic functions. This base is the irrational number e, which is given to sixteen digits by

$$e = 2.718281828459045 \cdots.$$

This number e is the value of a limit,

$$e = \lim_{n \to \infty} \left(1 + \frac{1}{n}\right)^n.$$

We can find approximations to the value of e by evaluating $(1 + 1/n)^n$ for various values of n. If we also evaluate

$$\left(1 + \frac{1}{n}\right)^{n+1} = \left(1 + \frac{1}{n}\right)\left(1 + \frac{1}{n}\right)^n > \left(1 + \frac{1}{n}\right)^n, \quad \text{if } n > 0,$$

we can find two values between which e must lie. This procedure can be formalized into a mathematical proof.

$$n = 10, \qquad \left(1 + \frac{1}{10}\right)^{10} \simeq 2.59374, \qquad \left(1 + \frac{1}{10}\right)^{11} \simeq 2.85311.$$

$$n = 20, \qquad \left(1 + \frac{1}{20}\right)^{20} \simeq 2.65330, \qquad \left(1 + \frac{1}{20}\right)^{21} \simeq 2.78437.$$

$$n = 100, \qquad \left(1 + \frac{1}{100}\right)^{100} \simeq 2.71404, \qquad \left(1 + \frac{1}{100}\right)^{101} \simeq 2.74118.$$

$$n = 10{,}000, \qquad \left(1 + \frac{1}{10{,}000}\right)^{10{,}000} \simeq 2.71825, \qquad \left(1 + \frac{1}{10{,}000}\right)^{10{,}001} \simeq 2.71852.$$

It seems evident from the above results that

$$2.71825 < e < 2.71852 ,$$

and by using larger and larger values of n, we can calculate an approximation to e to any desired accuracy. In practice, approximations to e are usually calculated by different procedures, but the method outlined here clearly demonstrates the fact that we can make the difference between the upper and lower approximations as small as we wish. In this way, we can establish that

$$e = \lim_{n \to \infty} \left(1 + \frac{1}{n}\right)^n$$

does exist. In fact the more general result,

$$\lim_{r \to \infty} \left(1 + \frac{1}{r}\right)^r = e , \quad \text{where } r \in Re,$$

can be proved.

Example. Show that

$$\lim_{n \to \infty} \left(1 + \frac{x}{n}\right)^n = e^x , \quad x \in Re^+ .$$

Solution: Put

$$\frac{n}{x} = u ;$$

then $u \in Re^+$, and

$$n = ux .$$

Then, as $n \to \infty$ and x is finite,

$$u \to \infty .$$

Therefore,

$$\lim_{n \to \infty} \left(1 + \frac{x}{n}\right)^n = \lim_{u \to \infty} \left(1 + \frac{1}{u}\right)^{ux}$$

$$= \lim_{u \to \infty} \left[\left(1 + \frac{1}{u}\right)^u\right]^x .$$

We may interchange the operations of taking the limit and forming a power; hence,

$$\lim_{n \to \infty} \left(1 + \frac{x}{n}\right)^n = \left[\lim_{u \to \infty} \left(1 + \frac{1}{u}\right)^u\right]^x$$

$$= e^x .$$

EXERCISE 11.2

1. Show that

$$\lim_{n \to \infty} \left(1 + \frac{1}{n}\right)^{xn} = e^x \quad \text{for } x \in Re .$$

2. Show that

$$\lim_{n \to \infty} \left(1 + \frac{1}{n}\right)^{n+1} = e.$$

3. Prove the identity

$$\left(1 + \frac{1}{n}\right)^n \left(1 - \frac{1}{n}\right)^{-n} = \left(1 + \frac{2}{n-1}\right)^n,$$

and then show that

$$\lim_{(n-1) \to \infty} \left(1 + \frac{2}{n-1}\right)^n = e^2.$$

Use these results to show that

$$\lim_{n \to \infty} \left(1 - \frac{1}{n}\right)^{-n} = e.$$

4. Show that

$$\lim_{n \to \infty} \left(1 - \frac{x}{n}\right)^n = e^{-x} \quad \text{for} \quad x \in Re^+$$

and hence that

$$\lim_{n \to \infty} \left(1 + \frac{x}{n}\right)^n = e^x \quad \text{for all} \quad x \in Re.$$

5. Assuming that the operations of forming a logarithm and finding a limit can be interchanged, show that

$$\log_{10} e = \lim_{n \to \infty} \left[\log_{10} \left(1 + \frac{1}{n}\right)^n\right].$$

11.3. The Derivative of the Logarithmic Function

The logarithmic function to the base e is called the natural logarithmic function; in symbols, we may use either

$$\log_e x \quad \text{or} \quad \ln x$$

for its value at x. x is frequently referred to as the argument of the logarithmic function,

$$\ln : x \to \ln x.$$

We shall now find the value of the derivative of the natural logarithmic function at x. Let

$$y = \ln x, \quad x \in Re^+ ;$$

then

$$y + \triangle y = \ln (x + \triangle x).$$

$$\therefore \quad \triangle y = \ln (x + \triangle x) - \ln x$$

$$= \ln \frac{x + \triangle x}{x}$$

$$= \ln \left(1 + \frac{\triangle x}{x}\right).$$

$$\therefore \quad \frac{\Delta y}{\Delta x} = \frac{1}{\Delta x} \ln\left(1 + \frac{\Delta x}{x}\right)$$

$$= \frac{1}{x}\left(\frac{x}{\Delta x}\right) \ln\left(1 + \frac{\Delta x}{x}\right)$$

$$= \frac{1}{x} \ln\left(1 + \frac{\Delta x}{x}\right)^{x/\Delta x}.$$

$$\therefore \quad D_x y = \lim_{\Delta x \to 0}\left[\frac{1}{x} \ln\left(1 + \frac{\Delta x}{x}\right)^{x/\Delta x}\right]$$

$$= \frac{1}{x} \cdot \ln\left[\lim_{\frac{\Delta x}{x} \to 0}\left(1 + \frac{\Delta x}{x}\right)^{x/\Delta x}\right]$$

$$= \frac{1}{x} \cdot \ln e$$

$$= \frac{1}{x} \cdot 1.$$

$$\therefore \quad D_x(\ln x) = \frac{1}{x}.$$

Example 1. Differentiate

   (a) $\ln 3x$,   (b) $\ln x^4$,   (c) $\ln(2x + 3)$.

Solution:

   (a) Let $y = \ln 3x$

and put

$$u = 3x$$

so that

$$y = \ln u.$$

Then

$$D_u y = \frac{1}{u},$$

and

$$D_x u = 3.$$

$$\therefore \quad D_x y = (D_u y)(D_x u)$$

$$= \left(\frac{1}{u}\right)(3)$$

$$= \left(\frac{1}{3x}\right)(3).$$

$$\therefore \quad D_x(\ln 3x) = \frac{1}{x}.$$

We easily verify this result by noting that $\ln 3x = \ln x + \ln 3$ and then differentiating.

(b) Let
$$y = \ln x^4$$

and put
$$u = x^4$$

so that
$$y = \ln u \, .$$

Then
$$D_u y = \frac{1}{u}$$

and
$$D_x u = 4x^3 \, .$$

$$\therefore \quad D_x y = (D_u y)\,(D_x u)$$

$$= \left(\frac{1}{u}\right)(4x^3)$$

$$= \frac{4x^3}{x^4} \, .$$

$$\therefore \quad D_x (\ln x^4) = \frac{4}{x} \, .$$

Verify this by noting that $\ln x^4 = 4 \ln x$ and then differentiating.

(c) Let
$$y = \ln (2x + 3)$$

and put
$$u = 2x + 3$$

so that
$$y = \ln u \, .$$

Then
$$D_u y = \frac{1}{u} \, ,$$

and
$$D_x u = 2 \, .$$

$$\therefore \quad D_x y = (D_u y)\,(D_x u)$$

$$= \left(\frac{1}{u}\right)(2) \, .$$

$$\therefore \quad D_x[\ln (2x + 3)] = \frac{2}{2x + 3} \, .$$

Example 2.   Differentiate $\ln (2x^2 + 3x - 5)$.

Solution:

$$D_x[\ln (2x^2 + 3x - 5)] = \frac{1}{2x^2 + 3x - 5}(4x + 3)$$

$$= \frac{4x + 3}{2x^2 + 3x - 5} \, .$$

EXERCISE 11.3

Differentiate each of the following.   (The values of x are such that the argument of the logarithmic function is positive.)

1. $\ln (3x)$

2. $\ln (\pi x)$

3. $3 \ln x$

4. $-2 \ln x$

5. $\ln (5 + 2x)$

6. $\ln (x - 2)$

7. $\ln (2x - 3)$

8. $\ln (4 - 3x)$

9. $\ln x^3$

10. $\ln x^{-5}$

11. $\ln (x^2 + 1)$

12. $\ln (x^3 + 8)$

13. $\ln (2x^2 + 4)$

14. $\ln (3 - 4x^3)$

15. $\ln (x^2 + 2x + 3)$

16. $\ln (x^2 - 6x + 5)$

17. $\ln \sqrt{x + 1}$

18. $\ln \sqrt{2 - x}$

19. $\ln \sqrt{x^2 + 1}$

20. $\ln \sqrt{x^3 - 8}$

21. $\ln (x^2 + 2x + 3)^{1/2}$

22. $\ln (x^2 - 2x)^{1/3}$

23. $\ln (x^2 + 1)^{-1/5}$

24. $\ln (2x + 3)^{2/3}$

25. $\ln (x + 2) (x + 3)$

26. $\ln (x - 1) (2x + 3)$

27. $\ln \dfrac{x + 2}{x + 3}$

28. $\ln \dfrac{x - 1}{2x + 3}$

29. $\ln \dfrac{x^2 + 1}{x + 1}$

30. $\ln (x^2 + 1) (x + 1)$

31. $x \ln x$

32. $(x + 1) \ln (2x + 1)$

33. $(x + 1) \ln (x^2 + 1)$

34. $x^2 \ln (1 - x^2)$

35. $\sqrt{1 + x} \ln (x + 2)$

36. $(x + 1)^2 \ln (x + 1)$

37. $(x^2 + 1)^{-1} \ln (x^2 + 1)$

38. $(2x + 3) \ln (x^2 + 3x)$

39. $[\ln (x^2 - 1)]^2$

40. $[\ln (x^2 + 1)]^3$

41. $\ln (\sin x)$

42. $\ln (\cos x)$

43. $\ln (1 - \cos^2 x)$

44. $\ln (1 + \tan^2 x)$

45. $\ln (\sec x)$

46. $\ln (\csc x)$

47. $\sin (\ln x)$

48. $\cos (\ln x^2)$

49. $\sin^2 (\ln x)$

50. $\cos (3 \ln x)$

11.4. The Derivative of the Exponential Function

The function

$$\exp : x \longrightarrow e^x$$

is so fundamental that it is frequently called *the* exponential function without any explicit statement with respect to the base e. With the use of natural logarithms, any exponential function to a different base can be expressed in terms of e as the base.

Consider a^x where a is any fixed positive real number. Then from the definition of a logarithm,

$$a = e^{\ln a},$$

and so

$$a^x = (e^{\ln a})^x$$
$$= e^{x \ln a}.$$

Correspondingly, if

$$y = \log_b x$$

then

$$x = b^y$$
$$= (e^{\ln b})^y$$
$$= e^{y \ln b}.$$

$$\therefore \quad \ln x = y \ln b,$$

$$\therefore \quad \ln x = (\log_b x)(\ln b);$$

that is,

$$\log_b x = \frac{\ln x}{\ln b}.$$

Note that, if we put $x = e$, then

$$\log_b e = \frac{1}{\ln b},$$

and so

$$\log_b x = (\log_b e) \ln x.$$

We shall now find the value of the derivative of the exponential function at x. Let

$$y = e^x;$$

then

$$\ln y = x.$$

Differentiating for y as an implicitly defined function of x, we obtain

$$\frac{1}{y} D_x y = 1;$$

$$\therefore \quad D_x y = y \; ;$$

that is,

$$D_x(e^x) = e^x \, .$$

We now see why the base e is so useful in mathematics: the exponential function to base e is its own derivative, and it is the only function for which this is true.

Example 1.   Differentiate

(a) e^{2x},   (b) e^{x^3},   (c) e^{3x-1}.

Solution:

(a) Let

$$y = e^{2x} \, ,$$

and put

$$u = 2x$$

so that

$$y = e^u \, .$$

Then

$$D_u y = e^u \, ,$$

and

$$D_x u = 2 \; ;$$

Therefore,

$$D_x y = (D_u y)(D_x u)$$
$$= (e^u)(2) \; ;$$

that is,

$$D_x(e^{2x}) = 2e^{2x} \, .$$

(b) Let

$$y = e^{x^3}$$

and put

$$u = x^3$$

so that

$$y = e^u \, .$$

Then

$$D_u y = e^u$$

and

$$D_x u = 3x^2 \, .$$

Hence,

$$D_x y = (D_u y)(D_x u)$$
$$= (e^u)(3x^2) \; ;$$

that is,

$$D_x(e^{x^3}) = 3x^2 \, e^{x^3} \, .$$

(c) Let
$$y = e^{3x-1}$$

and put
$$u = 3x - 1$$

so that
$$y = e^u$$

Then
$$D_u y = e^u ,$$

and
$$D_x u = 3 .$$

$$\therefore \quad D_x y = (D_u y)(D_x u)$$
$$= (e^u)(3) .$$

$$\therefore \quad D_x(e^{3x-1}) = 3e^{3x-1}$$

Example 2. Differentiate   (a) 3^x,   (b) $\log_{10}(x+2)$.

Solution:

(a)
$$3^x = e^{x \ln 3}.$$

Let
$$y = e^{x \ln 3} = 3^x ,$$

and put
$$u = x (\ln 3)$$

so that
$$y = e^u .$$

Then
$$D_x y = (e^u)(\ln 3)$$
$$= (e^{x \ln 3})(\ln 3).$$

$$\therefore \quad D_x(3^x) = 3^x \ln 3 .$$

(b)
$$\log_{10}(x+2) = \frac{\ln(x+2)}{\ln 10}$$
$$= (\log_{10} e) \ln(x+2) .$$

Let
$$y = (\log_{10} e) \ln(x+2) ,$$

and put
$$u = x + 2$$

so that
$$y = (\log_{10} e) \ln u .$$

Then

$$D_x y = (\log_{10} e)\left(\frac{1}{u}\right)(1) ;$$

$$\therefore \quad D_x[\log_{10}(x+2)] = \frac{\log_{10} e}{x+2}.$$

EXERCISE 11.4

Differentiate each of the following.

1. e^{3x} 2. e^{-2x} 3. e^{2x+3}

4. e^{4-3x} 5. $e^{-(x+1)}$ 6. e^{2x-4}

7. e^{x^2} 8. e^{-x^2} 9. e^{-x^3}

10. e^{x^5} 11. e^{1-x^2} 12. e^{1+x^2}

13. e^{2x^2+8} 14. e^{3x^2-9} 15. e^{x^2+2x+1}

16. $e^{(x+1)^2}$ 17. e^{x^2-2x-3} 18. e^{5-6x+x^2}

19. $e^{-(x+1)^3}$ 20. e^{2x-x^2} 21. $e^{1/x}$

22. $e^{1/(x+1)}$ 23. $e^{1/(x^2+1)}$ 24. $e^{1/(x^3-1)}$

25. xe^x 26. $x^2 e^x$ 27. $x^2 e^{2x}$

28. $(x+1)e^x$ 29. $(x+1)e^{(x+1)^2}$ 30. $(x^2+1)e^{(x-1)^2}$

31. e^{x^2-4x+3} 32. e^{2-x-x^2} 33. e^x/x

34. $\dfrac{e^x}{x^2}$ 35. $\dfrac{e^{x+1}}{x+1}$ 36. $\dfrac{e^{2x-1}}{2x+1}$

37. $e^{\sqrt{x}}$ 38. $e^{\pi x^2}$ 39. $\dfrac{1}{\pi}e^{x^2/2}$

40. $\frac{1}{3}e^{x-3}$ 41. $\log_{10}(x+2)$ 42. $\log_{10}(2x-3)$

43. $\log_{10} x^2$ 44. $\log_{10}(x^2+1)$ 45. $\log_3(x+2)$

46. $\log_5(2x+1)$ 47. $e^x \ln x$ 48. $e^{2x+1}\ln(2x+1)$

49. $\ln(e^{x^2})$ 50. $\ln(e^{2x+3})$ 51. $\sin(e^x)$

52. $\cos(e^x)$ 53. $\cos(e^{x^2})$ 54. $\sin(e^{-x^2})$

55. $e^{\sin x}$ 56. $e^{-\cos x}$ 57. $e^{\ln x}$

58. $e^{-\ln x^2}$ 59. $\sin(e^{x^2+1})$ 60. $e^{\cos(2x+1)}$

61. $\ln(\cos 2x)$ 62. $\ln(\tan x)$ 63. $\ln(xe^x)$

64. $\ln(x \cos x)$ 65. $\ln(x^2 \cos x)$ 66. $\ln(e^x \cos 2x)$

11.5. Applications of the Derivative

Problems in kinematics, maxima and minima, and rates arise involving exponential and logarithmic functions, and they may be solved by the usual methods.

Kinematics

Example 1. The velocity v of a particle moving against a resistance caused by friction is given by

$$v = 64\,(1 - e^{-t})\,.$$

What is the velocity (a) when $t = 0$? (b) as $t \to \infty$?   Find the acceleration a at any time and show also that

$$a = D_t v = 64 - v\,.$$

Solution:

$$v = 64\,(1 - e^{-t})\,.$$

When $t = 0$,

$$v = 0\,;$$

when $t \to \infty$,

$$v = 64 - 64 \lim_{t \to \infty} e^{-t}\,,$$

$$v = 64\,.$$

Therefore,

$$\begin{aligned} a = D_t v &= -64\,D_t\,(e^{-t}) \\ &= -64\,(e^{-t})\,(-1) \\ &= 64e^{-t}\,. \end{aligned}$$

Now

$$v = 64 - 64e^{-t}\,;$$

$$\therefore \quad 64e^{-t} = 64 - v\,;$$

$$\therefore \quad D_t v = 64 - v\,.$$

Rates of Growth

Example 2. A colony of bacteria on a culture plate grows at a rate given by

$$N = e^{t/2}$$

where N is the number of bacteria at a time t minutes from the start of the colony.   The colony forms a circular area A sq. cm. on the plate such that

$$A = \pi r^2 = N \cdot 10^{-12}\,.$$

Find formulae for A and r in terms of t and find $D_t N$, $D_t A$, and $D_t r$ in terms of t.

What are the values of N, A, and r after one hour?   Find the rate of increase with respect to time of N, A, and r after one hour.   (Note that $e^{30} \backsimeq 10^{13}$.)

Solution:

    (a) *The Rate of Increase of N*

$$N = e^{t/2} ;$$
(1)

therefore,

$$D_t N = \tfrac{1}{2} e^{t/2} .$$
(2)

    (b) *The Values of A and r*

$$A = N \cdot 10^{-12} ,$$

and from (1),

$$A = 10^{-12} e^{t/2} .$$
(3)

Also

$$A = \pi r^2 ;$$

therefore,

$$r = \left(\frac{A}{\pi} \right)^{1/2} ,$$

and from (3),

$$r = 10^{-6} \left(\frac{e^{t/2}}{\pi} \right)^{1/2} .$$
(4)

    (c) *The Rates of Increase of A and r*

$$A = N \cdot 10^{-12} ;$$

therefore,

$$D_N A = 10^{-12} ,$$
(5)

and

$$D_t A = (D_N A)(D_t N) .$$

From (2) and (5),

$$D_t A = (10^{-12})(\tfrac{1}{2} e^{t/2}) ,$$
$$= \tfrac{1}{2} \cdot 10^{-12} e^{t/2} .$$
(6)

    Now

$$A = \pi r^2 ,$$

and differentiating with respect to A, we obtain

$$1 = 2\pi r \cdot D_A r ;$$

therefore,

$$D_A r = \frac{1}{2\pi r} ,$$
(7)

and so

$$D_t r = (D_A r)(D_t A) ,$$

and from (6) and (7),

$$D_t r = \frac{1}{4\pi r} \cdot 10^{-12} e^{t/2} .$$
(8)

After one hour, $t = 60$; hence,

$$e^{t/2} = e^{30}$$
$$\simeq 10^{13},$$

and from (1),

$$N \simeq 10^{13}.$$

Therefore, from (3),

$$A \simeq 10^{-12} \cdot 10^{13}$$
$$= 10,$$

and from (4),

$$r \simeq 10^{-6} \left(\frac{10^{13}}{\pi} \right)^{1/2}$$
$$= \left(\frac{10}{\pi} \right)^{1/2}$$
$$\simeq 1.8.$$

Also, from (2),

$$D_t N = \tfrac{1}{2} e^{30}$$
$$\simeq \tfrac{1}{2} \cdot 10^{13}$$
$$= 5 \times 10^{12},$$

and from (6),

$$D_t A \simeq \tfrac{1}{2} \cdot 10^{-12} \cdot 10^{13}$$
$$= 5.$$

and from (8),

$$D_t r \simeq \frac{1}{4\pi(1.8)} \, 10^{-12} \cdot 10^{13}$$
$$= \frac{10}{4\pi(1.8)}$$
$$\simeq .45.$$

Maxima and Minima

Example 3. The attractive force between two oxygen atoms in a molecule is given approximately by

$$F = k\left(e^{-x} - 6e^{-2x}\right),$$

where x is the distance between the atomic centres, the radius of the oxygen atom being the unit of distance. Find the maximum value of F.

Solution:

$$F = k(e^{-x} - 6e^{-2x}) \, ;$$

$$\therefore \quad D_x F = k(-e^{-x} + 12e^{-2x}).$$

At a maximum, $D_x F = 0$; hence,

$$-e^{-x} + 12e^{-2x} = 0 ,$$
$$-e^{-x} + 12(e^{-x})^2 = 0 ,$$
$$e^{-x}(-1 + 12e^{-x}) = 0 .$$

Now,

$$e^{-x} \neq 0 ;$$

therefore,

$$-1 + 12e^{-x} = 0 ,$$
$$12e^{-x} = 1 ,$$
$$e^{-x} = \tfrac{1}{12} ,$$
$$e^x = 12 ,$$
$$\therefore \qquad x \simeq 2.5 .$$

Substituting in the equation for F, we obtain

$$\text{Maximum } F = k\left(\frac{1}{12} - 6\frac{1}{144}\right)$$
$$= k\left(\frac{1}{12} - \frac{1}{24}\right)$$
$$= \frac{k}{24} .$$

EXERCISE 11.5

1. The curve of the cables supporting a suspension bridge is given by
$$y = b\left(e^{x/a} + e^{-x/a}\right) .$$
Find the minimum value of y.

2. Find the maximum point and the points of inflection, if any, of
   (a) $f : x \to e^{-x^2}$,
   (b) $f : x \to xe^x$.
   Sketch each graph.   (These functions arise in the theory of probability.)

3. Find the stationary values and points of inflection, if any, of the curves
   (a) $y = x \ln x$,
   (b) $y = x - \ln x$.
   Sketch each graph.

4. The temperature T of a cooling solid at any time t is given by
$$T - T_1 = (T_0 - T_1)e^{-kt}$$
   where T_0 is the temperature originally,
   T_1 is the temperature of the surrounding air,
   and k is a rate constant.
   Find the rate of decrease of the temperature with time and show that
$$D_t T = -k(T - T_1) .$$

5. A radioactive substance decreases in mass according to the formula

$$M = M_0 e^{-.693t/t_0},$$

where M_0 is the original mass and t_0 is called the half life. Show that, when $t = t_0$, $M = \frac{1}{2}M_0$, and that

$$D_t M = \frac{-.693M}{t_0}.$$

6. The velocity v of a rocket ascending vertically against the acceleration due to gravity, g, under the thrust of its motors may be given approximately by

$$v = \frac{g}{k}(e^{kt} - 1) - gt, \quad 0 < t < t_0,$$

where

        t is the time since lift-off,

        t_0 is the time from lift-off to burn-out,

and k is a rate constant.

Find the acceleration at any time $t < t_0$ and give its values (a) when $t = 0$, (b) when $t = t_0$.

7. The potential energy V of an atom in the presence of all the other atoms in a crystal can be approximated by

$$V = -V_0 e^{-(r/a)^2}$$

where V_0 and a are constants. Such a potential is called a *potential well*. The force F on an atom in such a well is given by

$$F = D_r V.$$

Show that the potential is a minimum at the centre of the well where $r = 0$ and $-V_0$ is the minimum value. Show also that the force F has a maximum value when $r = a/\sqrt{2}$.

8. In some cases, the attractive force F between two nuclei can be given approximately by

$$F = k\left(\frac{1}{r} - \frac{1}{r}e^{-(r-a)/a}\right)$$

where

        r is the distance between the nuclei,

and a is the equilibrium distance between the nuclei.

Show that, at the maximum value of F,

$$e^{-(r-a)/a} = \frac{a}{r+a}. \tag{1}$$

By drawing sketch graphs of y against r for

$$y = \frac{a}{r+a} \quad \text{and} \quad y = e^{-(r-a)/a},$$

show that there is a solution of equation (1) for r in terms of a for which $r > a$.

11.6. Primitives and Integrals of Exponential and Logarithmic Functions

Since $D_x(e^x) = e^x$, it follows that the general solution of

$$D_x y = e^x$$

is

$$y = \int e^x dx = e^x + c;$$

that is, the exponential function is its own primitive. It also follows that the general solution of

$$D_x y = \frac{1}{x}$$

is

$$y = \int \frac{1}{x} \, dx = \ln x + c.$$

Example. Solve

(a) $D_x y = e^{3x}$,   (b) $D_x y = \dfrac{4}{x}$,   (c) $D_x y = \dfrac{2}{5 - 2x}$,

(d) $D_x y = xe^{x^2+1}$,   (e) $D_x y = \dfrac{x+1}{x^2 + 2x + 5}$.

Solutions:

(a) $$D_x(e^{3x}) = 3e^{3x} \, ;$$

therefore, the general solution of

$$D_x y = e^{3x}$$

is

$$y = \int e^{3x} dx = \tfrac{1}{3} e^{3x} + c.$$

(Check by differentiating again.)

(b) $$D_x(\ln x) = \frac{1}{x} \, ,$$

$$\therefore \quad D_x(4 \ln x) = \frac{4}{x} \, ,$$

or

$$D_x(\ln x^4) = \frac{4}{x} \, .$$

Hence, the general solution of

$$D_x y = \frac{4}{x}$$

is

$$y = \int \frac{4}{x} \, dx = 4 \ln x + c = \ln x^4 + c.$$

(c) $\qquad D_x[\ln(5 - 2x)] = \dfrac{1}{5 - 2x}(-2)$;

therefore, the general solution of

$$D_x y = \frac{2}{5 - 2x}$$

is

$$y = \int \frac{2}{5 - 2x}\, dx = -\ln(5 - 2x) + c.$$

(d) $\qquad D_x\left(e^{x^2+1}\right) = e^{x^2+1}(2x)$;

therefore, the general solution of

$$D_x y = x e^{x^2+1}$$

is

$$y = \int x e^{x^2+1}dx = \tfrac{1}{2}e^{x^2+1} + c.$$

(e) $\qquad D_x[\ln(x^2 + 2x + 5)] = \dfrac{1}{x^2 + 2x + 5}(2x + 2)$

$$= 2\,\frac{x + 1}{x^2 + 2x + 5}\ ;$$

therefore, the general solution of

$$D_x y = \frac{x + 1}{x^2 + 2x + 5}$$

is

$$y = \int \frac{x + 1}{x^2 + 2x + 5}\, dx = \tfrac{1}{2}\ln(x^2 + 2x + 5) + c$$

$$= \ln(x^2 + 2x + 5)^{1/2} + c.$$

EXERCISE 11.6

Find the general solution of each of the following.

1. $D_x y = e^{2x}$

2. $D_x y = e^{-2x}$

3. $D_x y = e^{3x-2}$

4. $D_x y = e^{4x+5}$

5. $D_x y = e^{3-5x}$

6. $D_x y = e^{-3-2x}$

7. $D_x y = x e^{x^2}$

8. $D_x y = x^2 e^{x^3}$

9. $D_x y = x^{-2} e^{x^{-1}}$

10. $D_x y = x^{-1/2} e^{x^{1/2}}$

11. $D_x y = \dfrac{3}{x}$

12. $D_x y = -\dfrac{2}{x}$

13. $D_x y = \dfrac{1}{x + 1}$

14. $D_x y = \dfrac{2}{x + 3}$

15. $D_x y = \dfrac{1}{1-x}$

16. $D_x y = \dfrac{1}{2-3x}$

17. $D_x y = \dfrac{2x}{1+x^2}$

18. $D_x y = \dfrac{x}{x^2-1}$

19. $D_x y = \dfrac{x}{1-x^2}$

20. $D_x y = \dfrac{x^2}{x^3-1}$

Integrate the following.

21. $\displaystyle\int e^{-5x}dx$

22. $\displaystyle\int e^{6x}dx$

23. $\displaystyle\int e^{x+4}dx$

24. $\displaystyle\int e^{2x-1}dx$

25. $\displaystyle\int e^{-x+2}dx$

26. $\displaystyle\int e^{-(x+2)}dx$

27. $\displaystyle\int e^{-3x+5}dx$

28. $\displaystyle\int e^{4x+1}dx$

29. $\displaystyle\int xe^{-x^2}dx$

30. $\displaystyle\int (x+1)e^{-(x+1)^2}dx$

31. $\displaystyle\int x^2 e^{-x^3}dx$

32. $\displaystyle\int x^3 e^{x^4+1}dx$

33. $\displaystyle\int \dfrac{1}{2-x}\,dx$

34. $\displaystyle\int \dfrac{1}{2x+3}\,dx$

35. $\displaystyle\int \dfrac{x}{x^2-4}\,dx$

36. $\displaystyle\int \dfrac{3x}{x^2+9}\,dx$

37. $\displaystyle\int \dfrac{3x^2}{x^3+8}\,dx$

38. $\displaystyle\int \dfrac{4x^3}{x^4+1}\,dx$

39. $\displaystyle\int \dfrac{x+3}{x^2+6x-7}\,dx$

40. $\displaystyle\int \dfrac{x+3}{x^2+x-6}\,dx$

11.7. Areas and Volumes

Example 1. Find the area bounded by the graph of $y = 3e^x$, the x-axis, and the lines $x = 0$ and $x = 1$.

Solution:

$$f(x) = 3e^x\ ;$$

$$\therefore\ \int f(x)\,dx = 3e^x + c.$$

$$_0A_1 = \left|\left[3e^x\right]_0^1\right|$$

$$= |3e - 3|\quad \simeq 5.1548.$$

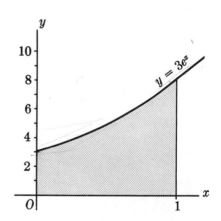

Example 2.   Find the area bounded by the graphs of $y = 1 - e^{-x/5}$, $y = \frac{1}{2}$ and $x = 0$.

Solution: The curve

$$y = 1 - e^{-x/5}$$

and the line

$$y = \frac{1}{2}$$

intersect for a value of x given by

$$\frac{1}{2} = 1 - e^{-x/5},$$

$$e^{-x/5} = \frac{1}{2},$$

$$e^{x/5} = 2,$$

$$\frac{x}{5} = \ln 2$$

$$\simeq .693,$$

$$x = 3.465.$$

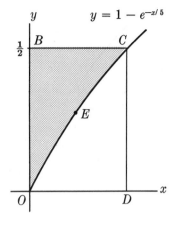

For the graph OEC,

$$f(x) = 1 - e^{-x/5}.$$

Also

$$D_x[e^{-x/5}] = -\tfrac{1}{5}e^x.$$

Hence, $$\text{Area } OECD = \int_0^{3.465} (1 - e^{-x/5}) \, dx$$

$$= \left[x + 5e^{-x/5} \right]_0^{3.465}$$

$$\simeq [3.465 + 5(\tfrac{1}{2})] - [0 + 5]$$

$$= (3.465 + 2.5) - 5$$

$$= .965.$$

$$\text{Area } OBCD = OB \times OD$$

$$\simeq \tfrac{1}{2} \times 3.465$$

$$\simeq 1.733.$$

The area required is

$$\text{Area } OBCE = \text{Area } OBCD - \text{Area } OECD$$

$$\simeq 1.733 - .965$$

$$= .768.$$

Example 3. Find the volume generated when the area between $y = x^{-1/2}$, $x = \frac{1}{4}$, $y = 0$, $x = 4$ is revolved

(a) about the x-axis   (b) about the y-axis.

Solution:

(a)   Element of volume $= \pi y^2 \, \triangle x$.

$$\therefore \quad \text{Volume of revolution} = \pi \int_{1/4}^{4} y^2 dx$$

$$= \pi \int_{1/4}^{4} x^{-1} dx$$

$$= \pi \Big[\ln x \Big]_{1/4}^{4}$$

$$= \pi [\ln 4 - \ln \tfrac{1}{4}]$$

$$= \pi [\ln 4 + \ln 4]$$

$$= 2\pi \ln 4$$

$$= 4\pi \ln 2.$$

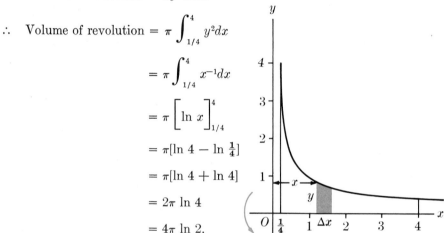

(b)   Element of volume $= 2\pi \, xy \, \triangle x$.

$$\therefore \quad \text{Volume of revolution} = 2\pi \int_{1/4}^{4} xy \, dx$$

$$= 2\pi \int_{1/4}^{4} x \cdot x^{-1/2} \, dx$$

$$= 2\pi \int_{1/4}^{4} x^{1/2} dx$$

$$= 2\pi \Big[\tfrac{2}{3} x^{3/2} \Big]_{1/4}^{4}$$

$$= \tfrac{4}{3}\pi [4^{3/2} - (\tfrac{1}{4})^{3/2}]$$

$$= \tfrac{4}{3}\pi [8 - \tfrac{1}{8}]$$

$$= \tfrac{4}{3}\pi \cdot \tfrac{63}{8}$$

$$= \tfrac{21}{2}\pi.$$

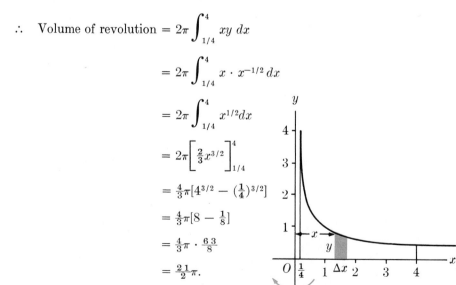

EXERCISE 11.7

Find the area bounded by these graphs:

1. $y = 10e^{-x}$, $x = -1, x = 1, y = 0$

2. $y = 2 - 2^x$, $x = 5$ and $y = 0$

3. $y = \dfrac{1}{x}$, $x = 1, x = 10$ and $y = 0$

4. $y = x^{-1}$, $x = 1$ and $y = .25$

5. $y = \frac{1}{2}$, $y = \dfrac{x^{-1}}{4}$ and $x = 1$

6. $y = 1 - e^{-x}$, $x = 0$ and $y = 1 - e^2$

7. $y = 2^x$, $x = 2$ and $y = 5^x$

8. $y = \dfrac{1}{x} - 1$, $x = 4$ and $y = 1 - \dfrac{1}{x}$

9. $y = \dfrac{4}{x}$ and $y + x = 5$ 10. $y = x + \dfrac{1}{x}$ and $y = 5.2$

Find the volumes generated when the areas bounded by the following graphs are revolved about the given axis.

11. $y = 10e^x$, $x = 0$, $y = 0$, $x = 5$ about x-axis

12. $y = 10e^{-x^2}$, $x = 0$, $y = 0$, $x = 5$ about y-axis

13. $y = 1 - \dfrac{1}{x}$, $x = 1$, $y = 0$, $x = 4$ about x-axis

14. $y = 1 - \dfrac{1}{x}$, $x = 1$, $y = 0$, $x = 4$ about y-axis

15. $y = 1 - \dfrac{1}{x^2}$, $x = 1$, $y = 0$, $x = 4$ about y-axis

11.8. The Equation $D_x y = ky$

If we differentiate

$$y = Ae^{kx},$$

where A is any constant, we find that

$$D_x y = Ake^{kx};$$

that is,

$$D_x y = ky.$$

This equation is very important in science and engineering, as many phenomena can be described by it.

Example 1.   Radium decays at a rate that is proportional to the mass of radium present.   The constant of proportionality is .000435.   How long does it take to reduce 100 grams of radium to 90 grams?   Show that only 50 grams are left after about 1600 years.

Solution: Let m be the mass of the radium in grams at any time t years; then the rate of decay is $-D_t m$.   Hence,

$$-D_t m = .000435\, m\,,$$
$$D_t m = (-.000435)\, m\,,$$

and so

$$m = A e^{-.000435 t}\,.$$

When $m = 100$, $t = 0$; therefore,

$$100 = A e^0\,,$$
$$A = 100\,,$$

and so

$$m = 100\, e^{-.000435 t}\,.$$

When $m = 90$, t is given by

$$90 = 100\, e^{-.000435 t}\,,$$

$$e^{.000435 t} = \frac{100}{90}$$

$$= 1.1 \mathrm{i}\,,$$
$$.000435\, t = \ln (1.1 \mathrm{i})$$
$$\simeq .10436\,,$$

$$t = \frac{1043.6}{4.35}$$
$$\simeq 240\,.$$

The radium is reduced to 90 grams in about 240 years.

When $t = 1600$,

$$m = 100\, e^{-.000435 \times 1600}$$
$$\simeq 49.86$$
$$\simeq 50\,.$$

After 1600 years, slightly more than half of the radium has decayed.

Example 2.   The population of a country on January 1, 1960, was 20,000,000, and the rate of increase in population [births + immigration] − [deaths + emigration] is 1.5% per year.   If we assume that the increase is compounded continuously, find when the population will have doubled to 40 millions.   When will it reach 80 millions?

Solution: Let P be the population in millions at a time t years after 1960; then

$$D_t P = \frac{1.5}{100} P,$$

and so

$$P = A e^{.015t}.$$

When $t = 0$, $P = 20$; therefore,

$$20 = A\,(1),$$

$$P = 20\,e^{.015t}.$$

When $P = 40$, t is given by

$$40 = 20\,e^{.015t},$$

$$.015t = \ln 2$$

$$\simeq .693,$$

$$t \simeq \frac{69.3}{1.5}$$

$$= 46.2.$$

The population will reach 40 millions in the year 2006 and will reach 80 millions in the year 2052 (*why?*).

EXERCISE 11.8

1. The growth of the population P of a country can be considered as a continuous process.   The rate of growth is proportional to the population at any time t, so that

$$D_t P = kP$$

where k is a constant.   Show that

$$P = P_0 e^{kt}$$

is a solution of this equation, where P_0 is the population at the origin of the time measurement.   If t is measured in years, find k so that

(a) the population doubles in 50 years,

(b) the population doubles in 30 years,

(c) the population doubles in 20 years.

2. In 1626, \$24 was paid for Manhattan Island. The island, the site of New York City, is worth 5×10^{10} dollars in 1966. If the \$24 had been invested at interest compounded continuously from 1626 to 1966, what rate of interest would have been required to give the same value today? (*Hint:* If P is the value at any time t, then

$$D_t P = \frac{r}{100} P$$

where r is the interest rate.)

3. The rate of change of air pressure p with altitude h is given by

$$D_h p = -\sigma,$$

where σ is the density of the air at a height h. Assuming Boyle's Law for gases in the form

$$\frac{p}{\sigma} = k$$

find p in terms of h.

4. An ingot of metal is cooling from an original temperature of 500°C to room temperature at 15°C. If the temperature of the ingot at a time t minutes after it starts to cool is T°C, then Newton's Law of Cooling states that

$$D_t T = -k(T - 15).$$

Show that

$$T = 485 e^{-kt} + 15$$

satisfies this equation and the condition that the original temperature at $t = 0$ is 500°C. What is the temperature after 30 minutes if $k = .02$? (*Hint:* Note that $D_t T = D_t (T - 15)$.)

5. The downward acceleration a of a man whose fall from a practice tower is being slowed by an open parachute is given by

$$a = D_t v = 32 - 10v,$$

where v is the velocity (in ft/sec).

Show that the velocity is given by

$$v = 3.2 (1 - e^{-10t})$$

if $v = 0$ at the beginning of the fall.

6. The rate at which a chemical compound dissolves is proportional to the difference between the concentration and the concentration of a saturated solution. Thus, if C is the concentration (in grams per litre) and the saturation concentration is 10,

$$\frac{dC}{dt} = k(10 - C).$$

Show that

$$C = 10(1 - e^{-kt}).$$

If $k = 1/100$ when the time is measured in minutes, what is the concentration after 1 hour? after 2 hours? after 5 hours?

Chapter Summary

The functions $x \to a^x$, $x \to \log_a x$

The exponential function $x \to e^x$

The natural logarithmic function $x \to \ln x$

$$D_x(e^x) = e^x \qquad\qquad D_x(e^{ax}) = ae^{ax} \qquad\qquad D_x(\ln x) = \frac{1}{x}$$

$$\int e^x dx = e^x + c \qquad\qquad \int e^{ax} dx = \frac{1}{a} e^{ax} + c \qquad\qquad \int \frac{1}{x}\, dx = \ln x + c$$

The equation $D_x y = ky$

REVIEW EXERCISE 11

Differentiate each of the following.

1. $\ln (3x - 4)$
2. $\ln (x^2 + 4)$
3. $\ln \sqrt{1 - x}$
4. $\ln \sqrt{9 - x^2}$
5. $(x + 2) \ln (x + 2)$
6. $x \ln x^2$
7. $\ln (\tan x)$
8. $\ln (\sin 2x)$
9. $\tan (\ln x)$
10. $\cos (\ln x^3)$
11. e^{4x}
12. e^{2x+3}
13. e^{x^2+4}
14. $e^{(x+1)^2}$
15. $e^{\sin x}$
16. $e^{\ln x^2}$
17. $x e^{x+2}$
18. $x^{-2} e^x$
19. $e^x \sin 2x$
20. $(\ln x)(\sin x)$

Find the general solution of each of the following.

21. $D_x y = e^{3x}$
22. $D_x y = e^{2x+1}$
23. $D_x y = x e^{x^2+1}$
24. $D_x y = x^{-3} e^{x^{-2}}$
25. $D_x y = \dfrac{4}{x}$
26. $D_x y = \dfrac{2}{x + 2}$
27. $D_x y = \dfrac{x}{x^2 - 1}$
28. $D_x y = \dfrac{x + 1}{x^2 + 2x + 3}$
29. $D_x y = e^{\sin x} \cos x$
30. $D_x y = \dfrac{\cos x}{\sin x}$

Integrate each of the following.

31. e^{-4x} 32. e^{3-x} 33. $x^2 e^x$

34. $(x+1)^{-2} e^{(x+1)^{-1}}$ 35. $-\dfrac{3}{x}$ 36. $\dfrac{1}{x+4}$

37. $\dfrac{x}{1-x^2}$ 38. $\dfrac{x^2+1}{x^3+3x}$ 39. $e^{\cos x} \sin x$

40. Find the area bounded by the graphs of $y = 10e^x$, $x = -1$, $y = 0$ and $x = 1$.

41. Find the area bounded by the graphs of $y = (2x+1)^{-1}$, $x = 4$ and $y = 4$.

42. Find the area between the graphs of $y = x^{-1}$ and $x + y = 5\frac{1}{5}$.

43. A fungoid growth in the shape of a sphere doubles its size every day, that is,
$$V = V_0(2^t),$$
where V is the volume of the growth and t is the time since the volume was V_0. Show that
$$D_t V = (\ln 2) V \simeq .693 \ V,$$
and find the rate at which the radius of the growth is changing.

44. The population of a country has a natural rate of increase of 15 per 1000 per year. In addition, 150,000 immigrate into the country each year. Thus, if the population is P, then
$$D_t P = \tfrac{15}{1000} P + 150{,}000.$$
Show that
$$P + 10{,}000{,}000 = (P_0 + 10{,}000{,}000)e^{.015t}$$
where t is the time in years measured from the time when the population is P_0. If P_0 is 10,000,000, how long does it take for the population to reach 20,000,000? 40,000,000? 100,000,000?

Find the volume generated when the area bounded by the graph is revolved about the given axis.

45. $y = 2e^{-x/2}$, $x = 0$, $y = 0$, $x = 10$ about x-axis

46. $y = 2e^{-x^2}$, $x = 0$, $y = 0$, $x = 2$ about y-axis

47. $y = x^{1/2} + x^{-1/2}$, $x = \frac{1}{4}$, $y = 0$, $x = 4$ about x-axis

Using (a) the trapezoidal rule and (b) Simpson's rule, each with five interval division points, evaluate the following definite integrals.

48. $\displaystyle\int_0^6 e^x dx$ 49. $\displaystyle\int_{1/4}^{7/4} x^{-1} dx$

Check the accuracy of the evaluation by integration.

12

POLAR CO-ORDINATES

12.1. Introduction

In this chapter we will study the polar co-ordinate system as an alternative to the Cartesian co-ordinate system for labelling points in a plane. This system will be useful in Chapter 13 in our study of complex numbers.

Select an arbitrary point O in the plane and call it the pole; select a ray with initial point at O (normally taken horizontally and to the right of O) and call it the polar axis. We will show that this point and ray form a frame of reference for a system of co-ordinates for the points in the plane. Let P be any point in the plane (Figure 12.1). Then P determines a real number r, the distance from O to P, and an angle θ (positive if measured counterclockwise from the polar axis).

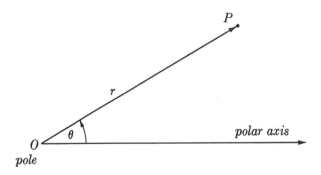

Figure 12.1

We call r the radius vector of P, and θ, the vectorial angle of P. Obviously θ is unique only up to an integral multiple of 2π radians. We call (r, θ) the polar co-ordinates of point P.

Example 1.   Plot the points with the following polar co-ordinates.

   (a) $(3, 0°)$ (b) $(4, 45°)$ (c) $(1, \pi)$ (d) $(3, -60°)$

Solution: In each case, in plotting (r, θ), we determine the ray with the given direction θ and then mark off r units in that direction.   The plotting of polar co-ordinates is greatly simplified by the use of polar co-ordinate graph paper, as shown in the diagram.

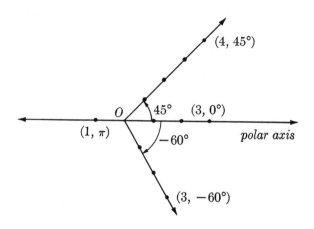

   If r is a negative number, the point with polar co-ordinates (r, θ) is plotted by first determining the ray with direction θ and then marking off r units along the ray in the *opposite* direction.

Example 2.   Plot the points with the following polar co-ordinates.

   (a) $(-3, 0°)$ (b) $(-4, 45°)$ (c) $(-1, \pi)$ (d) $(-3, -60°)$

Solution:

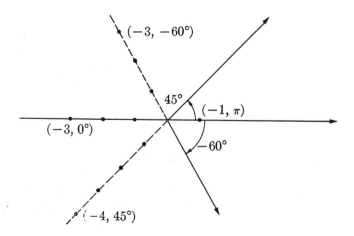

Example 3. Give two other sets of polar co-ordinates for the point with co-ordinates (3, 30°).

Solution: (3, 390°) and (−3, 210°) are two such sets.

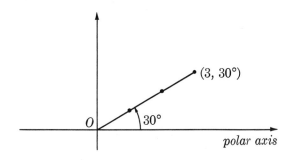

EXERCISE 12.1

In this exercise, use polar graph paper or a facsimile thereof for plotting points.

1. Plot the following points.
   (a) $P_1(4, 0°)$ (b) $P_2(0, 30°)$ (c) $P_3(5, 75°)$

   (d) $P_4(-5, 90°)$ (e) $P_5(-3, 300°)$ (f) $P_6\left(10\sqrt{2}, -\dfrac{\pi}{4}\right)$

   (g) $P_7(-12\sqrt{3}, -120°)$ (h) $P_8(-3, 390°)$ (i) $P_9(3, -150°)$

2. Give two additional sets of polar co-ordinates for the points in question (1).

3. Plot the following pairs of points.
   (a) $P_1(3, 30°)$ and $P_2(3, -30°)$ (b) $Q_1(5, 60°)$ and $Q_2(5, -60°)$
   (c) $R_1(2, 135°)$ and $R_2(-2, 45°)$ (d) $S_1(-4, 225°)$ and $S_2(4, -45°)$

4. Show that the points $P(r, \theta)$ and $Q(r, -\theta)$ or $Q(-r, 180° - \theta)$ are symmetric with respect to the polar axis.

5. Plot the following pairs of points.
   (a) $P_1(3, 30°)$ and $P_2(-3, 30°)$ (b) $Q_1(5, 60°)$ and $Q_2(-5, 60°)$
   (c) $R_1(2, 135°)$ and $R_2(2, 315°)$ (d) $S_1(-4, 225°)$ and $S_2(4, 225°)$

6. Show that the points $P(r, \theta)$ and $Q(-r, \theta)$ or $Q(r, 180° + \theta)$ are symmetric with respect to the pole.

7. Plot the following pairs of points.
   (a) $(4, 30°)$ and $(4, 150°)$ (b) $(2\sqrt{2}, 45°)$ and $(2\sqrt{2}, 135°)$
   (c) $(-\sqrt{3}, 120°)$ and $(\sqrt{3}, -120°)$ (d) $(4\sqrt{2}, 225°)$ and $(4\sqrt{2}, -45°)$

8. Show that the points (r, θ) and $(r, 180° - \theta)$ or $(-r, -\theta)$ are symmetric with respect to the line through O perpendicular to the polar axis.

9. If $0° \le \theta < 360°$, how many sets of polar co-ordinates does every point in the plane except the pole have? How many does the pole have?

10. Plot the following points.

$(4, 0°)$ $(4, 60°)$ $(4, 90°)$ $(4, 135°)$ $(4, 180°)$ $(4, 270°)$

11. What is the locus of points for which

(a) $r = 4$?   (b) $r = a$?

12. Plot the following points.

$(1, 60°)$ $(3, 60°)$ $(5, 60°)$ $(-2, 60°)$ $(-4, 60°)$

13. What is the locus of points for which

(a) $\theta = 60°$?   (b) $\theta = \theta_1$ (where θ_1 is a fixed angle)?

14. The following table of values is computed from the relation $r = 2 \cos \theta$.

θ	0°	30°	60°	90°	135°	180°	225°	270°	315°
$r = 2 \cos \theta$	2.0	1.7	1.0	0	−1.4	−2.0	−1.4	0	1.4

Plot the points (r, θ) determined by this table of values and draw a smooth curve through them. What does the curve seem to be?

15. Make a table similar to that in question (14) from the relation $r = 2 \sin \theta$, plot the corresponding points, and draw a smooth curve through them. What does the curve seem to be?

16. Repeat question (14) using the relation $r = 3 \sin \theta$.

17. What is the angle made with the polar axis by the line joining the points $(3, 60°)$ and $(4, 30°)$?

18. The following table of values is computed from the relation $r = 2 \sec \theta$.

θ	0°	30°	45°	60°	85°	95°	120°	135°	150°	180°
$r = 2 \sec \theta$	2.0	2.3	2.8	4.0	22.9	−22.9	−4.0	−2.8	−2.3	−2.0

Plot the points (r, θ) determined by this table of values and draw a smooth curve through them. What does this curve seem to be?

19. Why did we not use 90° in the table in question (18)?

20. Make a table similar to that in question (18) using suitable values of θ from 180° to 360°. Draw the corresponding curve.

12.2. Relation Between Polar and Rectangular Co-ordinates

Superimpose a frame of reference for a Cartesian co-ordinate system on a frame of reference for a polar co-ordinate system by placing the origin of the former on the pole of the latter and the positive x-axis along the polar axis (Figure 12.2).

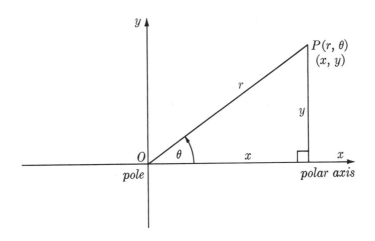

Figure 12.2

Then the point P in the plane will have rectangular co-ordinates (x, y) and polar co-ordinates (r, θ). The following relations between the rectangular and the polar co-ordinates may be read from the diagram.

$$x = r \cos \theta \qquad r = \sqrt{x^2 + y^2}$$
$$\text{and}$$
$$y = r \sin \theta \qquad \tan \theta = \frac{y}{x} \qquad \left(\text{that is, } \theta = \tan^{-1} \frac{y}{x} \right)$$

Example 1. Change $(2, 30°)$ to rectangular co-ordinates.

Solution:

$$x = 2 \cos 30° = 2 \cdot \frac{\sqrt{3}}{2} = \sqrt{3}.$$

$$y = 2 \sin 30° = 2 \cdot \frac{1}{2} = 1.$$

Therefore $(\sqrt{3}, 1)$ are the rectangular co-ordinates.

Example 2.   Change $(-2, -4)$ to polar co-ordinates.

Solution:

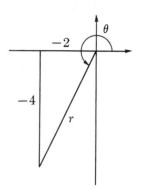

$$r = \sqrt{(-2)^2 + (-4)^2} = \sqrt{20} = 2\sqrt{5}$$

θ is the angle in quadrant III with

$$\tan \theta = \frac{-4}{-2} = 2 \, .$$

Therefore

$$\theta = 243° \quad \text{(nearest degree)}.$$

Therefore $(2\sqrt{5}, 243°)$ is one set of polar co-ordinates.

Note that in changing from rectangular to polar co-ordinates, a diagram (either drawn or mental) is almost essential in order to determine the quadrant of θ.

Example 3.   Change the rectangular equation $x^2 + y^2 = 2y$ to a polar equation.

Solution:

$$x^2 + y^2 = r^2 \quad \text{and} \quad y = r \sin \theta \, .$$

The equation $x^2 + y^2 = 2y$ becomes

$$r^2 = 2r \sin \theta \, .$$

Therefore $r = 2 \sin \theta$ is the required polar equation.

Example 4.   Change the polar equation $r^2 = 4 \cos 2\theta$ to one using rectangular co-ordinates.

Solution:

$$r^2 = x^2 + y^2 \quad \text{and} \quad 4 \cos 2\theta = 4(\cos^2\theta - \sin^2\theta)$$
$$= 4\left(\frac{x^2}{r^2} - \frac{y^2}{r^2}\right) = \frac{4}{r^2}(x^2 - y^2) \, .$$

The equation

$$r^2 = 4 \cos 2\theta$$

becomes

$$(r^2)^2 = 4 (x^2 - y^2) \, .$$

Therefore $(x^2 + y^2)^2 = 4 (x^2 - y^2)$ is the required rectangular equation.

EXERCISE 12.2

1. Change the following to rectangular co-ordinates.
   (a) $(4, 0°)$ (b) $(-3, 90°)$ (c) $(\sqrt{2}, 45°)$ (d) $(-6, 270°)$
   (e) $(4, 30°)$ (f) $(-2, -60°)$ (g) $(5, 120°)$ (h) $(-4, 135°)$
   (i) $(-3, 180°)$ (j) $(0, 45°)$ (k) $(-3, -45°)$ (l) $(-4, -90°)$

2. Change the following to polar co-ordinates $(0° \le \theta < 360°)$.
   (a) $(5, 0)$ (b) $(2, 2)$ (c) $(0, 6)$ (d) $(-4, -4)$
   (e) $(-3, 0)$ (f) $(0, -5)$ (g) $(0, 0)$ (h) $(4, -4\sqrt{3})$
   (i) $(-4\sqrt{3}, 4)$ (j) $(3, 4)$ (k) $(-5, 12)$ (l) $(-4, -3)$

3. Change the following to polar equations.
   (a) $x = 4$.   (b) $y = -3$.   (c) $x^2 + y^2 = 25$.
   (d) $3x - 5y = 0$.   (e) $3x - 4y + 6 = 0$.   (f) $xy = 4$.
   (g) $y^2 - 4x = 0$.   (h) $x^2 + y^2 - 2y = 0$.   (i) $x^2 + y^2 = 2x + 6y$.
   (j) $x^2 - y^2 = 9$.   (k) $x^2 - 4y^2 = 4$.   (l) $(x^2 + y^2)^2 = x^2 - y^2$.

4. Change the following to rectangular equations.
   (a) $r = 6$.   (b) $\theta = 30°$.   (c) $r = 3 \cos \theta$.

   (d) $r = \dfrac{6}{\sin \theta}$.   (e) $\dfrac{r}{\cos \theta} = 4$.   (f) $\dfrac{r}{\sin \theta} = 2$.

   (g) $r^2 \sin \theta \cos \theta = 1$.   (h) $r^2 = \dfrac{3}{\cos 2\theta}$.   (i) $r^2 = \dfrac{2}{\cot \theta}$.

   (j) $r = \dfrac{3}{\csc \theta}$.   (k) $r = \sin 2\theta$.   (l) $r = \dfrac{a}{\tan \theta}$.

5. What conic sections have the following polar equations?

   (a) $r = \dfrac{2}{1 + \cos \theta}$.   (b) $r = \dfrac{2}{2 + \cos \theta}$.   (c) $r = \dfrac{2}{1 + 2 \cos \theta}$.

12.3. Graphing Polar Relations

We have already encountered the graphs of certain polar relations in the problems of Exercise 12.1. We found the following results.

(1) The locus of points (r, θ) satisfying the relation $r = a$ is a circle, centre the pole, and radius a. This can be verified by changing $r = a$ to Cartesian co-ordinates. Given

$$r = a,$$

then

$$\sqrt{x^2 + y^2} = a.$$

Therefore

$$x^2 + y^2 = a^2.$$

(2) The locus of points (r, θ) satisfying the relation $\theta = \theta_1$ for fixed angle θ_1 is a straight line through the origin.   This again can be verified by changing to Cartesian co-ordinates.   Given

$$\theta = \theta_1 ,$$

then

$$\tan \theta = \tan \theta_1 ,$$

and

$$\frac{y}{x} = m, \quad \text{where } m = \tan \theta_1 .$$

therefore

$$y = mx .$$

(3) The locus of points (r, θ) satisfying the relation $r = a \cos \theta$ is a circle with centre $\left(\dfrac{a}{2}, 0\right)$ and radius $\dfrac{a}{2}$.   Given

$$r = a \cos \theta ,$$

then

$$r = a \frac{x}{r} .$$

$$r^2 = ax .$$

$$x^2 + y^2 - ax = 0 .$$

$$\left(x - \frac{a}{2}\right)^2 + y^2 = \frac{a^2}{4} .$$

Thus $r = a \cos \theta$ is the equation of a circle with centre $\left(\dfrac{a}{2}, 0\right)$ and radius $\dfrac{a}{2}$.

(4) The locus of points (r, θ) satisfying the relation $r = a \sin \theta$ is a circle with centre $\left(0, \dfrac{a}{2}\right)$ and radius $\dfrac{a}{2}$.   (It is left as an exercise for the student to convert this equation to a Cartesian equation.)

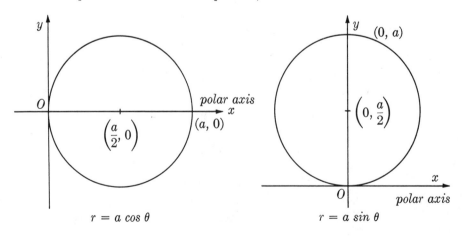

$r = a \cos \theta$ $r = a \sin \theta$

So far we have converted the given polar equation to a recognizable rectangular equation and have thus obtained the graph.   If this fails, we set up a table of values of co-ordinates (r, θ) of points on the graph of the given relation, plot the corresponding points, and draw a smooth curve through them.

The following facts may prove useful in sketching graphs of polar equations.

Tangents

If θ_1 is a real root of $f(\theta) = 0$, then the curve whose equation is $r = f(\theta)$ is tangent to the line $\theta = \theta_1$ at the pole.

Example 1.   In (3) above, $a \cos \theta = 0$ for $\theta = \pi/2$; the curve whose equation is $r = a \cos \theta$ is tangent to the line $\theta = \pi/2$ at the pole.

Symmetry About the Polar Axis

The points (r, θ) and $(r, -\theta)$ or $(-r, 180° - \theta)$ are symmetric with respect to the polar axis (see question (4), Exercise 12.1).   Hence a polar equation which is unchanged or changed to an equivalent equation when θ is replaced by $-\theta$ or when r is replaced by $-r$ and θ by $180° - \theta$, has a graph symmetric with respect to the polar axis.

Note that the curve $r = a \cos \theta = a \cos (-\theta)$ possesses this symmetry.   Also $-r = a \cos (\pi - \theta) = -a \cos \theta$ is equivalent to the equation $r = a \cos \theta$.

Example 2.   Show algebraically that the curve whose equation is $r = a(1 - \cos \theta)$ is symmetric about the polar axis.

Solution:
$$a[1 - \cos(-\theta)] = a(1 - \cos \theta) \, .$$

Therefore the graph of $r = a(1 - \cos \theta)$ is symmetric about the polar axis.

Symmetry About the Pole

The points (r, θ) and $(-r, \theta)$ or $(r, 180° + \theta)$ are symmetric with respect to the pole (see question (6), Exercise 12.1).   Hence a polar equation which is unchanged or changed to an equivalent one when r is replaced by $-r$ or θ is replaced by $180° + \theta$ has a graph which is symmetric with respect to the pole.

Example 3.   Show algebraically that the graph of $r^2 = 4 \sin 2\theta$ is symmetric with respect to the pole.

Solution:
$$r^2 = (-r)^2 = 4 \sin 2\theta \, .$$

Hence the graph is symmetric with respect to the pole.   Also
$$4 \sin 2 (\theta + 180°) = 4 \sin (2\theta + 360°) = 4 \sin 2\theta \, ,$$

which again shows that the graph is symmetric with respect to the pole.

Symmetry About the Line $\theta = \dfrac{\pi}{2}$

The points (r, θ) and $(r, 180° - \theta)$ or $(-r, -\theta)$ are symmetric with respect to the line $\theta = \pi/2$ (see question (8), Exercise 12.1), as are the points (r, θ) and $(-r, -\theta)$.   Hence a polar equation which is unchanged or changed into an equivalent equation when θ is replaced by $180° - \theta$, or when r is replaced by $-r$ and θ by $-\theta$, has a graph which is symmetric with respect to the line $\theta = \pi/2$.

Note that the curve $r = a \sin \theta = a \sin(\pi - \theta)$ possesses this symmetry.

Example 4.   Show algebraically that the graph of $r = 4 \sin 3\theta$ is symmetric with respect to the line $\theta = \dfrac{\pi}{2}$.

Solution:
$$4 \sin 3 (180° - \theta) = 4 \sin (540° - 3\theta)$$
$$= 4 \sin (180° - 3\theta)$$
$$= 4 \sin 3\theta .$$

Thus the graph is symmetric with respect to the line $\theta = \dfrac{\pi}{2}$.   (See Figure 12.4.)

Again,
$$-r = 4 \sin 3 (-\theta) ;$$

that is,
$$-r = -4 \sin 3\theta ,$$

is an equation equivalent to
$$r = 4 \sin 3\theta .$$

We summarize these criteria for symmetry in the following chart.

Same or equivalent equation if	implies symmetry about
θ replaced by $-\theta$ or θ replaced by $180° - \theta$ and r by $-r$	the polar axis, $\theta = 0$
θ replaced by $180° + \theta$ or r replaced by $-r$	the pole, $(0, 0)$
θ replaced by $180° - \theta$ or θ replaced by $-\theta$ and r by $-r$	the line $\theta = \dfrac{\pi}{2}$

These tests will be applied in the next section as an aid in plotting graphs of polar equations.

EXERCISE 12.3

1. Sketch the curves with the following polar equations. Either use a table of values to plot a number of points or change the equation to rectangular form.

   (a) $r = 3$.

   (b) $r = 0$.

   (c) $r = -2$.

   (d) $r = \cos\theta$.

   (e) $r = \sin\theta$.

   (f) $r = 4\cos\theta$.

   (g) $r = 3\sin\theta$.

   (h) $r = -2\cos\theta$.

   (i) $r = -4\sin\theta$.

   (j) $r = \sec\theta$.

   (k) $r = \operatorname{cosec}\theta$.

   (l) $r = 4\sec\theta$.

   (m) $r = 4\operatorname{cosec}\theta$.

   (n) $r = -\sec\theta$.

   (o) $r = -3\operatorname{cosec}\theta$.

2. Find the equations of the tangent lines at the pole to the curves with the following polar equations.

   (a) $r = 2\cos 2\theta$.

   (b) $r = 3\cos 3\theta$.

   (c) $r = 4(1 - \sin\theta)$.

   (d) $r = 4(1 + \cos\theta)$.

   (e) $r = 2(1 - 2\cos\theta)$.

   (f) $r = 3(\cos\theta - \sin\theta)$.

   (g) $r = \dfrac{2}{1 + \cos\theta}$.

   (h) $r = 4\sin\theta\tan\theta$.

   (i) $r = 2\cos(\theta - 30°)$.

3. Apply the tests for symmetry to the graphs with the following polar equations.

   (a) $r = 4\cos 2\theta$.

   (b) $r = 4\cos 3\theta$.

   (c) $r = \sin 2\theta$.

   (d) $r = 2\sin 4\theta$.

   (e) $r^2 = \sin\theta + \cos\theta$.

   (f) $r = \cos^4\theta$.

   (g) $r = 4(1 - \cos\theta)$.

   (h) $r = 4\tan\theta$.

   (i) $r = 2 + \cos\theta$.

   (j) $r = 2 + 3\cos\theta$.

   (k) $r = a\theta,\ a \in Re$.

   (l) $r^2 = 4\sin 2\theta$.

   (m) $r^2 = 9\cos 2\theta$.

   (n) $r = 2\cos(\theta - 30°)$.

   (o) $r = \dfrac{2}{1 + 2\cos\theta}$.

   (p) $r = \dfrac{2}{1 + \sin\theta}$.

   (q) $r = 4\sin\theta\tan\theta$.

   (r) $r = \cos\theta\cot\theta$.

4. State values of θ in the range $0° \le \theta < 360°$ for which r does not have real values in the following.

   (a) $r^2 = 4\sin\theta$.

   (b) $r^2 = \cos 2\theta$.

   (c) $r^2 + 2r = 2\cos\theta$.

   (d) $r^2 = 4\sec\theta$.

   (e) $r^2 = \tan\theta$.

   (f) $r^3 = 8\sin\theta$.

   (g) $r^2 = \dfrac{2}{1 + \sin\theta}$.

   (h) $r^2 = 4\sin\theta\tan\theta$.

   (i) $r^2 = \sin^3\theta$.

5. Find the points where the curves whose equations are given in question (4) intersect the polar axis.

6. Find the points common to the curves whose equations are given in the following.

   (a) $r = 3(1 - \cos\theta)$ and $r = 3\cos\theta$.

   (b) $r = 2\sin\theta$ and $r = 2\cos\theta$.

   (c) $r = 4\sin\theta$ and $r^2 = 8\cos 2\theta$.

12.4. Further Graphing of Polar Relations

We will now consider the graphs of some additional polar relations, making use of the techniques we have discussed in the preceding section.

Example 1. Sketch the curve whose equation is

$$r = 1 + 2 \cos \theta.$$

Solution:

(i) $1 + 2 \cos \theta = 0$ if $\cos \theta = -\frac{1}{2}$; that is, if $\theta = 120°$ or $240°$. Thus the lines $\theta = 120°$ and $\theta = 240°$ (shown in red) are tangent to the curve at the pole.

(ii) $1 + 2 \cos(-\theta) = 1 + 2 \cos \theta$.
Thus the curve is symmetric with respect to the polar axis.

(iii) We know that the graph of the relation $r = 2 \cos \theta$ is a circle with radius 1 and centre $(1, 0)$ (See curve marked (i) in Figure 12.3). We use this information to sketch the graph of $r = 1 + 2 \cos \theta$, by adding 1 to each value of r corresponding to θ in $r = 2 \cos \theta$. Thus, when $\theta = 0$, $r = 3$; when $\theta = 90°$, $r = 1$; the line $\theta = 120°$ is a tangent at the pole; when $\theta = 180°$, $r = -1$. Now r varies continuously as θ assumes values from $0°$ to $180°$; this allows us to sketch the branch of the curve marked (ii) in Figure 12.3.

Now, since the curve is symmetric with respect to the polar axis, we are able to sketch in the remaining half of the curve. (This half corresponds to values of θ in the range $180° \leq \theta \leq 360°$.)

Of course, we could also have obtained the information for plotting the key points on this curve by means of a table of values:

θ	0°	60°	90°	120°	180°
$\cos \theta$	1	.5	0	$-.5$	-1
$2 \cos \theta$	2	1	0	-1	-2
$r = 1 + 2 \cos \theta$	3	2	1	0	-1

A similar table will give the points corresponding to values of θ between $180°$ and $360°$.

We must emphasize that the circle whose equation is $r = 2 \cos \theta$ is shown in Figure 12.3 only for comparison purposes; it is not part of the curve whose equation is $r = 1 + 2 \cos \theta$.

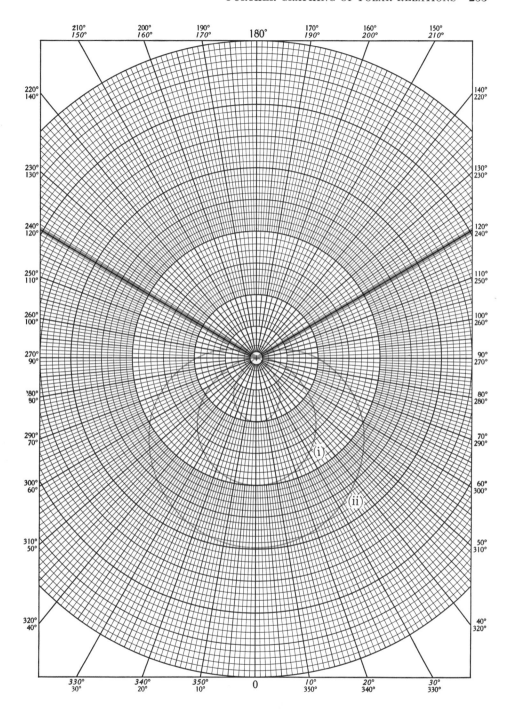

Figure 12.3. $r = 1 + 2 \cos \theta$

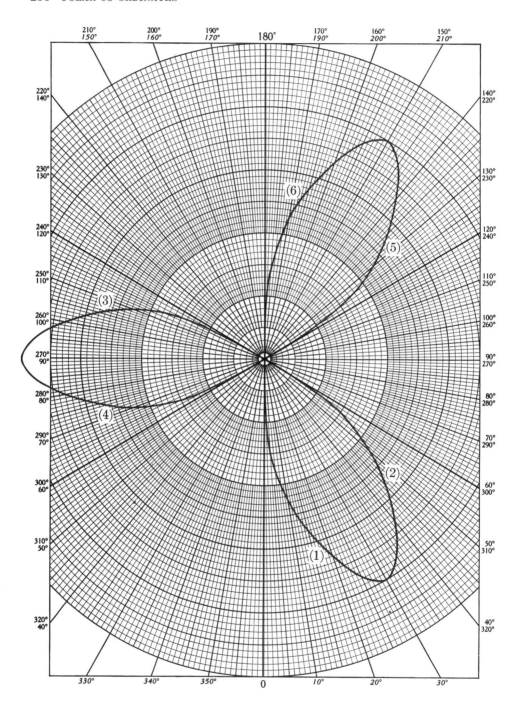

Figure 12.4. $r = 4 \sin 3\theta$ *The three-leaved rose*

Example 2.   Sketch the curve whose equation is

$$r = 4 \sin 3\theta.$$

Solution:

(i) $\sin 3\theta = 0$ if $3\theta = 0°, 180°, 360°, 540°, 720°, 900°, \ldots,$
that is, if

$$\theta = 0, 60°, 120°, 180°, 240°, 300°, \ldots .$$

The lines with these equations (shown in red in Figure 12.4) are all tangent to the curve at the pole.

(ii)   From Example 4, Section 12.3, we see that the graph is symmetric with respect to the line $\theta = \dfrac{\pi}{2}$.

(iii)   Now r will vary continuously with θ since the sine function is a continuous function. We may set up a table of values showing the co-ordinates (r, θ) of points on the curve. In so doing we should note that we would want to assign values to θ so that we know the values of $\sin 3\theta$. For example, if $\theta = 10°$, then $\sin 3\theta = \sin 30° = 0.5$.

However, in this case it is helpful to observe that:

as 3θ varies from	0° to 90°	90° to 180°	180° to 270°	270° to 360°	360° to 450°	450° to 540°
θ varies from	0° to 30°	30° to 60°	60° to 90°	90° to 120°	120° to 150°	150° to 180°
and r varies from	0 to 4	4 to 0	0 to −4	−4 to 0	0 to 4	4 to 0
producing branch numbered	(1)	(2)	(3)	(4)	(5)	(6)

With the information from this chart, the tangent lines from (i), and the symmetry from (ii), we can sketch the curve.

From the diagram, the reader will note that the curve has symmetry about the lines whose equations are

$$\theta = \frac{\pi}{6} \quad \text{and} \quad \theta = \frac{5\pi}{6}$$

as well as about the line whose equation is $\theta = \dfrac{\pi}{2}$.

These are not symmetries for which we have tests. However the reader may show that the curve whose equation is $r = f(\theta)$ is symmetric with respect to the line with equation $\theta = \dfrac{\pi}{6}$ if $f\left(\dfrac{\pi}{3} - \theta\right) = f(\theta)$. In this example, $r = 4 \sin 3\theta$ and

$$4 \sin 3\left(\frac{\pi}{3} - \theta\right) = 4 \sin (\pi - 3\theta)$$
$$= 4 \sin 3\theta.$$

Devise a similar test to show when the curve whose equation is $r = f(\theta)$ is

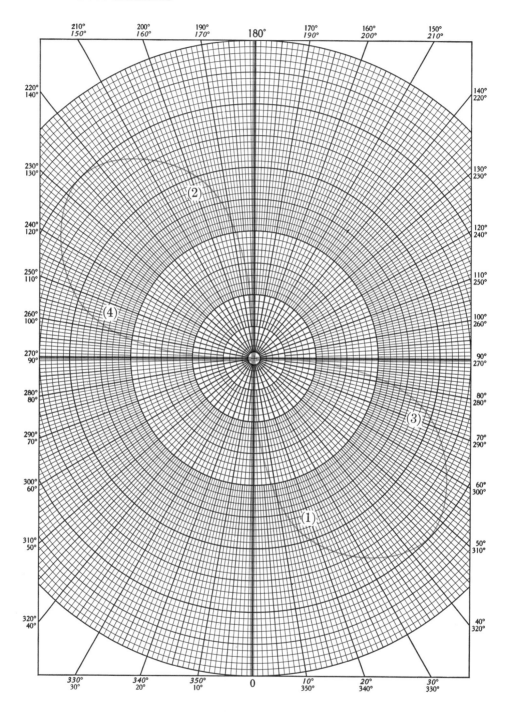

Figure 12.5. $r^2 = 4 \sin 2\theta$ *The lemniscate*

symmetric with respect to the line $\theta = \dfrac{5\pi}{6}$ and show algebraically that $r = 4 \sin 3\theta$ possesses this symmetry.

Example 3. Sketch the curve whose equation is

$$r^2 = 4 \sin 2\theta.$$

Solution:

(i) $4 \sin 2\theta = 0$ if

$$2\theta = 0°, 180°, 360°, 540°, \cdots,$$

that is, if

$$\theta = 0°, 90°, 180°, 270°, \cdots .$$

The lines with equations $\theta = 0°$, $\theta = 90°$, $\theta = 180°$, $\theta = 270°$ (shown in red in Figure 12.5) are tangent to the curve at the pole.

(ii) From question (31), Exercise 12.3, we see that the curve is symmetric with respect to the pole.

(iii) We note that, for real values of r, $\sin 2\theta$ must not have negative values. Hence there will be no part of the curve for values of 2θ ranging from 180° to 360° and from 540° to 720°, that is, for θ in the second and fourth quadrants.

As 2θ varies from	0 to 90°	90° to 180°
θ varies from	0 to 45°	45° to 90°
r^2 varies from	0 to 4	4 to 0
r varies from	0 to 2 (branch (1)) and 0 to -2 (branch (2))	2 to 0 (branch (3)) -2 to 0 (branch (4))

With this information, the tangent lines from (i), and the symmetry from (ii), we can sketch the curve (Figure 12.5). As θ varies from 180° to 270°, this curve is retraced.

From the diagram the reader will note symmetry about the line whose equation is $\theta = \dfrac{\pi}{4}$. Again the reader is asked to check that if a curve has equation $r = f(\theta)$, then it will be symmetric with respect to the line whose equation is $\theta = \dfrac{\pi}{4}$ if $f\left(\dfrac{\pi}{2} - \theta\right) = f(\theta)$. In this example, $r^2 = 4 \sin 2\theta$ and

$$4 \sin 2\left(\frac{\pi}{2} - \theta\right) = 4 \sin (\pi - 2\theta)$$
$$= 4 \sin 2\theta.$$

Similarly, this curve has symmetry with respect to the line whose equation is $\theta = \dfrac{3\pi}{4}$. This may be shown algebraically by checking that $f\left(\dfrac{3\pi}{2} - \theta\right) = f(\theta)$. In this example,

$$4 \sin 2\left(\frac{3\pi}{2} - \theta\right) = 4 \sin (3\pi - 2\theta)$$
$$= 4 \sin (\pi - 2\theta)$$
$$= 4 \sin 2\theta.$$

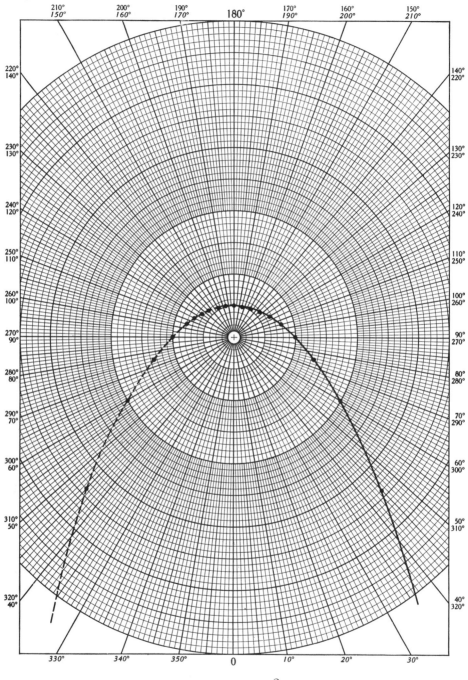

Figure 12.6. $r = \dfrac{2}{1 - \cos \theta}$

Whenever a curve possesses symmetry with respect to two lines intersecting at right angles, it possesses symmetry with respect to their point of intersection. We have already seen that this curve possesses symmetry with respect to the pole.

Example 4.   Sketch the curve whose equation is

$$r = \frac{2}{1 - \cos \theta}.$$

Solution:

(i)   The curve has no tangents at the pole.

(ii)   The curve is symmetric about the polar axis.   (Why?)

(iii)   We construct the following table of values.

θ	$\cos \theta$	$1 - \cos \theta$	$r = \dfrac{2}{1 - \cos \theta}$
0°	1.000	0	does not exist
15°	0.966	0.034	59
30°	0.866	0.134	15
45°	0.707	0.293	6.8
60°	0.500	0.500	4
75°	0.259	0.741	2.7
90°	0	1.000	2
105°	−0.259	1.259	1.6
120°	−0.500	1.500	1.3
135°	−0.707	1.707	1.2
150°	−0.866	1.866	1.07
165°	−0.966	1.966	1.02
180°	−1.000	2.000	1

Note that as θ approaches 0°, r approaches ∞.   The table shows approximations for r that can be used in our diagram.

The curve is sketched in Figure 12.6.   The top branch is obtained from the points with co-ordinates (r, θ) given in the table; the bottom branch is obtained from considerations of symmetry.   The curve is a parabola.   This may be checked by changing to the corresponding rectangular equation.

EXERCISE 12.4

Sketch the curves with the following equations.   (Refer to question (3), Exercise 12.3 for a discussion of their symmetry.)

1. $r = 4 \cos 2\theta$.

2. $r = 4 \cos 3\theta$.

3. $r = \sin 2\theta$.

4. $r = 2 \sin 4\theta$.

5. $r^2 = \sin \theta + \cos \theta$.

6. $r = \cos^4 \theta$.

7. $r = 4(1 - \cos \theta)$.

8. $r = 4 \tan \theta$.

9. $r = 2 + \cos \theta$.

10. $r = 2 + 3 \cos \theta$.

11. $r = a\theta,\ a \in Re$.

12. $r^2 = 4 \sin 2\theta$.

13. $r^2 = 9 \cos 2\theta$.

14. $r = 2 \cos (\theta - 30°)$.

15. $r = \dfrac{2}{1 + 2 \cos \theta}$.

12.5. The Derivative in Polar Co-ordinates

To study the interpretation of the derivative, $\frac{dr}{d\theta}$, for curves in polar co-ordinates, we must examine the diagram which will show the defining process.

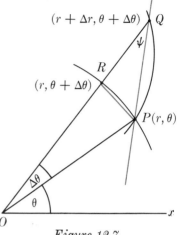

Figure 12.7

In the diagram,

O is the origin of the co-ordinate system;

O_x is the axis on which $\theta = 0$;

$P(r, \theta)$ is any point on the curve $r = f(\theta)$;

$Q(r + \Delta r, \ \theta + \Delta\theta)$ is a point close to P on the curve;

$R(r, \theta + \Delta\theta)$ is on OQ such that $OR = r$.

P and R then lie on a circle with radius r and centre O; line segment PR is a chord of this circle and $\triangle ORP$ is isosceles.

Hence,

$$\angle ORP = \angle OPR = \frac{\pi}{2} - \frac{\Delta\theta}{2}.$$

Therefore,

$$\frac{PR}{\sin \Delta\theta} = \frac{OR}{\sin\left(\dfrac{\pi}{2} - \dfrac{\Delta\theta}{2}\right)}; \qquad \text{Sine Law}$$

$$PR = \frac{r \sin \Delta\theta}{\cos \dfrac{\Delta\theta}{2}}$$

$$= \frac{r\left(2 \cos \dfrac{\Delta\theta}{2} \sin \dfrac{\Delta\theta}{2}\right)}{\cos \dfrac{\Delta\theta}{2}}$$

$$= 2r \sin \frac{\Delta\theta}{2}.$$

Let $\angle RQP = \psi$, then $\angle QPR = \dfrac{\pi}{2} - \dfrac{\Delta\theta}{2} - \psi$. Therefore, in $\triangle PQR$, the Sine Law gives

$$\frac{PR}{\sin RQP} = \frac{RQ}{\sin RPQ}$$

$$\frac{2\,r\,\sin\dfrac{\triangle\theta}{2}}{\sin\psi} = \frac{\triangle r}{\sin\left(\dfrac{\pi}{2} - \dfrac{\triangle\theta}{2} - \psi\right)}$$

$$= \frac{\triangle r}{\cos\left(\dfrac{\triangle\theta}{2} + \psi\right)}.$$

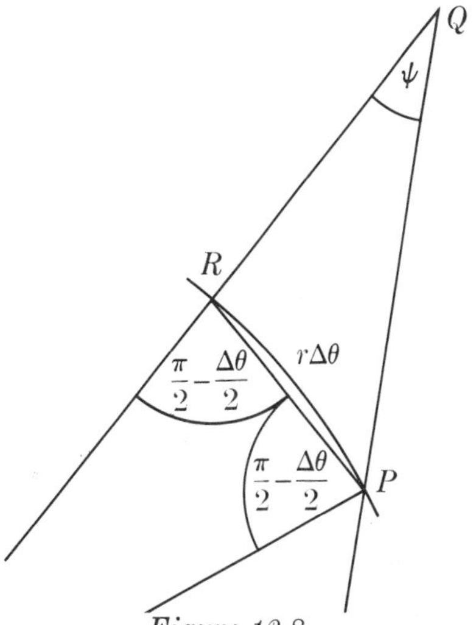

$$\therefore \quad \frac{\triangle r}{2r\,\sin\dfrac{\triangle\theta}{2}} = \frac{\cos\left(\psi + \dfrac{\triangle\theta}{2}\right)}{\sin\psi};$$

$$\frac{\triangle r}{r\,\triangle\theta}\cdot\frac{\dfrac{\triangle\theta}{2}}{\sin\dfrac{\triangle\theta}{2}} = \frac{\cos\left(\psi + \dfrac{\triangle\theta}{2}\right)}{\sin\psi}.$$

Figure 12.8

If we now let $\triangle\theta \rightarrow 0$,

then

$$\lim_{\triangle\theta\to0}\left(\frac{\triangle r}{\triangle\theta}\right) = \frac{dr}{d\theta};$$

$$\lim_{\triangle\theta\to0}\frac{\triangle\theta}{\sin\dfrac{\triangle\theta}{2}} = 1;$$

and

$$\lim_{\triangle\theta\to0}\frac{\cos\left(\psi + \dfrac{\triangle\theta}{2}\right)}{\sin\psi} = \cot\psi$$

so that

$$\frac{1}{r}\frac{dr}{d\theta} = \cot\psi.$$

Now ψ is the angle between RQ and PQ, and in the limit $\triangle\theta \rightarrow 0$ (and so $\triangle r \rightarrow 0$), PQ becomes the tangent to the curve $r = f(\theta)$, so that ψ becomes the angle between the radius vector and the tangent.

Thus,

$$\cot \psi = \frac{1}{r} \frac{dr}{d\theta}$$

gives us the value of the cotangent of the angle ψ between the radius vector and the tangent to the curve $r = f(\theta)$. Once we know the value of ψ, we can easily determine $\angle PMx$, the angle between the tangent and the θ-axis:

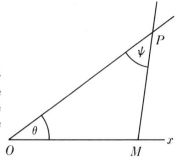

$$\angle PMx = \theta + \psi.$$

Figure 12.9

Example 1.   Find the angle between the θ-axis and the tangent at any point $P(r, \theta)$ on $r = a \cos \theta$.

Solution:

$$r = a \cos \theta.$$

$$\therefore \qquad \frac{dr}{d\theta} = -a \sin \theta.$$

$$\cot \psi = \frac{1}{r} \cdot \frac{dr}{d\theta}$$

$$= -\frac{a \sin \theta}{a \cos \theta}$$

$$= -\tan \theta = -\cot \left(\frac{\pi}{2} - \theta\right).$$

$$\therefore \qquad \psi = \pi - \left(\frac{\pi}{2} - \theta\right)$$

$$= \frac{\pi}{2} + \theta.$$

$$\therefore \qquad \angle PMx = \theta + \left(\frac{\pi}{2} + \theta\right)$$

$$= \frac{\pi}{2} + 2\theta.$$

Verify this result from the diagram and the properties of a circle.

Example 2.   Find the angle between the radius vector and the tangent at any point on the three-leaved rose, $r = 4 \sin 3\theta$. Where are the radius vector and tangent perpendicular?

Solution:

$$r = 4 \sin 3\theta.$$

$$\therefore \qquad \frac{dr}{d\theta} = -12 \cos 3\theta.$$

$$\therefore \quad \cot \psi = -\frac{12 \cos 3\theta}{4 \sin 3\theta}$$

$$= -3 \cot 3\theta.$$

$$\therefore \quad \psi = \text{arc cot } (-3 \cot 3\theta).$$

If the tangent and radius vector are perpendicular, then

$$\psi = \frac{\pi}{2}$$

and

$$\cot \psi = 0.$$

Hence, at those points where the tangent is perpendicular to the radius vector,

$$\cot 3\theta = 0$$

and

$$3\theta = \frac{\pi}{2}, \frac{3\pi}{2}, \frac{5\pi}{2}, \cdots;$$

$$\theta = \frac{\pi}{6}, \frac{\pi}{2}, \frac{5\pi}{6}, \cdots;$$

$$r = 4, -4, 4.$$

Therefore, the tangent and radius vector are perpendicular at $\left(4, \frac{\pi}{6}\right)$, $\left(-4, \frac{\pi}{2}\right)$, $\left(4, \frac{5\pi}{6}\right)$. Verify from the diagram on page 254.

EXERCISE 12.5

Find the angle between the radius vector and the tangent at any point $P(r, \theta)$ on the curves determined by the following equations in polar co-ordinates. Sketch the curve in each case.

1. $r = \sin \theta$
2. $r = 3 \cos \theta$
3. $r = -4 \sin \theta$

4. $r = \sec \theta$
5. $r = \text{cosec } \theta$
6. $r = 4(1 + \cos \theta)$

7. $r = 2 + \cos \theta$
8. $r = 1 + 2 \cos \theta$
9. $r = \dfrac{2}{1 + \cos \theta}$

10. $r = \dfrac{2}{1 + 2 \cos \theta}$ 11. $r^2 = 4 \sin \theta$ 12. $r^2 = \cos 2\theta$

13. $r^2 = \tan \theta$ 14. $r = 4 \sec \theta$

15. For each curve in questions 1 to 14 find any points (or equations to determine the value of θ at such points) where
   (a) the tangent is perpendicular to the radius vector;
   (b) the tangent is perpendicular to the θ-axis;
   (c) the tangent is parallel to the θ-axis.

12.6. Area in Polar Co-ordinates

Again, to study area in polar co-ordinates we will use a diagram to lead us to the defining integral.

The diagram shows a portion of the curve given by $r = f(\theta)$ with O as the origin. The radius vector $OA \, (\theta = \alpha)$, the curve $r = f(\theta)$ from A to B, and the radius vector $OB \, (\theta = \beta)$ bound an area which we wish to calculate.

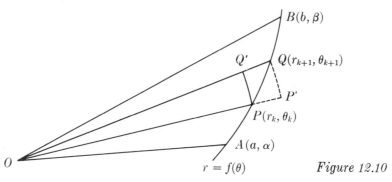

Figure 12.10

The radius vector from O to $P(r_k, \theta_k)$ and the radius vector from O to $Q(r_{k+1}, \theta_{k+1})$ together with the arc PQ bound an element of area.

Q' is where the circular arc of radius OP cuts OQ.

P' is where the circular arc of radius OQ cuts OP.

Hence, Q' has polar co-ordinates (r_k, θ_{k+1})

and P' has polar co-ordinates (r_{k+1}, θ_k).

Therefore,

$$\text{Area } OPQ' = \tfrac{1}{2}r_k^2(\theta_{k+1} - \theta_k)$$
$$= \tfrac{1}{2}[f(\theta_k)]^2 \, (\theta_{k+1} - \theta_k);$$

and

$$\text{Area } OP'Q = \tfrac{1}{2}r_{k+1}^2 \, (\theta_{k+1} - \theta_k)$$
$$= \tfrac{1}{2}[f(\theta_{k+1})]^2 \, (\theta_{k+1} - \theta_k).$$

The area of OPQ lies between these two and $f(\theta_k) \le f(\xi_k) \le f(\theta_{k+1})$ for $\theta_k \le \xi_k \le \theta_{k+1}$. So for some value ξ_k of θ, $\theta_k \le \xi_k \le \theta_{k+1}$,

$$\text{Area } OPQ = \tfrac{1}{2}[f(\xi_k)]^2 \, \triangle\theta_k,$$

where

$$\triangle\theta_k = \theta_{k+1} - \theta_k.$$

Hence, by the definition of the definite integral

$$\text{Area } OAB = \lim_{\triangle\theta_k \to 0} \sum_{\theta_k=\alpha}^{\theta_k=\beta} \tfrac{1}{2}[f(\xi_k)]^2 \, \triangle\theta_k$$

$$= \tfrac{1}{2} \int_\alpha^\beta [f(\theta)]^2 \, d\theta.$$

If we note that $r = f(\theta)$ this can be written as

$$\text{Area } OAB = \tfrac{1}{2} \int_\alpha^\beta r^2 \, d\theta.$$

Example 1.   Find the area in the closed curve $r = 2a \cos \theta$.

Solution:

At A, $r = 2a$ at $\theta = 0$,

and $r = -2a$ at $\theta = \pi$.

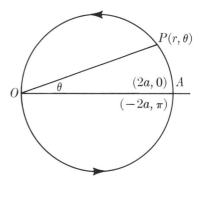

Therefore, $\text{Area} = \tfrac{1}{2} \int_0^\pi [2a \cos \theta]^2 \, d\theta$

$$= \tfrac{1}{2} \int_0^\pi 4a^2 \cos^2\theta \, d\theta$$

$$= 2a^2 \int_0^\pi \cos^2\theta \, d\theta$$

$$= a^2 \int_0^\pi [\cos 2\theta + 1] \, d\theta$$

$$= a^2 \left[\tfrac{1}{2} \sin 2\theta + \theta \right]_0^\pi$$

$$= a^2[\tfrac{1}{2} \cdot 0 + \pi - (\tfrac{1}{2} \cdot 0 + 0)]$$

$$= \pi a^2.$$

Example 2. Find the area enclosed by $r = 1 + 2 \cos \theta$ between $\theta = -\dfrac{2\pi}{3}$ and $\theta = +\dfrac{2\pi}{3}$.

Solution:

At A, $\qquad \theta = -\dfrac{2\pi}{3}$;

$$r = 1 + 2 \cos\left(-\dfrac{2\pi}{3}\right)$$

$$= 1 + 2(-\tfrac{1}{2})$$

$$= 0.$$

At B, $\qquad \theta = 0$;

$$r = 1 + 2 \cos (0)$$

$$= 1 + 2$$

$$= 3.$$

Again, at A, $\qquad \theta = +\dfrac{2\pi}{3}$;

$$r = 1 + 2 \cos\left(\dfrac{2\pi}{3}\right)$$

$$= 1 + 2(-\tfrac{1}{2})$$

$$= 0.$$

The diagram shows that from $\theta = -\dfrac{2\pi}{3}$ to $\theta = \dfrac{2\pi}{3}$, $r = 1 + 2 \cos \theta$ forms one closed loop.

$\therefore$ Area of loop $= \dfrac{1}{2} \displaystyle\int_{-2\pi/3}^{2\pi/3} (1 + 2 \cos \theta)^2 d\theta$

$$= \dfrac{1}{2} \int_{-2\pi/3}^{2\pi/3} (1 + 4 \cos \theta + 4 \cos^2\theta) d\theta$$

$$= \dfrac{1}{2} \left[\theta + 4 \sin \theta + 2(\tfrac{1}{2} \sin 2\theta + \theta) \right]_{-2\pi/3}^{2\pi/3} \qquad \text{(See Example 1.)}$$

$$= \dfrac{1}{2} \left[3\theta + 4 \sin \theta + \sin 2\theta \right]_{-2\pi/3}^{2\pi/3}$$

$$= \dfrac{1}{2} \left[3 \cdot \dfrac{2\pi}{3} + 4 \sin \dfrac{2\pi}{3} + \sin \dfrac{4\pi}{3} - \left(3\left(-\dfrac{2\pi}{3}\right) + 4 \sin \left(-\dfrac{2\pi}{3}\right) + \sin \left(-\dfrac{4\pi}{3}\right) \right) \right]$$

$$= \frac{1}{2}\left[2\pi + 4\frac{\sqrt{3}}{2} - \frac{\sqrt{3}}{2} - \left(-2\pi - 4\frac{\sqrt{3}}{2} + \frac{\sqrt{3}}{2}\right)\right]$$

$$= \frac{1}{2}\left[4\pi + \frac{6\sqrt{3}}{2}\right]$$

$$= 2\pi + \frac{3\sqrt{3}}{2}.$$

EXERCISE 12.6

Find the area enclosed by each loop of the curves given by:

1. $r = \sin \theta$ 2. $r = 3 \cos \theta$ 3. $r = -4 \cos \theta$

4. $r = \sin 2\theta$ 5. $r = 1 + \sin \theta$ 6. $r = 4(1 + \cos \theta)$

7. $r = 2 + \cos \theta$ 8. $r = 1 + 2 \cos \theta$ 9. $r^2 = 4 \sin \theta$

10. $r^2 = \cos 2\theta$

Chapter Summary

The polar co-ordinate system · pole · polar axis · radius vector · vectorial angle

Relation between polar and rectangular co-ordinates:

$$x = r \cos \theta. \qquad r = \sqrt{x^2 + y^2}.$$

$$y = r \sin \theta. \qquad \tan \theta = \frac{y}{x}.$$

Changing from polar to rectangular equations and vice versa

Graphing polar relations

Symmetry about (a) the polar axis, (b) the pole, (c) the line $\theta = \frac{\pi}{2}$

If ψ is the angle between the radius vector and the tangent to the curve $r = f(\theta)$,
then
$$\cot \psi = \frac{1}{r}\frac{dr}{d\theta}.$$

The tangent to $r = f(\theta)$ is perpendicular to the radius vector when
$$\frac{dr}{d\theta} = 0, \quad r \neq 0.$$

The area, A, bounded by the radius vector $OA(a, \alpha)$, the radius vector $OB(b, \beta)$
and the curve $r = f(\theta)$ is given by

$$A = \frac{1}{2}\int_{\alpha}^{\beta} r^2 d\theta.$$

Find the angle between the tangent and radius vector at the points stated on the
curves given.

REVIEW EXERCISE 12

1. Plot the following pairs of points.
   (a) $P_1(4, 60°)$, $Q_1(4, -60°)$ (b) $P_2(3, 120°)$, $Q_2(-3, 120°)$

2. What symmetry is demonstrated by the pairs of points in question (1)?

3. Change the following to rectangular co-ordinates.
   (a) $(3, 45°)$ (b) $(-2, 210°)$ (c) $(-5, 1080°)$ (d) $(-3, -90°)$

4. Change the following to polar co-ordinates.
   (a) $(0, 6)$ (b) $(-2, 0)$ (c) $(-2, 2\sqrt{3})$ (d) $(-4\sqrt{3}, -4)$

5. Change to polar equations.
   (a) $x^2 + y^2 - 2x = 0$.   (b) $2x - 5y = 0$.   (c) $y^2 + 9x = 0$.

6. Change to rectangular equations.
   (a) $r \sin \theta = 2$.   (b) $r^2 = \sin 2\theta$.   (c) $r = 2 \cot \theta$.

7. Sketch the curves with the following polar equations and identify the curve in each case.
   (a) $r = 4 \sin \theta$.   (b) $r = 4$.   (c) $r = -4 \cos \theta$.
   (d) $r = 4 \csc \theta$.   (e) $r = -5 \sec \theta$.   (f) $r = 2 \sec \theta$.

8. Sketch the curves with the following polar equations.
   (a) $r = 4 (1 - \sin \theta)$.   (b) $r^2 = 9 \sin 2\theta$.   (c) $r = 1 + 2 \sin \theta$.

   (d) $r^2 = 4 \sin \theta$.   (e) $r = \dfrac{2}{1 - \frac{1}{2} \sin \theta}$.   (f) $r = \dfrac{2}{1 + \frac{1}{2} \cos \theta}$.

9. When is the curve whose equation is $r = f(\theta)$ symmetric about the line $\theta = \theta_1$?

Find, at the given points, the angle between the radius vector and the tangent to the curves determined by the following equations.

10. $r = 2 \cos 2\theta$ at $(2, 0)$, $\left(0, \dfrac{\pi}{4}\right)$, $\left(-2, \dfrac{\pi}{2}\right)$.

11. $r = 4(1 + \sin \theta)$ at $(4, 0)$, $\left(8, \dfrac{\pi}{2}\right)$, $(4, \pi)$, $\left(0, \dfrac{3\pi}{2}\right)$.

12. $r = 4 \tan \theta$ at $(0, 0)$, $\left(4, \dfrac{\pi}{4}\right)$,   at $\theta = \dfrac{\pi}{2}$.

13. $r = \dfrac{2}{1 + \cos \theta}$ at $(1, 0)$, $\left(2, \dfrac{\pi}{2}\right)$,   at $\theta = \pi$.

14. $r^2 = \tan \theta$ at $(0, 0)$, $\left(1, \dfrac{\pi}{4}\right)$,   at $\theta = \dfrac{\pi}{2}$.

15. $r^2 = 4 \sin 2\theta$ at $(0, 0)$, $\left(2\sqrt{2}, \dfrac{\pi}{8}\right)$, $\left(4, \dfrac{\pi}{4}\right)$.

Find the area enclosed by one loop of the curves determined by the equations.

16. $r = 4 \sin \theta$ 17. $r = 6 \sin 3\theta$ 18. $r = 3 + 2 \sin \theta$ 19. $r^2 = 4 \sin 2\theta$

20. Find the area between the smaller and larger loops of $r = 1 + 2 \cos \theta$.

Chapter 13

COMPLEX NUMBERS

13.1. Origin and Definition

Systems of numbers have been invented by mathematicians down through the centuries as the need arose. One of the basic problems confronting mathematicians of the past was the problem of solving a given algebraic equation. This problem led in turn to the invention of the negative integers, the rational numbers, the irrational numbers, and zero. However, even with the set of real numbers comprising all infinite decimal numbers, man was unable to solve all simple polynomial equations.

We have seen that the solution set of the quadratic equation

$$ax^2 + bx + c = 0$$

is

$$\left\{ \frac{-b + \sqrt{b^2 - 4ac}}{2a} , \quad \frac{-b - \sqrt{b^2 - 4ac}}{2a} \right\}$$

and that formulae exist that give the roots of the cubic and quartic equations in terms of their coefficients. (See, for example, Section 9.2 of *Senior Mathematics 2**.) However, the roots of the quadratic equation are not always real numbers; the roots of the equation

$$x^2 + x + 4 = 0$$

are

$$\frac{-1 + \sqrt{-15}}{2} \quad \text{and} \quad \frac{-1 - \sqrt{-15}}{2},$$

and these are not real numbers since there is no real number whose square is -15. Thus we have need for the invention of a new set of numbers, the set C of complex numbers.

---

*Elliott, Fryer, Gardner, Hill, *Senior Mathematics 2*, Toronto, Holt, Rinehart and Winston, 1965.

We do not attempt to define "complex number" but content ourselves with the following statement. A complex number is one that can be represented by the numeral $a + bi$, where a and b are real numbers and i is a symbol with the property that $i^2 = -1$. Then $2 + 3i$, $4 - \frac{1}{2}i$, $\sqrt{2} + \pi i$ represent, or are numerals for, complex numbers; $3 - \sqrt{2}i$ or $3 - (\sqrt{2})i$ may be written $3 - i\sqrt{2}$ to avoid confusion with the root sign and avoid the use of parentheses.

There will be a numeral $a + bi$ corresponding to every ordered pair (a, b) of real numbers. For this reason, the ordered pair (a, b) can also be used as a numeral for the complex number it determines. Thus we may use $(2, 3)$, $(4, -\frac{1}{2})$, $(\sqrt{2}, \pi)$, and $(3, -\sqrt{2})$ as numerals for the above complex numbers.

The real number a is called the real part, or real component, or real coefficient of the complex number $a + bi$, and the real number b is called the imaginary part, or imaginary component, or imaginary coefficient of $a + bi$. We write

$$a = \text{Re } (a + bi) \quad \text{and} \quad b = \text{Im } (a + bi).$$

For example,

$$\text{Re } (-3 + 2i) = -3 \quad \text{and} \quad \text{Im } (-3 + 2i) = 2,$$

or

$$\text{Re } (-3, 2) = -3 \quad \text{and} \quad \text{Im } (-3, 2) = 2.$$

The name "imaginary coefficient" stems from the fact that i or $\sqrt{-1}$ was originally regarded as an "imaginary" number. Complex numbers have been in use for a long time and actually were accepted mathematically at a time when people still viewed negative numbers with suspicion. Now we realize that complex numbers are no more imaginary than any other type of number.

Complex numbers have important applications in electricity, elasticity, hydrodynamics, nucleonics, etc., branches of physical science and engineering in which the real number system is not sufficient to describe the physical processes.

If the complex number $x + yi$ is thought of essentially as the ordered pair (x, y) of real numbers, there is an obvious geometric representation of the complex number by the point in the Cartesian plane with co-ordinates (x, y). When we so represent a complex number, however, we do not use the names "x- and y-axes" for the perpendicular lines forming the frame of reference, and "Cartesian plane" for the plane so determined. Rather, we call these lines the real axis and the imaginary axis, and we call the resulting plane the complex plane or Argand plane (named after Jean Robert Argand who, in 1806, gave this geometrical representation of a complex number and used it to show that every algebraic equation has a root).

Example 1. Represent geometrically the complex numbers

$$1 + i, \quad -5 + 4i, \quad -3 - 2i, \quad 4 - 3i, \quad 6 + 0i, \quad 0 - 2i.$$

Solution: These complex numbers are represented, respectively, by the points $(1, 1)$, $(-5, 4)$, $(-3, -2)$, $(4, -3)$, $(6, 0)$, and $(0, -2)$ in the complex or Argand plane (Figure 13.1).

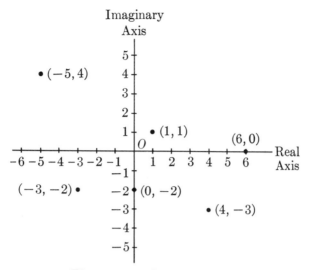

Figure 13.1. Argand Plane

Complex numbers of the form $a + 0i$ usually are written simply a. We will see later that there is a close connection between the subset of complex numbers of the form $a + 0i$ and the set of real numbers.

The complex number $x + yi$ also may be represented by the vector joining the origin to the point in the Argand plane with co-ordinates (x, y). Figure 13.2 shows the complex numbers of Example 1 represented as vectors.

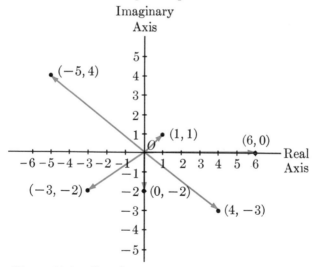

Figure 13.2. Complex numbers represented by vectors

The representation of a complex number as a vector allows us to associate an absolute value with a complex number; this is the absolute value or length of the vector representing the complex number.

DEFINITION. The absolute value or modulus or length $|x + yi|$ of the complex number $x + yi$ is defined to be

$$|x + yi| = \sqrt{x^2 + y^2}.$$

Example 2. Find the absolute values of the complex numbers of Example 1.

Solution:

$|1 + i| = \sqrt{1^2 + 1^2} = \sqrt{2}.$

$|-3 - 2i| = \sqrt{(-3)^2 + (-2)^2} = \sqrt{13}.$

$|6 + 0i| = \sqrt{6^2 + 0^2} = 6.$

$|-5 + 4i| = \sqrt{5^2 + 4^2} = \sqrt{41}.$

$|4 - 3i| = \sqrt{4^2 + (-3)^2} = 5.$

$|0 - 2i| = \sqrt{0^2 + (-2)^2} = 2.$

EXERCISE 13.1

1. Give (i) the real coefficient and (ii) the imaginary coefficient of the following.
   (a) $6 - i\sqrt{2}$ (b) $\frac{1}{2} + \frac{1}{2}i$ (c) $-\pi + 6i$ (d) $2x + 3yi$
   (e) $(4, 3)$ (f) $(0, -5)$ (g) $(\frac{1}{2}, -\sqrt{2})$ (h) $(5\sqrt{2} + 3, 0)$

2. Express the following complex numbers in the form $a + bi$.
   (a) $(3, -2)$ (b) $(0, 6)$ (c) $(2, 3 + \sqrt{2})$ (d) (x, y)

3. Express the following complex numbers in the form (a, b).
   (a) $5 - \frac{3}{2}i$ (b) $-\sqrt{2} + 3i$ (c) $\frac{2}{3} - \pi i$ (d) $p + qi$

4. Represent the following complex numbers by points in the Argand plane.
   (a) $6 + 4i$ (b) $-3 + 2i$ (c) $\frac{1}{2} + \frac{3}{2}i$ (d) $-4 - 2i$
   (e) $0 + 3i$ (f) $-3 + 0i$ (g) $\sqrt{2} + i\sqrt{2}$ (h) $\pi + 4i$

5. Give the absolute values of the complex numbers in question (4).

6. Represent the following complex numbers by vectors.
   (a) $3 + 4i$ (b) $5 - 2i$ (c) $-3 - 4i$ (d) $-2 + 6i$
   (e) $4 + 0i$ (f) $0 - 3i$ (g) $-3 + i\sqrt{2}$ (h) $-5 + 0i$

7. Give the absolute values of the complex numbers in question (6).

8. What complex number does the origin of the Argand plane represent?

9. What is the locus of points representing complex numbers of the form $0 + bi$?

10. What is the locus of points representing complex numbers of the form $a + 0i$?

11. What is the locus of points representing complex numbers whose real coefficients are equal to (a) their imaginary coefficients? (b) the negative of their imaginary coefficients?

12. Sketch the region in the Argand plane which represents complex numbers with absolute values less than or equal to unity.

13.2. Addition of Complex Numbers

In order to study the arithmetic of complex numbers, we must first know when two complex numbers are equal.

DEFINITION. $a + bi = c + di$ if and only if $a = c$ and $b = d$.

Thus two complex numbers are equal if and only if their real components are equal and their imaginary components are equal.

Example 1.   Are the following complex numbers equal?

(a) $2 + 3i$ and $\pi + i\sqrt{2}$ (b) $x + yi$ and $2 - \frac{1}{2}i$

Solution:

(a) $2 + 3i \neq \pi + i\sqrt{2}$ since $\text{Re}(2 + 3i) = 2$ and $\text{Re}(\pi + i\sqrt{2}) = \pi$ and $\pi \neq 2$; the imaginary parts are also unequal in this case.

(b) $x + yi = 2 - \frac{1}{2}i$ if and only if $x = 2$ and $y = -\frac{1}{2}$.

Example 2.   For what values of m and n will

$$(m + n) + (2m - n)i = 3 + 9i?$$

Solution: We have equality if and only if

$$m + n = 3$$

and

$$2m - n = 9.$$

Therefore $m = 4$, $n = -1$ are the required values.

If we assume that the expressions $a + bi$ and $c + di$ behave like linear polynomials in the symbol i, with the additional property that $i^2 = -1$, we may justify the result of the above definition as follows:
If

$$a + bi = c + di,$$

then

$$a - c = i(d - b),$$

and

$$(a - c)^2 = -(d - b)^2;$$

that is,

$$(a - c)^2 + (d - b)^2 = 0.$$

But $(a - c)^2$ and $(d - b)^2$ are both nonnegative real numbers and their sum can equal zero only if each is zero; therefore

$$a - c = b - d = 0 \quad \text{if} \quad a + bi = c + di.$$

Conversely, if $a = c$ and $b = d$, then certainly $a + bi = c + di$.

DEFINITION. Addition:

$$(a + bi) + (c + di) = (a + c) + (b + d)i.$$

This definition tells us that we may add complex numbers exactly as we add polynomials; for example,

$$(2 + 3x) + (4 + 7x) = 6 + 10x,$$

and similarly,

$$(2 + 3i) + (4 + 7i) = 6 + 10i.$$

The definition also shows us immediately that the set of complex numbers is closed under addition.

According to our definition,

$$(a + bi) + (0 + 0i) = a + bi,$$

so that the complex number $0 + 0i$ is the identity or zero for addition of complex numbers.   If there is no confusion, we will write simply 0 for this complex number.

We note that, by this definition of addition,

$$(7 - 3i) + (-7 + 3i) = 0 + 0i,$$

so that $(-7 + 3i)$ is the negative of the complex number $7 - 3i$; that is,

$$-7 + 3i = -(7 - 3i).$$

In general,

$$(a + bi) + (-a - bi) = (a - a) + (b - b)i = 0$$

and so

$$-(a + bi) = -a - bi \text{ is the additive inverse of } a + bi.$$

We may now define subtraction of complex numbers as follows.

DEFINITION. Subtraction:

$$(a + bi) - (c + di) = (a + bi) + (-c - di).$$

Thus to subtract a complex number, we add its additive inverse.

Example 3.

(a) Express $-(-3 + 2i)$ as a complex number in the form $a + bi$.

(b) Express $(5 + 4i) - (-3 + 2i)$ as a complex number in the form $a + bi$.

Solution:

(a)

$$-(-3 + 2i) = 3 - 2i.$$

(b)
$$(5 + 4i) - (-3 + 2i) = (5 + 4i) + [-(-3 + 2i)]$$
$$= (5 + 4i) + (3 - 2i)$$
$$= 8 + 2i.$$

The fact that addition of complex numbers is carried out in terms of addition of real numbers (the real and imaginary components of the complex numbers), shows us that addition of complex numbers is commutative and associative.   For example,

$$(3 + 2i) + (-7 + 4i) = -4 + 6i$$
$$= (-7 + 4i) + (3 + 2i).$$

In general
$$(a + bi) + (c + di) = (a + c) + (b + d)i$$
$$= (c + a) + (d + b)i$$
$$= (c + di) + (a + bi).$$

Thus addition of complex numbers is commutative.

Addition of complex numbers is associative; for example,

$$(4 + i) + [(-3 + 2i) + (6 - 4i)] = (4 + i) + (3 - 2i)$$
$$= 7 - i;$$

$$[(4 + i) + (-3 + 2i)] + (6 - 4i) = (1 + 3i) + (6 - 4i)$$
$$= 7 - i.$$

EXERCISE 13.2

1. Find the values of x and y so that the complex numbers in the following pairs are equal.

   (a) $6x + 3yi, 4 + 2i$

   (b) $x - 3yi, -\pi - i\sqrt{2}$

   (c) $x - (4 - y)i, -\frac{1}{2} + \frac{3}{2}i$

   (d) $x - (x + y)i, 3 + 0i$

   (e) $(x + 2y) + 3xi, -6 + 0i$

   (f) $(x + 2y) + 3xi, 0 - 6i$

   (g) $(x + y) + (2x - 3y)i, 3 - 2i$

   (h) $(4x - y) + (\frac{1}{2}x + y)i, -3 - 2i$

2. Add the following pairs of complex numbers.

   (a) $4 + 3i, 7 + 2i$

   (b) $6 - 3i, -2 + 4i$

   (c) $-\frac{1}{2} + 3i, -\frac{3}{2} - 2i$

   (d) $6 - 4i, 6 + 4i$

   (e) $-\frac{1}{2} - \frac{3}{2}i, \frac{5}{2} + i$

   (f) $-4 + \pi i, 4 + \pi i$

   (g) $\sqrt{2} + i, 3 + 2i$

   (h) $6\sqrt{2} + i, -3 + i\sqrt{2}$ (i) $\pi + 2i, \sqrt{3} + i\sqrt{2}$

3. State the additive inverses of the following in the form $a + bi$.

   (a) $5 - 2i$

   (b) $-3\sqrt{2} + \frac{1}{2}i$

   (c) $-\frac{1}{2} + \frac{\sqrt{3}}{2}i$

4. In the following, subtract the second complex number from the first.

(a) $6 + i$, $-4 + i$ (b) $3 - 2i$, $-2 - 5i$ (c) $-6 - 2i$, $-5 - 4i$

(d) $4 - \frac{1}{2}i$, $\frac{3}{2} + \frac{1}{2}i$ (e) $\frac{1}{2} + 3i$, $-2 - \frac{1}{2}i$ (f) $6 + 4i$, $-6 + 4i$

(g) $\sqrt{2} + 3i$, $5\sqrt{2} - i$ (h) $3\sqrt{2} + 4i$, $\pi + i\sqrt{2}$ (i) $\dfrac{1}{\sqrt{3}} + i$, $2 - i\sqrt{2}$

5. Verify that addition of complex numbers is associative using the following triples of complex numbers.

(a) $1 - i, 3 - 4i, 5 + 2i$ (b) $-6 + 2i, -4 - 3i, 5 - 6i$

6. Prove that the set of complex numbers is closed under subtraction.

7. Prove that addition of complex numbers is associative.

8. Solve the following equations for z.

(a) $(2 + 3i) + z = -4 + i$.   (b) $(-1 + 2i) + z = 5 - \frac{1}{2}i$.

(c) $(\sqrt{2} + i) - z = 4 + i\sqrt{2}$.   (d) $6 - i = z + (5 - \sqrt{2})i$.

9. Represent the complex numbers $z_1 = 5 + i$, $z_2 = 2 + 3i$, and their sum $z_1 + z_2$ geometrically.

10. Prove that the origin and the points representing $z_1, z_2,$ and $z_1 + z_2$ in question (9) are the vertices of a parallelogram.

11. Prove that the result in question (10) is true for every pair of complex numbers z_1 and z_2.

12. Interpret the result in question (11) using the vector representation for complex numbers.

13.3. Multiplication of Complex Numbers

DEFINITION. Multiplication:

$$(a + bi) \times (c + di) = (ac - bd) + (ad + bc)i.$$

This rather complicated looking definition tells us that we may multiply complex numbers in exactly the way that we multiply polynomials, bearing in mind that i^2 may be replaced by -1. For example,

$$(2 + 3x) \times (4 + x) = 8 + 2x + 12x + 3x^2$$
$$= 8 + 14x + 3x^2.$$

Similarly,

$$(2 + 3i) \times (4 + i) = 8 + 2i + 12i + 3i^2$$
$$= 8 + 14i + 3(-1)$$
$$= 5 + 14i.$$

$$(a + bi) \times (c + di) = ac + adi + bci + bdi^2$$
$$= ac + (ad + bc)i + bd(-1)$$
$$= (ac - bd) + (ad + bc)i.$$

The definition shows us immediately that the set of complex numbers is closed under multiplication.

The following examples indicate that multiplication of complex numbers is commutative and associative.

Example 1. Evaluate

(a) $(2 - 3i) \times (5 + i)$;   (b) $(5 + i) \times (2 - 3i)$.

Solution:

(a) $(2 - 3i) \times (5 + i) = 10 + 2i - 15i - 3i^2$
$$= 13 - 13i.$$

(b) $(5 + i) \times (2 - 3i) = 10 - 15i + 2i - 3i^2$
$$= 13 - 13i.$$

Therefore

$$(2 - 3i) \times (5 + i) = (5 + i) \times (2 - 3i).$$

Example 2. Evaluate

(a) $(1 + 2i) \times [(6 - i) \times (2 + 3i)]$,   (b) $[(1 + 2i) \times (6 - i)] \times (2 + 3i)$.

Solution:

(a) $(1 + 2i) \times [(6 - i) \times (2 + 3i)]$
$$= (1 + 2i) \times [12 - 2i + 18i - 3i^2]$$
$$= (1 + 2i) \times (15 + 16i)$$
$$= 15 + 16i + 30i + 32i^2$$
$$= -17 + 46i.$$

(b) $[(1 + 2i) \times (6 - i)] \times (2 + 3i)$
$$= [6 - i + 12i - 2i^2] \times (2 + 3i)$$
$$= (8 + 11i) \times (2 + 3i)$$
$$= 16 + 24i + 22i + 33i^2$$
$$= -17 + 46i.$$

Therefore

$$(1 + 2i) \times [(6 - i) \times (2 + 3i)] = [(1 + 2i) \times (6 - i)] \times (2 + 3i).$$

Note that

$$(a + bi) \times (1 + 0i) = a + bi,$$

so that $1 + 0i$ is the multiplicative identity or unit for the multiplication of complex numbers. When there can be no confusion, we will write 1 instead of $1 + 0i$.

Example 3.   If $z_1 = 2 - 5i$, $z_2 = -3 + 4i$, and $z_3 = -1 - 6i$, find

(a) $z_1(z_2 + z_3)$,   (b) $z_1z_2 + z_1z_3$.

Solution:

(a)
$$z_2 + z_3 = (-3 + 4i) + (-1 - 6i)$$
$$= -4 - 2i.$$

Therefore
$$z_1(z_2 + z_3) = (2 - 5i) \times (-4 - 2i)$$
$$= -18 + 16i.$$

(b)
$$z_1z_2 = (2 - 5i) \times (-3 + 4i)$$
$$= 14 + 23i.$$
$$z_1z_3 = (2 - 5i) \times (-1 - 6i)$$
$$= -32 - 7i.$$

Therefore
$$z_1z_2 + z_1z_3 = (14 + 23i) + (-32 - 7i)$$
$$= -18 + 16i.$$

We conclude that $z_1(z_2 + z_3) = z_1z_2 + z_1z_3$ for this particular triple of complex numbers z_1, z_2, and z_3.

If you examine closely the behaviour of complex numbers of the form $a + 0i$ under addition and multiplication, you will see that they behave in exactly the same way as the real numbers a.

complex numbers	*real numbers*
$(6 + 0i) + (2 + 0i) = 8 + 0i$	$6 + 2 = 8$
$(6 + 0i) \times (2 + 0i) = 12 + 0i$	$6 \times 2 = 12$

Because of this, mathematicians agree to identify the complex number $a + 0i$ with the real number a and even to write $a + 0i = a$ (as long as there is no possibility of confusion).

EXERCISE 13.3

1. Evaluate the following.

   (a) i^2 (b) i^5 (c) i^{16} (d) i^{99} (e) i^{999}

   (f) $-3i \times 2i^5$ (g) $\frac{1}{2}i^3 \times 4i$ (h) $-6i \times 4i^{19}$ (i) $i^3 \times i^{97}$ (j) $6i^{10} \times 4i^4$

2. Multiply the following pairs of complex numbers.

   (a) $4 + 3i$, $7 + 2i$ (b) $6 - 3i$, $-2 + 4i$ (c) $-\frac{1}{2} + 3i$, $-\frac{3}{2} - 2i$

   (d) $6 - 4i$, $6 + 4i$ (e) $-\frac{1}{2} - \frac{3}{2}i$, $\frac{5}{2} + i$ (f) $-4 + \pi i$, $4 + \pi i$

(g) $\sqrt{2} + i, 3 + 2i$ (h) $6\sqrt{2} + i, -3 + i\sqrt{2}$

(i) $4\sqrt{2} - 3i, \sqrt{2} + 2i$ (j) $-5 + i\sqrt{2}, -6 - 3i\sqrt{2}$

3. Use the following pairs of complex numbers to verify by example that multiplication of complex numbers is commutative.

  (a) $6 + i, -4 + i$ (b) $3 - 2i, -2 - 5i$ (c) $\frac{1}{2} + 3i, -2 - \frac{1}{2}i$

4. Prove that multiplication of complex numbers is commutative.

5. Use the following triples of complex numbers to verify by example that multiplication of complex numbers is associative and distributive over addition.

  (a) $3 - i, 5 + i, 2 - 3i$ (b) $6 + 2i, 5 - i\sqrt{2}, 5 + i\sqrt{2}$

6. (a) Verify that

$$(1 + 2i)[(3 - 2i) + (-5 - 4i)] = (1 + 2i)(3 - 2i) + (1 + 2i)(-5 - 4i).$$

  (b) What law is exemplified in (a)?

7. Find $uv, u^2 + v^2,$ and $u^3 - v^3,$ if $u = 2 - i$ and $v = -1 + 2i$.

8. Find w^3 if $w = 1 + i\sqrt{3}$.

9. If $u^3 = w^3$, does it necessarily follow that $u = w$?

10. If $u^2 + v^2 = 0$, does it necessarily follow that $u = v = 0$?

11. If $w = \cos \theta + i \sin \theta$, find w^2 and show that w^2 is equal to $\cos 2\theta + i \sin 2\theta$.

12. Write the multiplication table for the set of four numbers $\{1, i, -1, -i\}$, thereby showing that this set is closed under multiplication.

13. Prove that the product of two nonzero complex numbers is always nonzero.

14. Let $z = 4 + 3i$ and plot $z, iz, i^2z,$ and i^3z on the same diagram. Note that i may be considered as a rotation operator under multiplication; describe the rotation effect of i on z.

15. If $z = 1 - 2i\sqrt{2}$, plot $z, z^2,$ and z^3 on the same diagram.

16. Express the following complex numbers in the form $a + bi$.

  (a) $i^{17} + i^{28} + i^{43}$ (b) $(-1 + 2i)^4$

  (c) $\dfrac{(1 - i)^3}{\sqrt{2}}$ (d) $(4 - i)(5 + 2i)(3 - i)$

17. Prove that multiplication of complex numbers is associative and distributive over addition.

13.4. Complex Conjugates

DEFINITION.   Conjugate complex numbers, or complex conjugates, are pairs of complex numbers differing only in the sign of their imaginary coefficients.

For example, $6 - 3i$ and $6 + 3i$, $-4 + 0i$ and $-4 - 0i$, $0 - 6i$ and $0 + 6i$ are pairs of conjugate complex numbers or complex conjugates.

Example 1.   State the complex conjugates of the complex numbers

(a) $4 - 3i$,   (b) $-\dfrac{1}{2} + \dfrac{\sqrt{3}}{2}i$,

and in each case find the product of the given complex number and its conjugate.

Solution:

(a)   The complex conjugate of $4 - 3i$ is $4 + 3i$.

$$(4 - 3i) \times (4 + 3i) = 16 - 9i^2 = 25 .$$

(b)   The complex conjugate of $-\dfrac{1}{2} + \dfrac{\sqrt{3}}{2}i$ is $-\dfrac{1}{2} - \dfrac{\sqrt{3}}{2}i$.

$$\left(-\frac{1}{2} + \frac{\sqrt{3}}{2}i\right) \times \left(-\frac{1}{2} - \frac{\sqrt{3}}{2}i\right) = \left(-\frac{1}{2}\right)^2 - \left(\frac{\sqrt{3}}{2}\right)^2 i^2$$
$$= \frac{1}{4} + \frac{3}{4}$$
$$= 1 .$$

If we use the single letter z to represent the complex number $x + yi$, then we use the symbol $\bar{z}$ to represent the complex conjugate $x - yi$.   We have the following theorems.

Theorem 1. $z \times \bar{z}$ is a real number.

Proof:

$$z \times \bar{z} = (x + yi) \times (x - yi) = (x^2 + y^2) + 0i$$
$$= x^2 + y^2 .$$

(Recall that we have agreed to identify the real number a with the complex number $a + 0i$.)

Theorem 2. $z \times \bar{z} = |z|^2.$

Proof: From the preceding theorem, if $z = x + yi$, then

$$z \times \bar{z} = x^2 + y^2 .$$

Also

$$|z| = \sqrt{x^2 + y^2} .$$

Therefore

$$z \times \bar{z} = |z|^2 .$$

Example 2. Given $z_1 = 3 - 2i$ and $z_2 = -2 + 5i$, compare

$$\overline{z_1 + z_2} \quad \text{and} \quad \overline{z_1} + \overline{z_2}.$$

Solution:

$$z_1 + z_2 = (3 - 2i) + (-2 + 5i)$$
$$= 1 + 3i.$$

Hence

$$\overline{z_1 + z_2} = 1 - 3i.$$

$$\overline{z_1} = 3 + 2i \quad \text{and} \quad \overline{z_2} = -2 - 5i.$$

Hence

$$\overline{z_1} + \overline{z_2} = (3 + 2i) + (-2 - 5i)$$
$$= 1 - 3i.$$

Therefore

$$\overline{z_1 + z_2} = \overline{z_1} + \overline{z_2}$$

for these particular complex numbers z_1 and z_2.

The result in this example is proved in general in the following theorem.

Theorem 3. If z_1 and z_2 represent complex numbers, then

$$\overline{z_1 + z_2} = \overline{z_1} + \overline{z_2};$$

that is, the conjugate of the sum of two complex numbers is equal to the sum of their conjugates.

Proof: Let

$$z_1 = x_1 + iy_1 \quad \text{and} \quad z_2 = x_2 + iy_2.$$

Then

$$z_1 + z_2 = (x_1 + x_2) + i(y_1 + y_2)$$

and

$$\overline{z_1 + z_2} = (x_1 + x_2) - i(y_1 + y_2).$$

Also

$$\overline{z_1} = x_1 - iy_1 \quad \text{and} \quad \overline{z_2} = x_2 - iy_2,$$

so that

$$\overline{z_1} + \overline{z_2} = (x_1 - iy_1) + (x_2 - iy_2).$$
$$= (x_1 + x_2) - i(y_1 + y_2).$$

Therefore

$$\overline{z_1 + z_2} = \overline{z_1} + \overline{z_2}.$$

Example 3.   Given $z_1 = 2 - 5i$ and $z_2 = -3 + 2i$, compare

$$\overline{z_1 \times z_2} \quad \text{and} \quad \overline{z_1} \times \overline{z_2}.$$

Solution:

$$z_1 \times z_2 = (2 - 5i) \times (-3 + 2i)$$
$$= 4 + 19i.$$

Hence

$$\overline{z_1 \times z_2} = 4 - 19i.$$

$$\overline{z_1} = 2 + 5i \quad \text{and} \quad \overline{z_2} = -3 - 2i$$

Hence

$$\overline{z_1} \times \overline{z_2} = (2 + 5i) \times (-3 - 2i)$$
$$= 4 - 19i.$$

Therefore

$$\overline{z_1 \times z_2} = \overline{z_1} \times \overline{z_2}$$

for these particular complex numbers z_1 and z_2.

The result in this example is stated in general in the following theorem.

Theorem 4.   If z_1 and z_2 represent complex numbers, then

$$\overline{z_1 \times z_2} = \overline{z_1} \times \overline{z_2} ;$$

that is, the conjugate of the product of two complex numbers is equal to the product of their conjugates.

Proof: The proof is left as an exercise. (See question (9), Exercise 13.4).

Example 4.   Given $z = -4 - 9i$, compare $\overline{\overline{z}}$ and z.

Solution:

$$z = -4 - 9i.$$
$$\overline{z} = -4 + 9i.$$
$$\overline{\overline{z}} = -4 - 9i.$$

Therefore

$$\overline{\overline{z}} = z$$

for this particular complex number z.

The result in this example is stated in general in the following theorem; its proof is left as an exercise.   (See question (10), Exercise 13.4).

Theorem 5.   If z represents a complex number, then

$$\overline{\overline{z}} = z ;$$

that is, the conjugate of the conjugate of a complex number is equal to that complex number.

EXERCISE 13.4

1. State the conjugates of the following complex numbers.

   (a) $4 - 3i$ (b) $-5 - 4i$ (c) $4 + 0i$

   (d) $-3 - 3i$ (e) $0 - 5i$ (f) $8 + 5i$

2. Find $z + \bar{z}$ and $z - \bar{z}$ for each complex number in question (1).

3. Are any complex numbers equal to their own conjugates; if so, which ones?

4. Multiply the following complex numbers by their conjugates.

   (a) $6 - i$ (b) $-2 - 4i$ (c) $\frac{1}{2} + \frac{1}{2}i$ (d) $0 + 4i$

   (e) $2 - i\sqrt{3}$ (f) $4\sqrt{3} + 2i$ (g) $\frac{1}{2} + 0i$ (h) $-\frac{1}{2} - \frac{\sqrt{3}}{2}i$.

5. What is meant by the statements "The product of a complex number and its conjugate is a *real* number." and "The sum of a complex number and its conjugate is a *real* number."?

6. What is the connection between the geometrical representations of a complex number and its conjugate?

7. If $z_1 = 1 + i$, $z_2 = 4 - 3i$, and $z_3 = -1 - 2i$, find

   (a) $\overline{z_1 + z_2 + z_3}$ and $\bar{z_1} + \bar{z_2} + \bar{z_3}$,

   (b) $\overline{z_1 \times z_2 \times z_3}$ and $\bar{z_1} \times \bar{z_2} \times \bar{z_3}$,

   (c) $\overline{z_1 \times (z_2 + z_3)}$ and $\bar{z_1} \times \bar{z_2} + \bar{z_1} \times \bar{z_3}$.

8. Repeat question (7) if $z_1 = 5 - 2i$, $z_2 = -1 - i$, and $z_3 = 0 - 4i$.

9. Prove that $\bar{z_1} \times \bar{z_2} = \overline{z_1 \times z_2}$ for complex numbers z_1 and z_2.

10. Prove that $\bar{\bar{z_1}} = z_1$ for any complex number z_1.

11. Prove that $\overline{z_1 + z_2 + z_3} = \bar{z_1} + \bar{z_2} + \bar{z_3}$ for complex numbers z_1, z_2, and z_3.

12. Prove that $\overline{kz} = k\bar{z}$ if k is a real number and z is a complex number.

13. Prove that $\overline{z_1 \times z_2 \times z_3} = \bar{z_1} \times \bar{z_2} \times \bar{z_3}$ for complex numbers z_1, z_2, and z_3.

13.5. Division of Complex Numbers

In this section we consider the problem of dividing complex numbers.

Example 1. Express $\dfrac{2 - 3i}{4 + i}$ in the form $a + bi$.

Solution: We use the fact that the product of a complex number and its conjugate is essentially a real number. Since $4 - i$ is the conjugate of the denominator and $(4 - i)(4 + i) = 17$, we multiply the given expression by $\dfrac{4 - i}{4 - i}$ (which is equal to 1, the identity element for multiplication).

Then

$$\frac{2 - 3i}{4 + i} = \frac{2 - 3i}{4 + i} \times \frac{4 - i}{4 - i}$$

$$= \frac{5 - 14i}{17}$$

$$= \frac{5}{17} - \frac{14}{17}i \,.$$

Note that our operation here is similar to "rationalizing the denominator" (actually we are "realizing" the denominator). We may check that

$$\frac{2 - 3i}{4 + i} = \frac{5}{17} - \frac{14}{17}i \,,$$

by showing that

$$2 - 3i = (4 + i)\left(\frac{5}{17} - \frac{14}{17}i\right).$$

Division of a complex number by a nonzero complex number is always possible as in the example. The set of complex numbers is closed under division by non-zero complex numbers.

If $(a + bi)(c + di) = 1 + 0i = 1$, then $c + di$ is the multiplicative inverse of $a + bi$; by the definition of division as the inverse operation to multiplication, we have

$$c + di = \frac{1}{a + bi}\,.$$

Example 2. Find the multiplicative inverse of $4 - 3i$.

Solution: We are asked to find $\dfrac{1}{4 - 3i}\,.$

Now

$$\frac{1}{4 - 3i} = \frac{1}{4 - 3i} \times \frac{4 + 3i}{4 + 3i}$$

$$= \frac{4 + 3i}{16 + 9}$$

$$= \frac{4}{25} + \frac{3}{25}i \,.$$

Check:

$$(4 - 3i)\left(\frac{4}{25} + \frac{3}{25}i\right) = \frac{16}{25} - \frac{12}{25}i + \frac{12}{25}i - \frac{9}{25}i^2$$

$$= 1 + 0i$$

$$= 1 \,.$$

Every nonzero complex number will have a multiplicative inverse. (See question (4), Exercise 13.5.) As usual, the zero complex number $0 + 0i$ does not have a multiplicative inverse.

We are now in a position to review the properties of addition and multiplication as defined for complex numbers and to show that all the field postulates hold for the set of complex numbers with these operations.

(i) The set C of complex numbers is closed under the binary operations of addition and multiplication.

(ii) Addition of complex numbers is associative and commutative, $0 + 0i$ is the additive identity, and $-a - bi$ is the additive inverse of the complex number $a + bi$.

(iii) Multiplication of complex numbers is associative and commutative, $1 + 0i$ is the multiplicative identity, and every nonzero complex number has a multiplicative inverse.

(iv) Finally, multiplication of complex numbers is distributive over addition. Thus the complex numbers form a field under our definition of addition and multiplication.

There is one significant way in which the set of complex numbers differs from the set of real numbers. The set C of complex numbers is *not* an ordered set; that is, given two complex numbers z_1 and z_2, we can attach no significant meaning to either $z_1 > z_2$ or $z_1 < z_2$.

EXERCISE 13.5

1. Divide the first complex number in each of the following pairs by the second.
   (a) $4 + 3i$, $7 + 2i$ (b) $6 - 3i$, $-2 + 4i$ (c) $3 + 2i$, $-4 - 2i$
   (d) $-\frac{1}{2} + 3i$, $-\frac{3}{2} + 2i$ (e) $6 - 4i$, $6 + 4i$ (f) $-\frac{1}{2} - \frac{3}{2}i$, $\frac{5}{2} + i$
   (g) $-4 + \pi i$, $4 + \pi i$ (h) $\sqrt{2} + i$, $3 + 2i$ (i) $6\sqrt{2} + i$, $-3 + i\sqrt{2}$

2. Evaluate the following quotients in the form $a + bi$; multiply the resulting numbers to check. (The product should be 1.)
   (a) $\dfrac{6 - 3i}{1 + 2i}, \dfrac{1 + 2i}{6 - 3i}$ (b) $\dfrac{2 + i}{4 - 3i}, \dfrac{4 - 3i}{2 + i}$ (c) $\dfrac{1 + i\sqrt{2}}{4 + i\sqrt{3}}, \dfrac{4 + i\sqrt{3}}{1 + i\sqrt{2}}$

3. Find the multiplicative inverses of the following complex numbers. Check each result.
   (a) $4 + i$ (b) $3 - 2i$ (c) $6 + 3i$ (d) $-6 + 2i$
   (e) $\frac{1}{2} - \frac{1}{2}i$ (f) $\sqrt{3} + i$ (g) $2 - i\sqrt{2}$ (h) $\sqrt{3} + i\sqrt{2}$

4. Find the complex number which is the multiplicative inverse of the nonzero complex number $a + bi$.

5. Solve the following equations for z.
   (a) $(1 + i)z = 3 - 2i$ (b) $(-2 + 3i)z = 2 - 5i$
   (c) $(6 - 2i)z = -\frac{1}{2} + 3i$ (d) $(4 - 3i)z = 2$

6. Prove that the product of two complex numbers is zero if and only if at least one of the two complex numbers is zero.

13.6. Solution of Quadratic Equations

If a is a positive real number, the symbol $\sqrt{}$ in $\sqrt{a}$ can be considered as indicating a certain arithmetical operation; if a is a negative real number, it can no longer be so considered. However, just as $\sqrt{2}$ may be defined as a real number which is such that $\sqrt{2} \times \sqrt{2} = 2$, and by convention we take it to be the positive such number, so we may define $\sqrt{-2}$ to be a number which is such that $\sqrt{-2} \times \sqrt{-2} = -2$.

DEFINITION. If $a \in Re^+$, then $(\sqrt{-a})^2 = -a$.

Then, by the definition,

$$\sqrt{-1} \times \sqrt{-1} = -1 ;$$

that is, $\sqrt{-1} = i$. Further, if $a > 0$,

$$(i\sqrt{a}) \times (i\sqrt{a}) = i^2 a = (-1)a ;$$

that is,

$$(i\sqrt{a})^2 = -a .$$

Then, by convention,

$$i\sqrt{a} = \sqrt{-a} \text{ if } a > 0 .$$

Example 1. Evaluate the following.

   (a) $\sqrt{16} \times \sqrt{9}$ (b) $\sqrt{-16} \times \sqrt{9}$

   (c) $\sqrt{16} \times \sqrt{-9}$ (d) $\sqrt{-16} \times \sqrt{-9}$

Solution:

   (a) $\sqrt{16} \times \sqrt{9} = 4 \times 3 = 12$
$$= \sqrt{9 \times 16}.$$

   (b) $\sqrt{-16} \times \sqrt{9} = 4i \times 3 = 12i$
$$= \sqrt{-144} = \sqrt{-16 \times 9}.$$

   (c) $\sqrt{16} \times \sqrt{-9} = 4 \times 3i = 12i$
$$= \sqrt{-144} = \sqrt{16 \times -9}.$$

   (d) $\sqrt{-16} \times \sqrt{-9} = 4i \times 3i = 12i^2 = -12$
$$\neq \sqrt{(-16) \times (-9)} = \sqrt{144} = 12.$$

The results of Example 1 illustrate the validity of the following theorem.

Theorem. If $a, b \in Re$, then

$$\sqrt{a} \times \sqrt{b} = \sqrt{ab}$$

if and only if at least one of a or b is nonnegative.

Proof: The proof is required in question (11), Exercise 13.6.

With complex numbers at our disposal, we are now in a position to solve the general quadratic equation $ax^2 + bx + c = 0$. The solution set is

$$\left\{\frac{-b \pm \sqrt{b^2 - 4ac}}{2a}\right\}.$$

If

$$b^2 - 4ac \geq 0,$$

then the roots are real; if

$$b^2 - 4ac < 0,$$

then

$$b^2 - 4ac = -(4ac - b^2) \quad \text{and} \quad 4ac - b^2 > 0.$$

Hence, in this latter case,

$$\sqrt{b^2 - 4ac} = \sqrt{-(4ac - b^2)}$$
$$= \sqrt{-1}\sqrt{4ac - b^2}$$
$$= i\sqrt{4ac - b^2},$$

and the roots are the conjugate complex numbers

$$\frac{-b}{2a} + i\frac{\sqrt{4ac - b^2}}{2a} \quad \text{and} \quad \frac{-b}{2a} - i\frac{\sqrt{4ac - b^2}}{2a}.$$

Example 2. Solve the equation $x^2 + x + 4 = 0$.

Solution: The solution set is $\left\{\dfrac{-1 \pm \sqrt{-15}}{2}\right\}$; that is,

$$\left\{-\frac{1}{2} + \frac{i\sqrt{15}}{2}, \ -\frac{1}{2} - \frac{i\sqrt{15}}{2}\right\}.$$

With the invention of complex numbers, mathematicians reached the end of their quest as far as the solution of equations was concerned. No matter what polynomial equation is written, even with complex coefficients, the roots will be complex numbers. We cannot write a polynomial equation that does not have such a solution; there is never a need for a different type of number in such a situation.

The famous *Fundamental Theorem of Algebra* states the following.

The polynomial equation of degree n,

$$a_n z^n + a_{n-1} z^{n-1} + \cdots + a_2 z^2 + a_1 z + a_0 = 0,$$

in which the coefficients are complex numbers, always has at least one complex root. (The word *complex* includes, of course, real, rational, integral.)

With this theorem, which is not easily proved, we may readily prove by induction that such an equation has exactly n complex roots.

We have just considered the formula that gives the roots of the quadratic equation $ax^2 + bx + c = 0$ in terms of the coefficients a, b, and c; similar formulae exist for the cubic equation $ax^3 + bx^2 + cx + d = 0$ and the quartic equation $ax^4 + bx^3 + cx^2 + dx + e = 0$. Such formulae do not (and *cannot*) exist for equations of higher degree; however these equations still have roots. Various numerical methods exist to find the roots of such equations to any required degree of accuracy.

Example 3.   Solve the equation $2iz^2 - (4 + 3i)z + (3 - i) = 0$.

Solution: By the quadratic formula, the solution set is

$$\left\{ \frac{4 + 3i \pm \sqrt{(4 + 3i)^2 - 4(2i)(3 - i)}}{4i} \right\}.$$

Now

$$(4 + 3i)^2 - 4(2i)(3 - i) = 16 + 24i - 9 - 24i - 8$$
$$= -1,$$

and so the roots are

$$\frac{4 + 4i}{4i} = \frac{1}{i} + 1 \quad \text{and} \quad \frac{4 + 2i}{4i} = \frac{1}{i} + \frac{1}{2}$$

$$= 1 - i. \qquad\qquad = \frac{1}{2} - i.$$

The solution set is $\{1 - i, \frac{1}{2} - i\}$.

EXERCISE 13.6

1. Express the following as complex numbers in the form $a + bi$.
   (a) $\sqrt{-25}$
   (b) $\sqrt{16} - \sqrt{-9} - \sqrt{-64}$
   (c) $\sqrt{-4}\,\sqrt{25}$
   (d) $\sqrt{81}\,\sqrt{-16}$
   (e) $\sqrt{-9}\,\sqrt{-9}$
   (f) $\sqrt{-100}\,\sqrt{36}$
   (g) $\sqrt{-1}\,\sqrt{-8}$
   (h) $\sqrt{-65}\,\sqrt{-13}$
   (i) $\sqrt{-42}\,\sqrt{-14}$

2. Find the complex roots of the following equations.
   (a) $6x^2 - x + 2 = 0$.
   (b) $3x^2 - \sqrt{2}x + 1 = 0$.
   (c) $\sqrt{2}x^2 - 5x + 6\sqrt{2} = 0$.
   (d) $\sqrt{3}x^2 - x + \frac{4}{\sqrt{3}} = 0$.
   (e) $z^2 - iz + 4 = 0$.
   (f) $3z^2 + 2iz - 1 = 0$.
   (g) $iz^2 - 6z + 3i = 0$.
   (h) $2iz^2 + z - 3i = 0$.

3. Solve the equation of Example 3 of this section by first multiplying both members by i.

4. Find the complex roots of the following equations $ax^2 + bx + c = 0$; verify that the sum of the roots is $-\dfrac{b}{a}$ and the product of the roots is $\dfrac{c}{a}$.

(a) $x^2 + 5x + 8 = 0$.

(b) $2x^2 - 4x + 3 = 0$.

(c) $6x^2 - 5x + 2 = 0$.

(d) $3x^2 + x + 2 = 0$.

5. Show that the sum of the roots of the equation $ax^2 + bx + c = 0$ is always $-\dfrac{b}{a}$ if the coefficients a, b, and c are real numbers.

6. In question (5), show that the product of the roots is always $\dfrac{c}{a}$.

7. What are the roots of the equation
$$[x - (1 + i)]\,[x - (2 - i)] = 0\,?$$

8. Write the equation in question (7) in the form $ax^2 + bx + c = 0$. Does the sum of the roots equal $-\dfrac{b}{a}$? Does the product of the roots equal $\dfrac{c}{a}$? Explain.

9. Show that if the roots of a quadratic equation with real coefficients are complex numbers, they are conjugate complex numbers. Why is this not violated in question (7)?

10. Form quadratic equations with the following pairs of roots.

(a) $2 \pm i$

(b) $-3 \pm 2i$

(c) $0 \pm i$

(d) $-\sqrt{2} \pm 3i$

(e) $6 \pm i\sqrt{3}$

(f) $\frac{1}{2} \pm \frac{1}{2}i\sqrt{2}$

11. Prove the theorem of this section: If a, $b \in Re$, then
$$\sqrt{a} \times \sqrt{b} = \sqrt{ab}$$
if and only if at least one of a or b is nonnegative.

13.7. The Polar Form of a Complex Number

The complex number $x + yi$ is represented geometrically by the point P in the Argand plane with co-ordinates (x, y) or, equivalently, by the vector joining the origin to this point (Figure 13.3). In this way we have a one-to-one correspondence between the set of complex numbers and the set of points in the Argand plane (or the set of vectors in the Argand plane with initial point at the origin).

We have already associated a magnitude or length or absolute value with the complex number $z = x + yi$, namely, the nonnegative length of the vector representing the complex number,
$$|x + yi| = \sqrt{x^2 + y^2}.$$

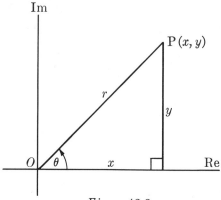

Figure 13.3

Usually we use the letter r to represent the length of the vector associated with the complex number z;

$$r = |z| = \sqrt{x^2 + y^2}\,.$$

Now the vector OP determines an angle θ (a positive number of radians is measured counterclockwise from the real or horizontal axis). This angle is called the argument of the complex number z;

$$\theta = \text{Arg}\, z\,.$$

The term "angle of z" is also used for θ. Note that a complex number z does not determine a unique angle θ, since obviously

$$\text{Arg}\, z = \theta + 2k\pi\,, \quad k \in I.$$

Thus each complex number z will determine an infinite number of ordered pairs (r, θ) consisting of a nonnegative real number and an angle. However such an ordered pair will determine a unique point in the Argand plane and thus determine a unique complex number z. There is a many-to-one correspondence between the set of ordered pairs (r, θ) and the set of complex numbers.

From Figure 13.3 we see that

$$\frac{x}{r} = \cos \theta \quad \text{and} \quad \frac{y}{r} = \sin \theta\,;$$

that is,

$$x = r \cos \theta \quad \text{and} \quad y = r \sin \theta\,.$$

We may then write

$$z = x + yi$$
$$= r \cos \theta + ir \sin \theta$$
$$= r (\cos \theta + i \sin \theta)\,.$$

$x + yi$ is called the Cartesian or rectangular form of the complex number and $r(\cos \theta + i \sin \theta)$ is known as the polar form of the complex number z (so called because r and θ are polar co-ordinates for the corresponding point in the plane; polar co-ordinates were discussed in Chapter 12). This form is often abbreviated as

$$z = r(\cos \theta + i \sin \theta) = r \operatorname{cis} \theta,$$

read "$r \cos \theta$ plus $i \sin \theta$." Of course, since

$$\cos \theta = \cos(\theta + 2k\pi) \quad \text{and} \quad \sin \theta = \sin(\theta + 2k\pi),$$

the polar form of a complex number is not unique.

$$z = r \operatorname{cis} \theta = r \operatorname{cis}(\theta + 2k\pi).$$

This is a very important fact in later work with complex numbers.

There is no difficulty in changing from the polar form

$$z = r(\cos \theta + i \sin \theta)$$

to the rectangular form

$$x + yi;$$

we merely evaluate $\cos \theta$ and $\sin \theta$ (possibly using tables) and multiply by r.

Example 1. Find the rectangular form of the complex number

$$z = 2\sqrt{2}\left(\cos \frac{\pi}{4} + i \sin \frac{\pi}{4}\right).$$

Solution: Since

$$\cos \frac{\pi}{4} = \sin \frac{\pi}{4} = \frac{1}{\sqrt{2}},$$

therefore

$$z = 2\sqrt{2}\left(\frac{1}{\sqrt{2}} + i\frac{1}{\sqrt{2}}\right) = 2 + 2i.$$

Example 2. Find the rectangular form of the complex number

$$z = 3 \operatorname{cis} 127°.$$

Solution: From tables, $\cos 127° = -0.6018$ and $\sin 127° = 0.7986$. Therefore

$$z = 3(-0.6018 + 0.7986i)$$
$$= -1.8054 + 2.3958i.$$

In changing from rectangular to polar form, a diagram such as that in Figure 13.3 is useful. We plot the complex number in rectangular form and indicate r and θ on the diagram.

Example 3.   Find the polar form of the complex number $z = 3 + 3i$.

Solution:

$$r = \sqrt{3^2 + 3^2} = 3\sqrt{2}.$$

$$\tan \theta = \frac{3}{3} = 1,$$

and

θ is in quadrant I.

Hence

$$\theta = \frac{\pi}{4},$$

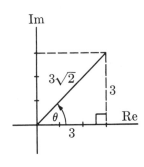

and therefore

$$z = 3\sqrt{2} \text{ cis} \left(\frac{\pi}{4} + 2k\pi\right).$$

Example 4.   Find the polar form of the complex number $z = -\sqrt{3} - i$.

Solution:

$$r = \sqrt{(-\sqrt{3})^2 + (-1)^2} = 2.$$

$$\tan \theta = \frac{-1}{-\sqrt{3}} = \frac{1}{\sqrt{3}}$$

and

θ is in quadrant III.

Hence

$$\theta = 210°,$$

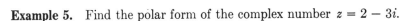

and therefore

$$z = 2 \text{ cis} (210 + 360k)°.$$

Example 5.   Find the polar form of the complex number $z = 2 - 3i$.

Solution:

$$r = \sqrt{2^2 + (-3)^2} = \sqrt{13}.$$

$$\tan \theta = \frac{-3}{2} = -1.5$$

and

θ is in quadrant IV.

Hence

$$\theta = 304°, \quad \text{(to nearest degree}$$
$$\text{from tables),}$$

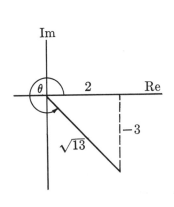

and therefore

$$z = \sqrt{13} \text{ cis} (304 + 360k)°.$$

EXERCISE 13.7

1. Plot each of the following complex numbers and write them in rectangular form.

   (a) $4(\cos 0° + i \sin 0°)$ (b) $10(\cos 180° + i \sin 180°)$

   (c) $3\left(\cos \dfrac{\pi}{2} + i \sin \dfrac{\pi}{2}\right)$ (d) $5\left(\cos \dfrac{3\pi}{2} + i \sin \dfrac{3\pi}{2}\right)$

   (e) cis 4π (f) 3 cis$(-\pi)$ (g) 5 cis $\dfrac{5\pi}{2}$

   (h) 2 cis $30°$ (i) 3 cis $135°$ (j) 5 cis $420°$

   (k) 7 cis $720°$ (l) 4 cis $(-60)°$ (m) cis $225°$

   (n) 3 cis $600°$ (o) 2 cis $\dfrac{7\pi}{6}$ (p) 3 cis $\dfrac{13\pi}{6}$

   (q) cis 99π (r) 3 cis $150°$ (s) 6 cis $210°$

2. Plot each of the following complex numbers and write them in polar form using θ in the range $0° \leq \theta < 360°$.

   (a) 4 (b) $3i$ (c) -2

   (d) $-i$ (e) $1 + i\sqrt{3}$ (f) $1 - i\sqrt{3}$

   (g) $-1 + i\sqrt{3}$ (h) $-1 - i\sqrt{3}$ (i) $6 + 6i$

   (j) $-2\sqrt{3} + 2i$ (k) $-5i$ (l) $-6 - 6i\sqrt{3}$

   (m) $-3 + 3i\sqrt{3}$ (n) $-4 - 4i$ (o) 10

   (p) $-\dfrac{1}{2} + \dfrac{\sqrt{3}}{2}i$ (q) $-\sqrt{2}$ (r) $\sqrt{3} - i$

3. Write the general polar form of the following complex numbers.

   (a) 4 (b) -2 (c) i

   (d) $-6i$ (e) $-\sqrt{3} + i$ (f) $3\sqrt{2} - 3i\sqrt{2}$

4. Find the rectangular form of the following complex numbers.

   (a) 2 cis $40°$ (b) 3 cis $100°$ (c) cis $200°$

   (d) 3 cis $190°$ (e) 2 cis $275°$ (f) 4 cis $2°$

5. What is the argument of the following complex numbers with $a \in Re^+$?

   (a) $a + 0i$ (b) $-a + 0i$ (c) $0 + ai$ (d) $0 - ai$

6. Explain why it is essential to use a diagram (at least a mental one) in expressing $a + bi$ in polar form.

7. Prove that if z has polar form r cis θ, then $\bar{z}$ has polar form r cis $(-\theta)$.

8. Use the result in question (7) to give the polar form of the conjugates of the following complex numbers. Change each number to its polar form first.

   (a) 6 (b) $6i$ (c) -6 (d) $-6i$

   (e) $1 + i$ (f) $3 - 3i$ (g) $\sqrt{3} - i$ (h) $1 - i\sqrt{3}$

13.8. Multiplication and Division of Complex Numbers in Polar Form

Theorem 1.   If $z_1 = r_1 \text{ cis } \theta_1$ and $z_2 = r_2 \text{ cis } \theta_2$, then

$$z_1 z_2 = r_1 r_2 \text{ cis } (\theta_1 + \theta_2) .$$

In words, "The absolute value of the product of two complex numbers is the *product* of their absolute values; the argument of the product of two complex numbers is the *sum* of their arguments."

The result of this theorem shows that multiplication of complex numbers is simpler when the complex numbers are in polar form than when they are in rectangular form.

Proof of Theorem:

$$z_1 = r_1(\cos \theta_1 + i \sin \theta_1) \quad \text{and} \quad z_2 = r_2(\cos \theta_2 + i \sin \theta_2) .$$

Therefore

$$
\begin{aligned}
z_1 z_2 &= r_1 r_2(\cos \theta_1 + i \sin \theta_1)(\cos \theta_2 + i \sin \theta_2) \\
&= r_1 r_2[\cos \theta_1 \cos \theta_2 + i^2 \sin \theta_1 \sin \theta_2 + i \cos \theta_1 \sin \theta_2 + i \sin \theta_1 \cos \theta_2] \\
&= r_1 r_2[(\cos \theta_1 \cos \theta_2 - \sin \theta_1 \sin \theta_2) + i(\sin \theta_1 \cos \theta_2 + \cos \theta_1 \sin \theta_2)] \\
&= r_1 r_2[\cos(\theta_1 + \theta_2) + i \sin (\theta_1 + \theta_2)] \\
&= r_1 r_2 \text{ cis } (\theta_1 + \theta_2), \quad \text{as required.}
\end{aligned}
$$

Example 1.   Find the product of $3 \text{ cis } 15°$ and $2 \text{ cis } 30°$ in the form $a + bi$.

Solution:

$$
\begin{aligned}
(3 \text{ cis } 15°)(2 \text{ cis } 30°) &= 6 \text{ cis } 45° \\
&= 6\left(\frac{1}{\sqrt{2}} + \frac{i}{\sqrt{2}}\right) \\
&= 3\sqrt{2} + 3i\sqrt{2} .
\end{aligned}
$$

Division of complex numbers in polar form is dealt with in the following theorem.

Theorem 2.   If $z_1 = r_1 \text{ cis } \theta_1$ and $z_2 = r_2 \text{ cis } \theta_2$, with $z_2 \neq 0$, then

$$\frac{z_1}{z_2} = \frac{r_1}{r_2} \text{ cis } (\theta_1 - \theta_2) .$$

In words, "The absolute value of a quotient of two complex numbers is the *quotient* of their absolute values; the argument of the quotient of two complex numbers is the *difference* of their arguments."

Proof of Theorem: By definition, $\dfrac{r_1 \text{ cis } \theta_1}{r_2 \text{ cis } \theta_2}$ is the complex number $r \text{ cis } \theta$ such that

$$(r \text{ cis } \theta)(r_2 \text{ cis } \theta_2) = r_1 \text{ cis } \theta_1 ;$$

that is,
$$rr_2 \operatorname{cis}(\theta + \theta_2) = r_1 \operatorname{cis} \theta_1.$$

Hence
$$rr_2 = r_1 \quad \text{and} \quad \theta + \theta_2 = \theta_1 + 2k\pi,$$
$$r = \frac{r_1}{r_2} \quad \text{and} \quad \theta = \theta_1 - \theta_2 + 2k\pi.$$

Therefore
$$\frac{r_1 \operatorname{cis} \theta_1}{r_2 \operatorname{cis} \theta_2} = \frac{r_1}{r_2} \operatorname{cis}(\theta_1 - \theta_2), \quad \text{as required.}$$

Example 2. Find the quotient $10 \operatorname{cis} 105° \div 5 \operatorname{cis} 75°$ in the form $a + bi$.

Solution:
$$\frac{10 \operatorname{cis} 105°}{5 \operatorname{cis} 75°} = 2 \operatorname{cis} 30°$$
$$= 2\left(\frac{\sqrt{3}}{2} + \frac{i}{2}\right)$$
$$= \sqrt{3} + i.$$

EXERCISE 13.8

1. Perform the following indicated operations and write the answers in rectangular form.

   (a) $2 \operatorname{cis} 45° \cdot 3 \operatorname{cis} 0°$

   (b) $4 \operatorname{cis} 25° \cdot 2 \operatorname{cis} 65°$

   (c) $2 \operatorname{cis} \pi \cdot 2 \operatorname{cis} \dfrac{\pi}{2}$

   (d) $\operatorname{cis} 60° \cdot \operatorname{cis} 120°$

   (e) $4 \operatorname{cis} 0° \div 2 \operatorname{cis} 45°$

   (f) $4 \operatorname{cis} 70° \div 3 \operatorname{cis} 25°$

   (g) $\operatorname{cis} \pi \div 2 \operatorname{cis} \dfrac{\pi}{2}$

   (h) $\operatorname{cis} 60° \div \operatorname{cis} 120°$

   (i) $3 \operatorname{cis} 100° \cdot 4 \operatorname{cis} 20°$

   (j) $2 \operatorname{cis} 380° \div 5 \operatorname{cis} 200°$

   (k) $4 \operatorname{cis} 100° \cdot 3 \operatorname{cis} 35°$

   (l) $5 \operatorname{cis} 270° \div \frac{1}{2} \operatorname{cis} 45°$

2. If $z = r \operatorname{cis} \theta$, show that $z^2 = r^2 \operatorname{cis} 2\theta$.

3. Find the squares of the following complex numbers.

   (a) $3 \operatorname{cis} 30°$ (b) $\sqrt{2} \operatorname{cis} 45°$ (c) $3 \operatorname{cis} 60°$

4. If $z = r \operatorname{cis} \theta$, $z \neq 0$, find the multiplicative inverse of z in polar form.

5. Find the multiplicative inverses of the following complex numbers.

   (a) $2 \operatorname{cis} 60°$ (b) $\frac{1}{2} \operatorname{cis}(-30°)$ (c) $\sqrt{2} \operatorname{cis} 135°$

6. (a) If $z = \sqrt{2} \operatorname{cis} 15°$, find z^4.   (b) If $z = \sqrt[4]{2} \operatorname{cis} 22\frac{1}{2}°$, find z^8.

13.9. De Moivre's Theorem

In question (2), Exercise 13.8, the first theorem of Section 13.8, namely, "If $z_1 = r_1$ cis θ_1, and $z_2 = r_2$ cis θ_2, then $z_1 z_2 = r_1 r_2$ cis $(\theta_1 + \theta_2)$.", was used to prove that

$$\text{if} \quad z = r \text{ cis } \theta, \quad \text{then} \quad z^2 = r^2 \text{ cis } 2\theta .$$

This is a special case of a very important theorem known as De Moivre's Theorem.

De Moivre's Theorem

$$(r \text{ cis } \theta)^n = r^n \text{ cis } n\theta, \quad n \in C .$$

(Abraham de Moivre (1667-1754) was born in France but spent most of his life in England. He was a friend of Newton and made important contributions to mathematics, especially in the theory of probability.)

Proof of De Moivre's Theorem if $n \in N$: We use mathematical induction. Let S be the set of positive integers for which De Moivre's Theorem is true.

(1) $1 \in S$, since $(r \text{ cis } \theta)^1 = r$ cis 1θ.

(2) Assume $k \in S$; that is, assume

$$(r \text{ cis } \theta)^k = r^k \text{ cis } k\theta.$$

Then

$$\begin{aligned}
(r \text{ cis } \theta)^{k+1} &= (r \text{ cis } \theta)^k \cdot r \text{ cis } \theta \\
&= r^k \text{ cis } k\theta \cdot r \text{ cis } \theta \\
&= r^{k+1} \text{ cis } (k+1)\theta \quad \text{(mult. in polar form).}
\end{aligned}$$

Therefore $k + 1 \in S$ whenever $k \in S$.
Therefore $S = N$ and De Moivre's Theorem

$$(r \text{ cis } \theta)^n = r^n \text{ cis } n\theta$$

is true for all positive integers n.

De Moivre's Theorem allows us to compute powers of complex numbers written in polar form.

Example 1. Calculate $(1 - i)^{100}$.

Solution:

$$1 - i = \sqrt{2} \text{ cis } \left(-\frac{\pi}{4}\right).$$
$$\begin{aligned}
(1 - i)^{100} &= (\sqrt{2})^{100} \text{ cis } (-25\pi) \\
&= 2^{50} \text{ cis } \pi \\
&= 2^{50} (-1 + 0i) \\
&= -2^{50} .
\end{aligned}$$

The validity of De Moivre's Theorem for negative integers and rational numbers is demonstrated in the following examples.

Example 2.   Show that $(r \text{ cis } \theta)^{-8} = r^{-8} \text{ cis } (-8\theta)$.

Solution:

$$(r \text{ cis } \theta)^{-8} = \frac{1}{(r \text{ cis } \theta)^8}$$

$$= \frac{1}{r^8 \text{ cis } 8\theta} \qquad \text{(De Moivre's)}$$

$$= \frac{1}{r^8} \text{ cis } (0 - 8\theta) \qquad \text{(division of complex numbers)}$$

$$= r^{-8} \text{ cis } (-8\theta), \qquad \text{as required.}$$

Example 3.   Show that $\cos \frac{2}{3}\theta + i \sin \frac{2}{3}\theta$ is a value of $(\cos \theta + i \sin \theta)^{\frac{2}{3}}$.

Solution:

$$\left(\cos \frac{\theta}{3} + i \sin \frac{\theta}{3}\right)^3 = \cos \theta + i \sin \theta$$

so that

$$\cos \frac{\theta}{3} + i \sin \frac{\theta}{3} \text{ is a value of } (\cos \theta + i \sin \theta)^{\frac{1}{3}}.$$

Also,

$$\left(\cos \frac{\theta}{3} + i \sin \frac{\theta}{3}\right)^2 = \cos \frac{2\theta}{3} + i \sin \frac{2\theta}{3}$$

so that

$$\cos \frac{2\theta}{3} + i \sin \frac{2\theta}{3} \text{ is a value of } (\cos \theta + i \sin \theta)^{\frac{2}{3}}.$$

The following example shows how De Moivre's Theorem and the Binomial Theorem can be combined to produce certain multiple angle formulae used in trigonometry.

Example 4.   Express $\cos 3\theta$ and $\sin 3\theta$ in terms of $\cos \theta$ and $\sin \theta$.

Solution:

$$\cos 3\theta + i \sin 3\theta = (\cos \theta + i \sin \theta)^3 \qquad \text{(De Moivre's)}$$

$$= \cos^3\theta + 3i \cos^2\theta \sin \theta + 3i^2 \cos \theta \sin^2\theta + i^3 \sin^3\theta$$

$$\text{(binomial)}$$

$$= (\cos^3\theta - 3 \cos \theta \sin^2\theta) + i (3 \cos^2\theta \sin \theta - \sin^3\theta).$$

Therefore

$$\cos 3\theta = \cos^3\theta - 3 \cos \theta \sin^2\theta$$

and

$$\sin 3\theta = 3 \cos^2\theta \sin \theta - \sin^3\theta, \qquad \text{as required.}$$

EXERCISE 13.9

1. Use De Moivre's Theorem to evaluate the following products; express each result in rectangular form.

(a) $(\cos 15° + i \sin 15°)^4$

(b) $(\cos 45° + i \sin 45°)^8$

(c) $(\cos 20° + i \sin 20°)^{-9}$

(d) $(\cos 15° + i \sin 15°)^{-4}$

(e) $\left(2 \operatorname{cis} \dfrac{\pi}{4}\right)^2$

(f) $\left(3 \operatorname{cis} \dfrac{\pi}{6}\right)^4$

(g) $\left(\dfrac{1}{2} \operatorname{cis} \dfrac{2\pi}{3}\right)^3$

(h) $(2 \operatorname{cis} 15°)^{-2}$

(i) $(3 \operatorname{cis} 72°)^5$

(j) $(3 \operatorname{cis} 90°)^{-2}$

(k) $\dfrac{(1 + i)^7(-1 + i)^5}{(-1 - i)^3}$

(l) $\dfrac{(\sqrt{3} + i)^4(-1 + i)^6}{(1 + i)^4}$

(m) $(\sqrt{3} - i)^9$

(n) i^{83}

(o) $(-1 - i)^{-8}$

(p) $\left(-\dfrac{\sqrt{3}}{2} + \dfrac{1}{2}i\right)^{-6}$

(q) $(\sqrt{3} + i)^4(-1 + i)^6$

(r) $\dfrac{(\sqrt{3} - i)^{12}(1 + i)^8}{\left(-\dfrac{1}{2} - \dfrac{i\sqrt{3}}{2}\right)^6}$

2. If $A = 2 \operatorname{cis} 120°$ and $B = \frac{1}{2} \operatorname{cis} 30°$, find the following in rectangular form.

(a) A^6 (b) B^{10} (c) A^4B^5 (d) A^9/B^6

3. Use De Moivre's Theorem and the Binomial Theorem to find formulae for the following.

(a) $\sin 2\theta$ and $\cos 2\theta$

(b) $\sin 4\theta$ and $\cos 4\theta$

(c) $\sin 5\theta$ and $\cos 5\theta$

(d) $\sin 6\theta$ and $\cos 6\theta$

4. Prove that De Moivre's Theorem is true for all negative integers n .

5. Prove that if m is rational, then $\cos m\theta + i \sin m\theta$ is one of the values of $(\cos \theta + i \sin \theta)^m$.

13.10. Roots of Complex Numbers

If u and z are complex numbers such that $u^p = z$, for some integer p , then u is a pth root of z , and we write $u = z^{1/p}$.

We may use De Moivre's Theorem to find roots of a complex number as in the following examples. We will assume that De Moivre's Theorem holds for all rational exponents.

Example 1. Find the cube root of $64i$.

Solution: To apply De Moivre's Theorem, we use the polar form of the complex number.

$$64i = 64\left(\cos\frac{\pi}{2} + i\sin\frac{\pi}{2}\right)$$

$$= 64 \operatorname{cis}\left(\frac{\pi}{2} + 2k\pi\right), \quad k \in I.$$

If Z is a cube root of $64 \operatorname{cis}\left(\frac{\pi}{2} + 2k\pi\right)$, then

$$Z^3 = 64 \operatorname{cis}\left(\frac{\pi}{2} + 2k\pi\right),$$

and

$$Z = \left[64 \operatorname{cis}\left(\frac{\pi}{2} + 2k\pi\right)\right]^{1/3}$$

$$= 4 \operatorname{cis}\left(\frac{\pi}{6} + \frac{2k\pi}{3}\right).$$

There would seem to be an infinite number of cube roots, since k can have any integral value but in fact they are not all distinct.

Let Z_k be the cube root corresponding to the integer k. Then

$$Z_0 = 4 \operatorname{cis}\frac{\pi}{6} = 4\left(\frac{\sqrt{3}}{2} + \frac{i}{2}\right) = 2\sqrt{3} + 2i\ ;$$

$$Z_1 = 4 \operatorname{cis}\frac{5\pi}{6} = 4\left(-\frac{\sqrt{3}}{2} + \frac{i}{2}\right) = -2\sqrt{3} + 2i\ ;$$

$$Z_2 = 4 \operatorname{cis}\frac{9\pi}{6} = 4(0 - i) = -4i\ ;$$

$$Z_3 = 4 \operatorname{cis}\frac{13\pi}{6} = 4 \operatorname{cis}\frac{\pi}{6} = Z_0\ ;$$

$$Z_4 = 4 \operatorname{cis}\frac{17\pi}{6} = 4 \operatorname{cis}\frac{5\pi}{6} = Z_1\ ;$$

$$Z_5 = 4 \operatorname{cis}\frac{21\pi}{6} = 4 \operatorname{cis}\frac{9\pi}{6} = Z_2\ ; \quad \text{etc.}$$

Thus $64i$ has three distinct cube roots since, for any integer t,

$$Z_{3t} = Z_0, \quad Z_{3t+1} = Z_1, \quad \text{and} \quad Z_{3t+2} = Z_2.$$

The three distinct cube roots of $64i$ may be plotted on the Argand plane; the points representing these cube roots lie on a circle about the origin of radius 4 and the vectors representing these cube roots divide this circle into three equal sectors.

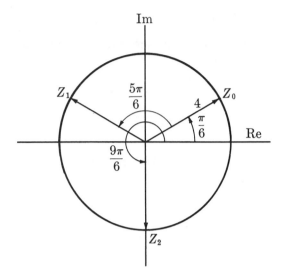

The three complex numbers Z_0, Z_1, and Z_2 of Example 1 are distinct solutions of the polynomial equation

$$Z^3 - 64i = 0 .$$

We may call such an equation, a pure equation of degree 3.   **By a pure equation** of degree n, we mean an equation of the form

$$z^n - A = 0 ,$$

where A is a complex number.

Example 2.   Find the solution set of the equation $z^4 - 16 = 0$.

Solution: We require the fourth roots Z of 16.   Write

$$16 = 16 \operatorname{cis} (0 + 2k\pi) ;$$

then

$$Z = [16 \operatorname{cis} (0 + 2k\pi)]^{1/4}$$
$$= 2 \operatorname{cis} \frac{k\pi}{2} ,$$

and therefore

$$Z_0 = 2 \operatorname{cis} 0 = 2 ,$$
$$Z_1 = 2 \operatorname{cis} \frac{\pi}{2} = 2i ,$$
$$Z_2 = 2 \operatorname{cis} \pi = -2 ,$$
$$Z_3 = 2 \operatorname{cis} \frac{3\pi}{2} = -2i .$$

Again, $Z_4 = Z_0$, $Z_5 = Z_1$, $Z_6 = Z_2$, $Z_7 = Z_3$, etc., so that there are four distinct fourth roots of 16. If we plot these fourth roots on the Argand plane, the corresponding points lie on a circle, centre the origin, radius 2, and the corresponding vectors divide the circle into four equal sectors.

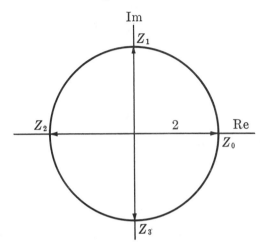

The solution set of $z^4 - 16 = 0$ is $\{2, 2i, -2, -2i\}$.

In general, to find the pth roots Z of a complex number z, we write z in general polar form

$$z = r \operatorname{cis} (\theta + 2k\pi),$$

and apply De Moivre's Theorem to obtain

$$Z = [r \operatorname{cis} (\theta + 2k\pi)]^{1/p}$$
$$= r^{1/p} \operatorname{cis} \left(\frac{\theta + 2k\pi}{p} \right).$$

Note that $r^{1/p}$ is the real positive pth root of the positive real number r. The p distinct roots Z_0, Z_1, $\cdots$, Z_{p-1} are obtained by replacing k in turn by 0, 1, 2, $\cdots$, $p - 1$.

EXERCISE 13.10

1. Find the following indicated roots; leave the answers in polar form if they involve angles θ for which $\cos \theta$ and $\sin \theta$ are not well known. Represent the roots graphically.

   (a) square roots of $9i$

   (b) square roots of $-4i$

   (c) square roots of 16 cis 120°

   (d) cube roots of 8 cis 180°

   (e) cube roots of 27

   (f) cube roots of $-8i$

(g) sixth roots of 81 cis 180°   (h) fifth roots of 32 cis 150°

(i) sixth roots of 1   (j) fourth roots of -64

(k) cube roots of -1 (l) fourth roots of $-8 + 8i\sqrt{3}$

(m) sixth roots of i (n) fifth roots of $-4(1 - i)$

(o) square roots of $1 - i\sqrt{3}$ (p) eighth roots of $\frac{1}{2}(i\sqrt{3} - 1)$

2. Find the solution sets of the following equations.

(a) $z^3 = 64$ (b) $z^2 = 16i$

(c) $z^4 + 81 = 0$ (d) $z^5 = 32$

(e) $z^5 + 1 = 0$ (f) $z^2 + 1 - i\sqrt{3} = 0$

(g) $z^4 + 4 + 4i\sqrt{3} = 0$ (h) $z^3 = 2 + i$

3. Use tables to find approximations to the square roots of

(a) $3 + 4i$ (b) $5 - 12i$

4. Find approximate roots of the equation

$$z^2 - (5 + i)z + 4 - \frac{i}{2} = 0 \,.$$

Chapter Summary

Complex number · Numeral for a complex number in the form $a + bi$ with $i^2 = -1$, a, b real, or (a, b) with a, b real · Imaginary and real coefficient or component

Geometric representation of complex numbers · Argand plane

Absolute value or modulus or length of a complex number

Equality of complex numbers

Addition of complex numbers

Properties of addition: commutative, associative, existence of identity, existence of negatives

Multiplication of complex numbers

Properties of multiplication: commutative, associative, existence of identity, existence of inverses for nonzero complex numbers, distributivity

Complex conjugates

Division of complex numbers

Solution of quadratic equations with complex roots

Polar form of a complex number

Multiplication and division of complex numbers in polar form

De Moivre's Theorem

Roots of complex numbers

REVIEW EXERCISE 13

1. State the real and imaginary coefficients of the following complex numbers,
   (a) $3 + 5i$ (b) $4 - i$ (c) $-\frac{1}{2} + 2i$ (d) $5 + 0i$
   and represent them by points in the Argand plane.

2. Give the absolute values of the complex numbers in question (1).

3. If $z_1 = 3 - 2i$ and $z_2 = -4 + 5i$, find the following numbers and their absolute values.
   (a) $z_1 + z_2$ (b) $z_2 + z_1$ (c) $z_1 - z_2$ (d) $z_2 - z_1$

4. If $z_1 = -4 - 3i$, $z_2 = -1 + 5i$, and $z_3 = 0 - 4i$, find the following.
   (a) $(z_1 + z_2) + z_3$ (b) $z_1 + (z_2 + z_3)$ (c) $z_1 - z_2 - z_3$

5. Solve for z.
   (a) $(3 - 5i) + z = -2 + 4i$.   (b) $5 - 3i = z + (4 - 2i)$.

6. Represent geometrically, the complex numbers $z_1 = 5 - 2i$, $z_2 = -3 + 4i$, and $z_1 + z_2$, and show that the three points used, together with the origin, form a parallelogram.

7. If $z_1 = 5 + 2i$, $z_2 = -3 + i$, $z_3 = -4 - 3i$, find the following.
   (a) $z_1 z_2$ (b) $z_2 z_1$ (c) $(z_1 z_2)z_3$ (d) $z_1(z_2 z_3)$
   (e) $z_1(z_2 + z_3)$ (f) $z_1 z_2 + z_1 z_3$ (g) $(z_1 + z_2)z_3$ (h) $z_1 z_3 + z_2 z_3$

8. For the complex numbers of question (7), find the following.
   (a) $z_1 + \overline{z_1}$ (b) $z_2 + \overline{z_2}$ (c) $z_3 + \overline{z_3}$ (d) $z_1 \overline{z_1}$
   (e) $z_2 \overline{z_2}$ (f) $z_3 \overline{z_3}$ (g) $\overline{z_1 + z_2}$ (h) $\overline{z_1} + \overline{z_2}$
   (i) $\overline{z_1 z_2}$ (j) $\overline{z_1} \overline{z_2}$ (k) $\overline{z_1 z_2 z_3}$ (l) $\overline{z_1} \overline{z_2} \overline{z_3}$

9. For the complex numbers of question (7), find the following
   (a) $\dfrac{z_1}{z_2}$ (b) $\dfrac{z_2}{z_3}$ (c) $\dfrac{z_3}{z_1}$ (d) $\dfrac{z_1}{z_2} \cdot \dfrac{z_2}{z_3} \cdot \dfrac{z_3}{z_1}$

   (e) $\dfrac{1}{z_1}$ (f) $\dfrac{1}{z_2}$ (g) $\dfrac{1}{z_3}$ (h) $\dfrac{1}{z_1 z_2 z_3}$

10. Solve the following equations for z.
    (a) $(4 - 3i)z = 5 + 2i$.   (b) $(-3 + 2i)z = 6$.

11. Plot the following complex numbers and give their rectangular form.
    (a) $4 \operatorname{cis} 0°$ (b) $3 \operatorname{cis} 225°$ (c) $2 \operatorname{cis} 210°$ (d) $4 \operatorname{cis} 100\pi$

12. Plot the following complex numbers and give their polar form $(0° \le \theta < 360°)$.
    (a) 6 (b) $-\dfrac{1}{2} - \dfrac{\sqrt{3}}{2}i$ (c) $-3\sqrt{3} + 3i$ (d) $\sqrt{3} + i$

13. Perform the indicated operations and give the answer in rectangular form.

(a) $5 \text{ cis } 30° \cdot 3 \text{ cis } 60°$ (b) $6 \text{ cis } 85° \div 3 \text{ cis } 40°$

(c) $(\sqrt{2} \text{ cis } 15°)^4$ (d) $(\sqrt{3} \text{ cis } 30°)^3$

(e) $\dfrac{1}{2 \text{ cis } 30°}$ (f) $\dfrac{3}{4 \text{ cis } 45°}$

14. Use De Moivre's Theorem to evaluate the following.

(a) $(1 - i)^9$ (b) $(\sqrt{3} + i)^8$

15. Find the following indicated roots and represent the roots graphically.

(a) cube roots of $27i$ (b) fifth roots of $8 - 8i\sqrt{3}$

16. Find the solution sets of the following equations.

(a) $z^4 + 81i = 0$ (b) $z^4 - 4 + 4i\sqrt{3} = 0$

17. Verify algebraically that

(a) $(r \text{ cis } \theta)^{-5} = \dfrac{1}{r^5} \text{ cis } (-5\theta),$

(b) cis $\frac{5}{2}\theta$ is one of the values of $(\text{cis } \theta)^{\frac{5}{2}}$,

(c) cis $(-\frac{3}{4}\theta)$ is one of the values of $(\text{cis } \theta)^{-\frac{3}{4}}$.

POWERS, ROOTS, AND RECIPROCALS 1—100

n	n^2	n^3	$\sqrt{n}$	$\sqrt[3]{n}$	$1/n$	n	n^2	n^3	$\sqrt{n}$	$\sqrt[3]{n}$	$1/n$
1	1	1	1.000	1.000	1.0000	51	2,601	132,651	7.141	3.708	.0196
2	4	8	1.414	1.260	.5000	52	2,704	140,608	7.211	3.733	.0192
3	9	27	1.732	1.442	.3333	53	2,809	148,877	7.280	3.756	.0189
4	16	64	2.000	1.587	.2500	54	2,916	157,464	7.348	3.780	.0185
5	25	125	2.236	1.710	.2000	55	3,025	166,375	7.416	3.803	.0182
6	36	216	2.449	1.817	.1667	56	3,136	175,616	7.483	3.826	.0179
7	49	343	2.646	1.913	.1429	57	3,249	185,193	7.550	3.849	.0175
8	64	512	2.828	2.000	.1250	58	3,364	195,112	7.616	3.871	.0172
9	81	729	3.000	2.080	.1111	59	3,481	205,379	7.681	3.893	.0169
10	100	1,000	3.162	2.154	.1000	60	3,600	216,000	7.746	3.915	.0167
11	121	1,331	3.317	2.224	.0909	61	3,721	226,981	7.810	3.936	.0164
12	144	1,728	3.464	2.289	.0833	62	3,844	238,328	7.874	3.958	.0161
13	169	2,197	3.606	2.351	.0769	63	3,969	250,047	7.937	3.979	.0159
14	196	2,744	3.742	2.410	.0714	64	4,096	262,144	8.000	4.000	.0156
15	225	3,375	3.873	2.466	.0667	65	4,225	274,625	8.062	4.021	.0154
16	256	4,096	4.000	2.520	.0625	66	4,356	287,496	8.124	4.041	.0152
17	289	4,913	4.123	2.571	.0588	67	4,489	300,763	8.185	4.062	.0149
18	324	5,832	4.243	2.621	.0556	68	4,624	314,432	8.246	4.082	.0147
19	361	6,859	4.359	2.668	.0526	69	4,761	328,509	8.307	4.102	.0145
20	400	8,000	4.472	2.714	.0500	70	4,900	343,000	8.367	4.121	.0143
21	441	9,261	4.583	2.759	.0476	71	5,041	357,911	8.426	4.141	.0141
22	484	10,648	4.690	2.802	.0455	72	5,184	373,248	8.485	4.160	.0139
23	529	12,167	4.796	2.844	.0435	73	5,329	389,017	8.544	4.179	.0137
24	576	13,824	4.899	2.884	.0417	74	5,476	405,224	8.602	4.198	.0135
25	625	15,625	5.000	2.924	.0400	75	5,625	421,875	8.660	4.217	.0133
26	676	17,576	5.099	2.962	.0385	76	5,776	438,976	8.718	4.236	.0132
27	729	19,683	5.196	3.000	.0370	77	5,929	456,533	8.775	4.254	.0130
28	784	21,952	5.292	3.037	.0357	78	6,084	474,552	8.832	4.273	.0128
29	841	24,389	5.385	3.072	.0345	79	6,241	493,039	8.888	4.291	.0127
30	900	27,000	5.477	3.107	.0333	80	6,400	512,000	8.944	4.309	.0125
31	961	29,791	5.568	3.141	.0323	81	6,561	531,441	9.000	4.327	.0123
32	1,024	32,768	5.657	3.175	.0312	82	6,724	551,368	9.055	4.344	.0122
33	1,089	35,937	5.745	3.208	.0303	83	6,889	571,787	9.110	4.362	.0120
34	1,156	39,304	5.831	3.240	.0294	84	7,056	592,704	9.165	4.380	.0119
35	1,225	42,875	5.916	3.271	.0286	85	7,225	614,125	9.220	4.397	.0118
36	1,296	46,656	6.000	3.302	.0278	86	7,396	636,056	9.274	4.414	.0116
37	1,369	50,653	6.083	3.332	.0270	87	7,569	658,503	9.327	4.431	.0115
38	1,444	54,872	6.164	3.362	.0263	88	7,744	681,472	9.381	4.448	.0114
39	1,521	59,319	6.245	3.391	.0256	89	7,921	704,969	9.434	4.465	.0112
40	1,600	64,000	6.325	3,420	.0250	90	8,100	729,000	9.487	4.481	.0111
41	1,681	68,921	6.403	3.448	.0244	91	8,281	753,571	9.539	4.498	.0110
42	1,764	74,088	6.481	3.476	.0238	92	8,464	778,688	9.592	4.514	.0109
43	1,849	79,507	6.557	3.503	.0233	93	8,649	804,357	9.644	4.531	.0108
44	1,936	85,184	6.633	3.530	.0227	94	8,836	830,584	9.695	4.547	.0106
45	2,025	91,125	6.708	3.557	.0222	95	9,025	857,375	9.747	4.563	.0105
46	2,116	97,336	6.782	3.583	.0217	96	9,216	884,736	9.798	4.579	.0104
47	2,209	103,823	6.856	3.609	.0213	97	9,409	912,673	9.849	4.595	.0103
48	2,304	110,592	6.928	3.634	.0208	98	9,604	941,192	9.899	4.610	.0102
49	2,401	117,649	7.000	3.659	.0204	99	9,801	970,299	9.950	4.626	.0101
50	2,500	125,000	7.071	3.684	.0200	100	10,000	1,000,000	10.000	4.642	.0100

TRIGONOMETRIC FUNCTIONS

Angle		Sine	Cosine	Tangent	Cotangent	Secant	Cosecant
Degrees	Radians						
0°	.0000	.0000	1.0000	.0000	undefined	1.000	undefined
1°	.0175	.0175	.9998	.0175	57.2900	1.000	57.30
2°	.0349	.0349	.9994	.0349	28.6363	1.001	28.65
3°	.0524	.0523	.9986	.0524	19.0811	1.001	19.11
4°	.0698	.0698	.9976	.0699	14.3007	1.002	14.34
5°	.0873	.0872	.9962	.0875	11.4301	1.004	11.47
6°	.1047	.1045	.9945	.1051	9.5144	1.006	9.567
7°	.1222	.1219	.9925	.1228	8.1443	1.008	8.206
8°	.1396	.1392	.9903	.1405	7.1154	1.010	7.185
9°	.1571	.1564	.9877	.1584	6.3138	1.012	6.392
10°	.1745	.1736	.9848	.1763	5.6713	1.015	5.759
11°	.1920	.1908	.9816	.1944	5.1446	1.019	5.241
12°	.2094	.2079	.9781	.2126	4.7046	1.022	4.810
13°	.2269	.2250	.9744	.2309	4.3315	1.026	4.445
14°	.2443	.2419	.9703	.2493	4.0108	1.031	4.134
15°	.2618	.2588	.9659	.2679	3.7321	1.035	3.864
16°	.2793	.2756	.9613	.2867	3.4874	1.040	3.628
17°	.2967	.2924	.9563	.3057	3.2709	1.046	3.420
18°	.3142	.3090	.9511	.3249	3.0777	1.051	3.236
19°	.3316	.3256	.9455	.3443	2.9042	1.058	3.072
20°	.3491	.3420	.9397	.3640	2.7475	1.064	2.924
21°	.3665	.3584	.9336	.3839	2.6051	1.071	2.790
22°	.3840	.3746	.9272	.4040	2.4751	1.079	2.669
23°	.4014	.3907	.9205	.4245	2.3559	1.086	2.559
24°	.4189	.4067	.9135	.4452	2.2460	1.095	2.459
25°	.4363	.4226	.9063	.4663	2.1445	1.103	2.366
26°	.4538	.4384	.8988	.4877	2.0503	1.113	2.281
27°	.4712	.4540	.8910	.5095	1.9626	1.122	2.203
28°	.4887	.4695	.8829	.5317	1.8807	1.133	2.130
29°	.5061	.4848	.8746	.5543	1.8040	1.143	2.063
30°	.5236	.5000	.8660	.5774	1.7321	1.155	2.000
31°	.5411	.5150	.8572	.6009	1.6643	1.167	1.942
32°	.5585	.5299	.8480	.6249	1.6003	1.179	1.887
33°	.5760	.5446	.8387	.6494	1.5399	1.192	1.836
34°	.5934	.5592	.8290	.6745	1.4826	1.206	1.788
35°	.6109	.5736	.8192	.7002	1.4281	1.221	1.743
36°	.6283	.5878	.8090	.7265	1.3764	1.236	1.701
37°	.6458	.6018	.7986	.7536	1.3270	1.252	1.662
38°	.6632	.6157	.7880	.7813	1.2799	1.269	1.624
39°	.6807	.6293	.7771	.8098	1.2349	1.287	1.589
40°	.6981	.6428	.7660	.8391	1.1918	1.305	1.556
41°	.7156	.6561	.7547	.8693	1.1504	1.325	1.524
42°	.7330	.6691	.7431	.9004	1.1106	1.346	1.494
43°	.7505	.6820	.7314	.9325	1.0724	1.367	1.466
44°	.7679	.6947	.7193	.9657	1.0355	1.390	1.440
45°	.7854	.7071	.7071	1.0000	1.0000	1.414	1.414

TRIGONOMETRIC FUNCTIONS

Angle		Sine	Cosine	Tangent	Cotangent	Secant	Cosecant
Degrees	Radians						
45°	.7854	.7071	.7071	1.0000	1.0000	1.414	1.414
46°	.8029	.7193	.6947	1.0355	.9657	1.440	1.390
47°	.8203	.7314	.6820	1.0724	.9325	1.466	1.367
48°	.8378	.7431	.6691	1.1106	.9004	1.494	1.346
49°	.8552	.7547	.6561	1.1504	.8693	1.524	1.325
50°	.8727	.7660	.6428	1.1918	.8391	1.556	1.305
51°	.8901	.7771	.6293	1.2349	.8098	1.589	1.287
52°	.9076	.7880	.6157	1.2799	.7813	1.624	1.269
53°	.9250	.7986	.6018	1.3270	.7536	1.662	1.252
54°	.9425	.8090	.5878	1.3764	.7265	1.701	1.236
55°	.9599	.8192	.5736	1.4281	.7002	1.743	1.221
56°	.9774	.8290	.5592	1.4826	.6745	1.788	1.206
57°	.9948	.8387	.5446	1.5399	.6494	1.836	1.192
58°	1.0123	.8480	.5299	1.6003	.6249	1.887	1.179
59°	1.0297	.8572	.5150	1.6643	.6009	1.942	1.167
60°	1.0472	.8660	.5000	1.7321	.5774	2.000	1.155
61°	1.0647	.8746	.4848	1.8040	.5543	2.063	1.143
62°	1.0821	.8829	.4695	1.8807	.5317	2.130	1.133
63°	1.0996	.8910	.4540	1.9626	.5095	2.203	1.122
64°	1.1170	.8988	.4384	2.0503	.4877	2.281	1.113
65°	1.1345	.9063	.4226	2.1445	.4663	2.366	1.103
66°	1.1519	.9135	.4067	2.2460	.4452	2.459	1.095
67°	1.1694	.9205	.3907	2.3559	.4245	2.559	1.086
68°	1.1868	.9272	.3746	2.4751	.4040	2.669	1.079
69°	1.2043	.9336	.3584	2.6051	.3839	2.790	1.071
70°	1.2217	.9397	.3420	2.7475	.3640	2.924	1.064
71°	1.2392	.9455	.3256	2.9042	.3443	3.072	1.058
72°	1.2566	.9511	.3090	3.0777	.3249	3.236	1.051
73°	1.2741	.9563	.2924	3.2709	.3057	3.420	1.046
74°	1.2915	.9613	.2756	3.4874	.2867	3.628	1.040
75°	1.3090	.9659	.2588	3.7321	.2679	3.864	1.035
76°	1.3265	.9703	.2419	4.0108	.2493	4.134	1.031
77°	1.3439	.9744	.2250	4.3315	.2309	4.445	1.026
78°	1.3614	.9781	.2079	4.7046	.2126	4.810	1.022
79°	1.3788	.9816	.1908	5.1446	.1944	5.241	1.019
80°	1.3963	.9848	.1736	5.6713	.1763	5.759	1.015
81°	1.4137	.9877	.1564	6.3138	.1584	6.392	1.012
82°	1.4312	.9903	.1392	7.1154	.1405	7.185	1.010
83°	1.4486	.9925	.1219	8.1443	.1228	8.206	1.008
84°	1.4661	.9945	.1045	9.5144	.1051	9.567	1.006
85°	1.4835	.9962	.0872	11.4301	.0875	11.47	1.004
86°	1.5010	.9976	.0698	14.3007	.0699	14.34	1.002
87°	1.5184	.9986	.0523	19.0811	.0524	19.11	1.001
88°	1.5359	.9994	.0349	28.6363	.0349	28.65	1.001
89°	1.5533	.9998	.0175	57.2900	.0175	57.30	1.000
90°	1.5708	1.0000	.0000	undefined	.0000	undefined	1.000

THE LOGARITHMIC FUNCTION TO BASE 10

	0	1	2	3	4	5	6	7	8	9
10	0000	0043	0086	0128	0170	0212	0253	0294	0334	0374
11	0414	0453	0492	0531	0569	0607	0645	0682	0719	0755
12	0792	0828	0864	0899	0934	0969	1004	1038	1072	1106
13	1139	1173	1206	1239	1271	1303	1335	1367	1399	1430
14	1461	1492	1523	1553	1584	1614	1644	1673	1703	1732
15	1761	1790	1818	1847	1875	1903	1931	1959	1987	2014
16	2041	2068	2095	2122	2148	2175	2201	2227	2253	2279
17	2304	2330	2355	2380	2405	2430	2455	2480	2504	2529
18	2553	2577	2601	2625	2648	2672	2695	2718	2742	2765
19	2788	2810	2833	2856	2878	2900	2923	2945	2967	2989
20	3010	3032	3054	3075	3096	3118	3139	3160	3181	3201
21	3222	3243	3263	3284	3304	3324	3345	3365	3385	3404
22	3424	3444	3464	3483	3502	3522	3541	3560	3579	3598
23	3617	3636	3655	3674	3692	3711	3729	3747	3766	3784
24	3802	3820	3838	3856	3874	3892	3909	3927	3945	3962
25	3979	3997	4014	4031	4048	4065	4082	4099	4116	4133
26	4150	4166	4183	4200	4216	4232	4249	4265	4281	4298
27	4314	4330	4346	4362	4378	4393	4409	4425	4440	4456
28	4472	4487	4502	4518	4533	4548	4564	4579	4594	4609
29	4624	4639	4654	4669	4683	4698	4713	4728	4742	4757
30	4771	4786	4800	4814	4829	4843	4857	4871	4886	4900
31	4914	4928	4942	4955	4969	4983	4997	5011	5024	5038
32	5051	5065	5079	5092	5105	5119	5132	5145	5159	5172
33	5185	5198	5211	5224	5237	5250	5263	5276	5289	5302
34	5315	5328	5340	5353	5366	5378	5391	5403	5416	5428
35	5441	5453	5465	5478	5490	5502	5514	5527	5539	5551
36	5563	5575	5587	5599	5611	5623	5635	5647	5658	5670
37	5682	5694	5705	5717	5729	5740	5752	5763	5775	5786
38	5798	5809	5821	5832	5843	5855	5866	5877	5888	5899
39	5911	5922	5933	5944	5955	5966	5977	5988	5999	6010
40	6021	6031	6042	6053	6064	6075	6085	6096	6107	6117
41	6128	6138	6149	6160	6170	6180	6191	6201	6212	6222
42	6232	6243	6253	6263	6274	6284	6294	6304	6314	6325
43	6335	6345	6355	6365	6375	6385	6395	6405	6415	6425
44	6435	6444	6454	6464	6474	6484	6493	6503	6513	6522
45	6532	6542	6551	6561	6571	6580	6590	6599	6609	6618
46	6628	6637	6646	6656	6665	6675	6684	6693	6702	6712
47	6721	6730	6739	6749	6758	6767	6776	6785	6794	6803
48	6812	6821	6830	6839	6848	6857	6866	6875	6884	6893
49	6902	6911	6920	6928	6937	6946	6955	6964	6972	6981
50	6990	6998	7007	7016	7024	7033	7042	7050	7059	7067
51	7076	7084	7093	7101	7110	7118	7126	7135	7143	7152
52	7160	7168	7177	7185	7193	7202	7210	7218	7226	7235
53	7243	7251	7259	7267	7275	7284	7292	7300	7308	7316
54	7324	7332	7340	7348	7356	7364	7372	7380	7388	7396

THE LOGARITHMIC FUNCTION TO BASE 10

	0	1	2	3	4	5	6	7	8	9
55	7404	7412	7419	7427	7435	7443	7451	7459	7466	7474
56	7482	7490	7497	7505	7513	7520	7528	7536	7543	7551
57	7559	7566	7574	7582	7589	7597	7604	7612	7619	7627
58	7634	7642	7649	7657	7664	7672	7679	7686	7694	7701
59	7709	7716	7723	7731	7738	7745	7752	7760	7767	7774
60	7782	7789	7796	7803	7810	7818	7825	7832	7839	7846
61	7853	7860	7868	7875	7882	7889	7896	7903	7910	7917
62	7924	7931	7938	7945	7952	7959	7966	7973	7980	7987
63	7993	8000	8007	8014	8021	8028	8035	8041	8048	8055
64	8062	8069	8075	8082	8089	8096	8102	8109	8116	8122
65	8129	8136	8142	8149	8156	8162	8169	8176	8182	8189
66	8195	8202	8209	8215	8222	8228	8235	8241	8248	8254
67	8261	8267	8274	8280	8287	8293	8299	8306	8312	8319
68	8325	8331	8338	8344	8351	8357	8363	8370	8376	8382
69	8388	8395	8401	8407	8414	8420	8426	8432	8439	8445
70	8451	8457	8463	8470	8476	8482	8488	8494	8500	8506
71	8513	8519	8525	8531	8537	8543	8549	8555	8561	8567
72	8573	8579	8585	8591	8597	8603	8609	8615	8621	8627
73	8633	8639	8645	8651	8657	8663	8669	8675	8681	8686
74	8692	8698	8704	8710	8716	8722	8727	8733	8739	8745
75	8751	8756	8762	8768	8774	8779	8785	8791	8797	8802
76	8808	8814	8820	8825	8831	8837	8842	8848	8854	8859
77	8865	8871	8876	8882	8887	8893	8899	8904	8910	8915
78	8921	8927	8932	8938	8943	8949	8954	8960	8965	8971
79	8976	8982	8987	8993	8998	9004	9009	9015	9020	9025
80	9031	9036	9042	9047	9053	9058	9063	9069	9074	9079
81	9085	9090	9096	9101	9106	9112	9117	9122	9128	9133
82	9138	9143	9149	9154	9159	9165	9170	9175	9180	9186
83	9191	9196	9201	9206	9212	9217	9222	9227	9232	9238
84	9243	9248	9253	9258	9263	9269	9274	9279	9284	9289
85	9294	9299	9304	9309	9315	9320	9325	9330	9335	9340
86	9345	9350	9355	9360	9365	9370	9375	9380	9385	9390
87	9395	9400	9405	9410	9415	9420	9425	9430	9435	9440
88	9445	9450	9455	9460	9465	9469	9474	9479	9484	9489
89	9494	9499	9504	9509	9513	9518	9523	9528	9533	9538
90	9542	9547	9552	9557	9562	9566	9571	9576	9581	9586
91	9590	9595	9600	9605	9609	9614	9619	9624	9628	9633
92	9638	9643	9647	9652	9657	9661	9666	9671	9675	9680
93	9685	9689	9694	9699	9703	9708	9713	9717	9722	9727
94	9731	9736	9741	9745	9750	9754	9759	9763	9768	9773
95	9777	9782	9786	9791	9795	9800	9805	9809	9814	9818
96	9823	9827	9832	9836	9841	9845	9850	9854	9859	9863
97	9868	9872	9877	9881	9886	9890	9894	9899	9903	9908
98	9912	9917	9921	9926	9930	9934	9939	9943	9948	9952
99	9956	9961	9965	9969	9974	9978	9983	9987	9991	9996

THE EXPONENTIAL FUNCTION TO BASE 10

	0	1	2	3	4	5	6	7	8	9
.00	1000	1002	1005	1007	1009	1012	1014	1016	1019	1021
.01	1023	1026	1028	1030	1033	1035	1038	1040	1042	1045
.02	1047	1050	1052	1054	1057	1059	1062	1064	1067	1069
.03	1072	1074	1076	1079	1081	1084	1086	1089	1091	1094
.04	1096	1099	1102	1104	1107	1109	1112	1114	1117	1119
.05	1122	1125	1127	1130	1132	1135	1138	1140	1143	1146
.06	1148	1151	1153	1156	1159	1161	1164	1167	1169	1172
.07	1175	1178	1180	1183	1186	1189	1191	1194	1197	1199
.08	1202	1205	1208	1211	1213	1216	1219	1222	1225	1227
.09	1230	1233	1236	1239	1242	1245	1247	1250	1253	1256
.10	1259	1262	1265	1268	1271	1274	1276	1279	1282	1285
.11	1288	1291	1294	1297	1300	1303	1306	1309	1312	1315
.12	1318	1321	1324	1327	1330	1334	1337	1340	1343	1346
.13	1349	1352	1355	1358	1361	1365	1368	1371	1374	1377
.14	1380	1384	1387	1390	1393	1396	1400	1403	1406	1409
.15	1413	1416	1419	1422	1426	1429	1432	1435	1439	1442
.16	1445	1449	1452	1455	1459	1462	1466	1469	1472	1476
.17	1479	1483	1486	1489	1493	1496	1500	1503	1507	1510
.18	1514	1517	1521	1524	1528	1531	1535	1538	1542	1545
.19	1549	1552	1556	1560	1563	1567	1570	1574	1578	1581
.20	1585	1589	1592	1596	1600	1603	1607	1611	1614	1618
.21	1622	1626	1629	1633	1637	1641	1644	1648	1652	1656
.22	1660	1663	1667	1671	1675	1679	1683	1687	1690	1694
.23	1698	1702	1706	1710	1714	1718	1722	1726	1730	1734
.24	1738	1742	1746	1750	1754	1758	1762	1766	1770	1774
.25	1778	1782	1786	1791	1795	1799	1803	1807	1811	1816
.26	1820	1824	1828	1832	1837	1841	1845	1849	1854	1858
.27	1862	1866	1871	1875	1879	1884	1888	1892	1897	1901
.28	1905	1910	1914	1919	1923	1928	1932	1936	1941	1945
.29	1950	1954	1959	1963	1968	1972	1977	1982	1986	1991
.30	1995	2000	2004	2009	2014	2018	2023	2028	2032	2037
.31	2042	2046	2051	2056	2061	2065	2070	2075	2080	2084
.32	2089	2094	2099	2104	2109	2113	2118	2123	2128	2133
.33	2138	2143	2148	2153	2158	2163	2168	2173	2178	2183
.34	2188	2193	2198	2203	2208	2213	2218	2223	2228	2234
.35	2239	2244	2249	2254	2259	2265	2270	2275	2280	2286
.36	2291	2296	2301	2307	2312	2317	2323	2328	2333	2339
.37	2344	2350	2355	2360	2366	2371	2377	2382	2388	2393
.38	2399	2404	2410	2415	2421	2427	2432	2438	2443	2449
.39	2455	2460	2466	2472	2477	2483	2489	2495	2500	2506
.40	2512	2518	2523	2529	2535	2541	2547	2553	2559	2564
.41	2570	2576	2582	2588	2594	2600	2606	2612	2618	2624
.42	2630	2636	2642	2649	2655	2661	2667	2673	2679	2685
.43	2692	2698	2704	2710	2716	2723	2729	2735	2742	2748
.44	2754	2761	2767	2773	2780	2786	2793	2799	2805	2812
.45	2818	2825	2831	2838	2844	2851	2858	2864	2871	2877
.46	2884	2891	2897	2904	2911	2917	2924	2931	2938	2944
.47	2951	2958	2965	2972	2979	2985	2992	2999	3006	3013
.48	3020	3027	3034	3041	3048	3055	3062	3069	3076	3083
.49	3090	3097	3105	3112	3119	3126	3133	3141	3148	3155

THE EXPONENTIAL FUNCTION TO BASE 10

	0	1	2	3	4	5	6	7	8	9
.50	3162	3170	3177	3184	3192	3199	3206	3214	3221	3228
.51	3236	3243	3251	3258	3266	3273	3281	3289	3296	3304
.52	3311	3319	3327	3334	3342	3350	3357	3365	3373	3381
.53	3388	3396	3404	3412	3420	3428	3436	3443	3451	3459
.54	3467	3475	3483	3491	3499	3508	3516	3524	3532	3540
.55	3548	3556	3565	3573	3581	3589	3597	3606	3614	3622
.56	3631	3639	3648	3656	3664	3673	3681	3690	3698	3707
.57	3715	3724	3733	3741	3750	3758	3767	3776	3784	3793
.58	3802	3811	3819	3828	3837	3846	3855	3864	3873	3882
.59	3890	3899	3908	3917	3926	3936	3945	3954	3963	3972
.60	3981	3990	3999	4009	4018	4027	4036	4046	4055	4064
.61	4074	4083	4093	4102	4111	4121	4130	4140	4150	4159
.62	4169	4178	4188	4198	4207	4217	4227	4236	4246	4256
.63	4266	4276	4285	4295	4305	4315	4325	4335	4345	4355
.64	4365	4375	4385	4395	4406	4416	4426	4436	4446	4457
.65	4467	4477	4487	4498	4508	4519	4529	4539	4550	4560
.66	4571	4581	4592	4603	4613	4624	4634	4645	4656	4667
.67	4677	4688	4699	4710	4721	4732	4742	4753	4764	4775
.68	4786	4797	4808	4819	4831	4842	4853	4864	4875	4887
.69	4898	4909	4920	4932	4943	4955	4966	4977	4989	5000
.70	5012	5023	5035	5047	5058	5070	5082	5093	5105	5117
.71	5129	5140	5152	5164	5176	5188	5200	5212	5224	5236
.72	5248	5260	5272	5284	5297	5309	5321	5333	5346	5358
.73	5370	5383	5395	5408	5420	5433	5445	5458	5470	5483
.74	5495	5508	5521	5534	5546	5559	5572	5585	5598	5610
.75	5623	5636	5649	5662	5675	5689	5702	5715	5728	5741
.76	5754	5768	5781	5794	5808	5821	5834	5848	5861	5875
.77	5888	5902	5916	5929	5943	5957	5970	5984	5998	6012
.78	6026	6039	6053	6067	6081	6095	6109	6124	6138	6152
.79	6166	6180	6194	6209	6223	6237	6252	6266	6281	6295
.80	6310	6324	6339	6353	6368	6383	6397	6412	6427	6442
.81	6457	6471	6486	6501	6516	6531	6546	6561	6577	6592
.82	6607	6622	6637	6653	6668	6683	6699	6714	6730	6745
.83	6761	6776	6792	6808	6823	6839	6855	6871	6887	6902
.84	6918	6934	6950	6966	6982	6998	7015	7031	7047	7063
.85	7079	7096	7112	7129	7145	7161	7178	7194	7211	7228
.86	7244	7261	7278	7295	7311	7328	7345	7362	7379	7396
.87	7413	7430	7447	7464	7482	7499	7516	7534	7551	7568
.88	7586	7603	7621	7638	7656	7674	7691	7709	7727	7745
.89	7762	7780	7798	7816	7834	7852	7870	7889	7907	7925
.90	7943	7962	7980	7998	8017	8035	8054	8072	8091	8110
.91	8128	8147	8166	8185	8204	8222	8241	8260	8279	8299
.92	8318	8337	8356	8375	8395	8414	8433	8453	8472	8492
.93	8511	8531	8551	8570	8590	8610	8630	8650	8670	8690
.94	8710	8730	8750	8770	8790	8810	8831	8851	8872	8892
.95	8913	8933	8954	8974	8995	9016	9036	9057	9078	9099
.96	9120	9141	9162	9183	9204	9226	9247	9268	9290	9311
.97	9333	9354	9376	9397	9419	9441	9462	9484	9506	9528
.98	9550	9572	9594	9616	9638	9661	9683	9705	9727	9750
.99	9772	9795	9817	9840	9863	9886	9908	9931	9954	9977

THE LOGARITHMIC FUNCTION TO BASE e

This table contains logarithms of numbers from 1 to 10 to the base e. To obtain the natural logarithms of other numbers, use the formulas:

$$\ln (10^r\, N) = \ln N + \ln 10^r$$

$$\ln \left(\frac{N}{10^r}\right) = \ln N - \ln 10^r$$

$\ln 10\ = 2.302585$	$\ln 10^4 =\ \ 9.210340$
$\ln 10^2 = 4.605170$	$\ln 10^5 = 11.512925$
$\ln 10^3 = 6.907755$	$\ln 10^6 = 13.815511$

N	0	1	2	3	4	5	6	7	8	9
1.0	0.0 0000	0995	1980	2956	3922	4879	5827	6766	7696	8618
1.1	0.0 9531	*0436	*1333	*2222	*3103	*3976	*4842	*5700	*6551	*7395
1.2	0.1 8232	9062	9885	*0701	*1511	*2314	*3111	*3902	*4686	*5464
1.3	0.2 6236	7003	7763	8518	9267	*0010	*0748	*1481	*2208	*2930
1.4	0.3 3647	4359	5066	5767	6464	7156	7844	8526	9204	9878
1.5	0.4 0547	1211	1871	2527	3178	3825	4469	5108	5742	6373
1.6	0.4 7000	7623	8243	8858	9470	*0078	*0682	*1282	*1879	*2473
1.7	0.5 3063	3649	4232	4812	5389	5962	6531	7098	7661	8222
1.8	0.5 8779	9333	9884	*0432	*0977	*1519	*2078	*2594	*3127	*3658
1.9	0.6 4185	4710	5233	5752	6269	6783	7294	7803	8310	8813
2.0	0.6 9315	9813	*0310	*0804	*1295	*1784	*2271	*2755	*3237	*3716
2.1	0.7 4194	4669	5142	5612	6081	6547	7011	7473	7932	8390
2.2	0.7 8846	9299	9751	*0200	*0648	*1093	*1536	*1978	*2418	*2855
2.3	0.8 3291	3725	4157	4587	5015	5442	5866	6289	6710	7129
2.4	0.8 7547	7963	8377	8789	9200	9609	*0016	*0422	*0826	*1228
2.5	0.9 1629	2028	2426	2822	3216	3609	4001	4391	4779	5166
2.6	0.9 5551	5935	6317	6698	7078	7456	7833	8208	8582	8954
2.7	0.9 9325	9695	*0063	*0430	*0796	*1160	*1523	*1885	*2245	*2604
2.8	1.0 2962	3318	3674	4028	4380	4732	5082	5431	5779	6126
2.9	1.0 6471	6815	7158	7500	7841	8181	8519	8856	9192	9527
3.0	1.0 9861	*0194	*0526	*0856	*1186	*1514	*1841	*2168	*2493	*2817
3.1	1.1 3140	3462	3783	4103	4422	4740	5057	5373	5688	6002
3.2	1.1 6315	6627	6938	7248	7557	7865	8173	8479	8784	9089
3.3	1.1 9392	9695	9996	*0297	*0597	*0896	*1194	*1491	*1788	*2083
3.4	1.2 2378	2671	2964	3256	3547	3837	4127	4415	4703	4990
3.5	1.2 5276	5562	5846	6130	6413	6695	6976	7257	5736	7815
3.6	1.2 8093	8371	8647	8923	9198	9473	9746	*0019	*0291	*0563
3.7	1.3 0833	1103	1372	1641	1909	2176	2442	2708	2972	3237
3.8	1.3 3500	3763	4025	4286	4547	4807	5067	5325	5584	5841
3.9	1.3 6098	6354	6609	6864	7118	7372	7624	7877	8128	8379
4.0	1.3 8629	8879	9128	9377	9624	9872	*0118	*0364	*0610	*0854
4.1	1.4 1099	1342	1585	1828	2070	2311	2552	2792	3031	3270
4.2	1.4 3508	3746	3984	4220	4456	4692	4927	5161	5395	5629
4.3	1.4 5862	6094	6326	6557	6787	7018	7247	7476	7705	7933
4.4	1.4 8160	8387	8614	8840	9065	9290	9515	9739	9962	*0185
4.5	1.5 0408	0630	0851	1072	1293	1513	1732	1951	2170	2388
4.6	1.5 2606	2823	3039	3256	3471	3687	3902	4116	4330	4543
4.7	1.5 4756	4969	5181	5393	5604	5814	6025	6235	6444	6653
4.8	1.5 6862	7070	7277	7485	7691	7898	8104	8309	8515	8719
4.9	1.5 8924	9127	9331	9534	9737	9939	*0141	*0342	*0543	*0744
5.0	1.6 0944	1144	1343	1542	1741	1939	2137	2334	2531	2728

THE LOGARITHMIC FUNCTION TO BASE e

N	0	1	2	3	4	5	6	7	8	9
5.1	1.6 2924	3120	3315	3511	3705	3900	4094	4287	4481	4673
5.2	1.6 4866	5058	5250	5441	5632	5823	6013	6203	6393	6582
5.3	1.6 6771	6959	7147	7335	7523	7710	7896	8083	8269	8455
5.4	1.6 8640	8825	9010	9194	9378	9562	9745	9928	*0111	*0293
5.5	1.7 0475	0656	0838	1019	1199	1380	1560	1740	1919	2098
5.6	1.7 2277	2455	2633	2811	2988	3166	3342	3519	3695	3871
5.7	1.7 4047	4222	4397	4572	4746	4920	5094	5267	5440	5613
5.8	1.7 5786	5958	6130	6302	6473	6644	6815	6985	7156	7326
5.9	1.7 7495	7665	7843	8002	8171	8339	8507	8675	8842	9009
6.0	1.7 9176	9342	9509	9675	9840	*0006	*0171	*0336	*0500	*0665
6.1	1.8 0829	0993	1156	1319	1482	1645	1808	1970	2132	2294
6.2	1.8 2455	2616	2777	2938	3098	3258	3418	3578	3737	3896
6.3	1.8 4055	4214	4372	4530	4688	4845	5003	5160	5317	5473
6.4	1.8 5630	5786	5942	6097	6253	6408	6563	6718	6872	7026
6.5	1.8 7180	7334	7487	7641	7794	7947	8099	8251	8403	8555
6.6	1.8 8707	8858	9010	9160	9311	9462	9612	9762	9912	*0061
6.7	1.9 0211	0360	0509	0658	0806	0954	1102	1250	1398	1545
6.8	1.9 1692	1839	1986	2132	2279	2425	2571	2716	2862	3007
6.9	1.9 3152	3297	3442	3586	3730	3874	4018	4162	4305	4448
7.0	1.9 4591	4734	4876	5019	5161	5303	5445	5586	5727	5869
7.1	1.9 6009	6150	6291	6431	6571	6711	6851	6991	7130	7269
7.2	1.9 7408	7547	7685	7824	7962	8100	8238	8376	8513	8650
7.3	1.9 8787	8924	9061	9198	9334	9470	9606	9742	9877	*0013
7.4	2.0 0148	0283	0418	0553	0687	0821	0956	1089	1223	1357
7.5	2.0 1490	1624	1757	1890	2022	2155	2287	2419	2551	2683
7.6	2.0 2815	2946	3078	3209	3340	3471	3601	3732	3862	3992
7.7	2.0 4122	4252	4381	4511	4640	4769	4898	5027	5156	5284
7.8	2.0 5412	5540	5668	5796	5924	6051	6179	6306	6433	6560
7.9	2.0 6686	6813	6939	7065	7191	7317	7443	7568	7694	7819
8.0	2.0 7944	8069	8194	8318	8443	8567	8691	8815	8939	9063
8.1	2.0 9186	9310	9433	9556	9679	9802	9924	*0047	*0169	*0291
8.2	2.1 0413	0535	0657	0779	0900	1021	1142	1263	1384	1505
8.3	2.1 1626	1746	1866	1986	2106	2226	2346	2465	2585	2704
8.4	2.1 2823	2942	3061	3180	3298	3417	3535	3653	3771	3889
8.5	2.1 4007	4124	4242	4359	4476	4593	4710	4827	4943	5060
8.6	2.1 5176	5292	5409	5524	5640	5756	5871	5987	6102	6217
8.7	2.1 6332	6447	6562	6677	6791	6905	7020	7134	7248	7361
8.8	2.1 7475	7589	7702	7816	7929	8042	8155	8267	8380	8493
8.9	2.1 8605	8717	8830	8942	9054	9165	9277	9389	9500	9611
9.0	2.1 9722	9834	9944	*0055	*0166	*0276	*0387	*0497	*0607	*0717
9.1	2.2 0827	0937	1047	1157	1266	1375	1485	1594	1703	1812
9.2	2.2 1920	2029	2138	2246	2354	2462	2570	2678	2786	2894
9.3	2.2 3001	3109	3216	3324	3431	3538	3645	3751	3858	3965
9.4	2.2 4071	4177	4284	4390	4496	4601	4707	4813	4918	5024
9.5	2.2 5129	5234	5339	5444	5549	5654	5759	5863	5968	6072
9.6	2.2 6176	6280	6384	6488	6592	6696	6799	6903	7006	7109
9.7	2.2 7213	7316	7419	7521	7624	7727	7829	7932	8034	8136
9.8	2.2 8238	8340	8442	8544	8646	8747	8849	8950	9051	9152
9.9	2.2 9253	9354	9455	9556	9657	9757	9858	9958	*0058	*0158
10.0	2.3 0259	0358	0458	0558	0658	0757	0857	0956	1055	1154

THE EXPONENTIAL FUNCTION TO BASE e

For values of x not given in the table, the exponential function e^x may be found approximately by the use of a table of common logarithms in connection with the relation

$$\log e^x = 0.43429x.$$

x	e^x	e^{-x}	x	x	e^x	e^{-x}	x
0.0	1.0000	1.0000	0.0	3.3	27.113	.03688	3.3
0.1	1.1052	.90484	0.1	3.4	29.964	.03337	3.4
0.2	1.2214	.81873	0.2	3.5	33.115	.03020	3.5
0.3	1.3499	.74082	0.3	3.6	36.598	.02732	3.6
0.4	1.4918	.67032	0.4	3.7	40.447	.02472	3.7
0.5	1.6487	.60653	0.5	3.8	44.701	.02237	3.8
0.6	1.8221	.54881	0.6	3.9	49.402	.02024	3.9
0.7	2.0138	.49659	0.7	4.0	54.598	.01832	4.0
0.8	2.2255	.44933	0.8	4.1	60.340	.01657	4.1
0.9	2.4596	.40657	0.9	4.2	66.686	.01500	4.2
1.0	2.7183	.36788	1.0	4.3	73.700	.01357	4.3
1.1	3.0042	.33287	1.1	4.4	81.451	.01228	4.4
1.2	3.3201	.30119	1.2	4.5	90.017	.01111	4.5
1.3	3.6693	.27253	1.3	4.6	99.484	.01005	4.6
1.4	4.0552	.24660	1.4	4.7	109.95	.00910	4.7
1.5	4.4817	.22313	1.5	4.8	121.51	.00823	4.8
1.6	4.9530	.20190	1.6	4.9	134.29	.00745	4.9
1.7	5.4739	.18268	1.7	5.0	148.41	.00674	5.0
1.8	6.0496	.16530	1.8	5.1	164.02	.00610	5.1
1.9	6.6859	.14957	1.9	5.2	181.27	.00552	5.2
2.0	7.3891	.13534	2.0	5.3	200.34	.00499	5.3
2.1	8.1662	.12246	2.1	5.4	221.41	.00452	5.4
2.2	9.0250	.11080	2.2	5.5	244.69	.00409	5.5
2.3	9.9742	.10026	2.3	5.6	270.43	.00370	5.6
2.4	11.023	.09072	2.4	5.7	298.87	.00335	5.7
2.5	12.182	.08208	2.5	5.8	330.30	.00303	5.8
2.6	13.464	.07427	2.6	5.9	365.04	.00274	5.9
2.7	14.880	.06721	2.7	6.0	403.43	.00248	6.0
2.8	16.445	.06081	2.8	6.1	445.86	.00224	6.1
2.9	18.174	.05502	2.9	6.2	492.75	.00203	6.2
3.0	20.086	.04979	3.0	6.3	544.57	.00184	6.3
3.1	22.198	.04505	3.1	6.4	601.85	.00166	6.4
3.2	24.533	.04076	3.2	6.5	665.14	.00150	6.5

ANSWERS

Chapter 1

EXERCISE 1.1 (page 2)

1. (a) $2x - y + 1 = 0.$ (b) $2x - y - 2 = 0.$ (c) $2x - y + 5 = 0.$
(d) $2x - y - 7 = 0.$ (e) $2x - y + 1 = 0.$

2. (a) $2x - y - 1 = 0.$ (b) $3x + y - 9 = 0.$ (c) $x + 2y - 8 = 0.$
(d) $7x - 3y - 5 = 0.$ (e) $3x - 5y + 9 = 0.$ (f) $x - 2y + 4 = 0.$
(g) $x - 3y + 7 = 0.$ (h) $2x + y - 7 = 0.$ (i) $x + 3y - 11 = 0.$
(j) $5x + 3y - 19 = 0.$ (k) $\pi x + y - 3 - 2\pi = 0.$ (l) $\sqrt{2}x - y + 3 - 2\sqrt{2} = 0.$

3. Lines (a), (c);   lines (b), (g);   lines (e), (j);   lines (f), (h).

4. (a) 2.   (b) 0.   (c) 0.   (d) 7.   (e) $\frac{5}{2}$.   (f) Not defined.

5. (a) Lines (b), (c).   (b) Line (f).

EXERCISE 1.2 (page 4)

1. (a) 5.   (b) 3.   (c) 4.   (d) 0.   (e) -4.   (f) 1.

2. (a) 30.   (b) 40.   (c) 10.

3. (a) 2.   (b) 4.   (c) -38.   (d) $-\frac{4}{3}$.   (e) $\frac{8}{15}$.   (f) Not defined.

EXERCISE 1.3 (page 7)

1.

	(a)		(b)		(c)		(d)	
	$y = x^2$	Slope	$y = x^3$	Slope	$y = \dfrac{1}{x}$	Slope	$y = x^2 + 2x$	Slope
$x = 1$	1		1		1		3	
$x = 1.5$	2.25	2.5	3.375	4.75	$\frac{2}{3}$	$-\frac{2}{3}$	5.25	4.5
$x = 1.2$	1.44	2.2	1.728	3.64	$\frac{5}{6}$	$-\frac{5}{6}$	3.84	4.2
$x = 1.1$	1.21	2.1	1.331	3.31	$\frac{10}{11}$	$-\frac{10}{11}$	3.41	4.1
$x = 1.01$	1.0201	2.01	1.030301	3.0301	$\frac{100}{101}$	$-\frac{100}{101}$	3.0401	4.01
$x = 1.001$	1.002001	2.001	1.003003001	3.003001	$\frac{1000}{1001}$	$-\frac{1000}{1001}$	3.004001	4.001
Est. slope at $x = 1$		2		3		-1		4

2.

	(a)		(b)		(c)		(d)	
	$y = 4x^2$	Slope	$y = 2x^3$	Slope	$y = \dfrac{10}{x}$	Slope	$y = x + \dfrac{1}{x}$	Slope
$x = 3$	36		54		$\frac{10}{3}$		$\frac{10}{3}$	
$x = 2.5$	25	22	31.25	45.5	4.0	$-1.3\dot{3}$	2.9	$.86\dot{6}$
$x = 2.9$	33.64	23.6	48.778	52.22	3.4483	-1.15	3.24483	.885
$x = 2.95$	34.81	23.80	51.34475	53.105	3.3898	-1.13	3.28898	.887
$x = 2.99$	35.7604	23.96	53.461798	53.8202	3.3445	-1.12	3.32445	.888
Est. slope at $x = 3$		24		54		$-1.1\dot{1}$		$.88\dot{8}$

3.

	(a) $y = \dfrac{x^2}{5}$	Slope	(b) $y = \dfrac{x^3}{10}$	Slope	(c) $y = \dfrac{25}{x}$	Slope	(d) $y = 5x - 10$	Slope
$x = 5$	5		12.5		5		15	
$x = 5.5$	6.05	2.1	16.6375	8.275	4.5̇4̇5̇	$-.9091$	17.5	5
$x = 4.5$	4.05	1.9	9.1125	6.775	5.5̇5̇5̇	$-1.111̇$	12.5	5
$x = 5.1$	5.202	2.02	13.2651	7.651	4.9020	$-.980$	15.5	5
$x = 4.9$	4.802	1.98	11.7649	7.351	5.1020	-1.020	14.5	5
$x = 5.01$	5.02002	2.002	12.5751501	7.515	4.9900	-1.000	15.05	5
$x = 4.99$	4.98002	1.998	12.4251499	7.485	5.0100	-1.000	14.95	5
Est. slope at $x = 5$		2		7.5		-1.000		5

4.

	(a) $y = \dfrac{x^2}{5}$	Slope	(b) $y = \dfrac{x^3}{10}$	Slope	(c) $y = \dfrac{25}{x}$	Slope	(d) $y = 5x - 10$	Slope
$x = -2$	.8		$-.8$		-12.5		-20	
$x = -2.5$	1.25	$-.9$	-1.5625	1.525	-10	-5.0	-22.5	5
$x = -1.5$	.45	$-.7$	$-.3375$	.925	$-16.6̇$	$-8.3̇3̇$	-17.5	5
$x = -2.1$	.882	$-.82$	$-.9261$	1.261	-11.9048	-5.952	-20.5	5
$x = -1.9$	.722	$-.78$	$-.6859$	1.141	-13.1579	$-.6579$	-19.5	5
$x = -2.01$	.80802	$-.802$	$-.81206$	1.206	-12.4378	-6.22	-20.05	5
$x = -1.99$	.79202	$-.798$	$-.78806$	1.194	-12.5628	-6.28	-19.95	5
Est. slope at $x = -2$		$-.8$		1.2		-6.25		5

5. (a) 6. (b) -2. (c) -8. (d) 4.

EXERCISE 1.4 (page 9)

3. 4.999999999 and 5.000000001. **4.** (3.33333, 11.11108); (3.33334, 11.11115).

5. $[\pi - .00001, (\pi - .00001)^2]$; $[\pi + .00001, (\pi + .00001)^2]$; or (3.141, 9.866); (3.142, 9.872).

EXERCISE 1.5 (page 11)

1. (a) 4. (b) 6. **2.** $2x_1$.

3. (a) 20. (b) 1. (c) -10. (d) $2n$. (e) $\frac{1}{2}$. (f) -2.8.

4. (a) (4, 16). (b) $(-2.5, 6.25)$. (c) (.1, .01). (d) $(2n, 4n^2)$. (e) $(-.1\dot{6}, .02\dot{7})$. (f) $(-5 \times 10^7, 2.5 \times 10^{15})$.

5. $0 < |k| < (2x_1 \times 10^{-10} + 10^{-20})$; $0 < |l| < 10^{-10}$. **6.** $0 < |h| < 10^{-24}$.

EXERCISE 1.6 (page 14)

2. $2 - 2a$. **3.** $2ax_1$.

4. (a) $2x + 2$. (b) $12x - 5$. (c) $2x - 4$. (d) $6 - 2x$. (e) $2x - 7$. (f) $2x + 3$. (g) $8 - 6x$. (h) $-1 - 24x$. (i) $6x + 6$. (j) $4 - 8x$. (k) $10x + 10$. (l) $-12 + 6x$. (m) $2\pi x + \sqrt{2}$. (n) $\frac{2}{3}x - \frac{2}{3}$.

5. (a) 6; −4. (b) 19; −41. (c) 0; −10. (d) 2; 12. (e) −3; −13.
(f) 7; −3. (g) −4; 26. (h) −49; 71. (i) 18; −12. (j) −12; 28.
(k) 30; −20. (l) 0; −30. (m) $4\pi + \sqrt{2}$; $-6\pi + \sqrt{2}$. (n) $\frac{2}{3}$; $-2\frac{2}{3}$.

EXERCISE 1.7 (page 17)

1. $3ax^2$. **2.** $3ax^2 + 2bx + c$.

3. (a) $15x^2$. (b) $3x^2 - 4$. (c) $x^2/4$. (d) $x - x^2/2$. (e) $-9x^2$.
(f) $3 - 6x^2$. (g) $3x^2 - 4x + 1$.
(h) $6x^2 + 16x + 6$. (i) $3x^2 + 8x + 1$. (j) $3x^2$.

4. (a) 32. (b) 0. (c) 9. (d) 3. (e) −88. (f) 0.

EXERCISE 1.8 (page 19)

1. (a) Slope is negative, and the absolute value of the slope is large.
(b) Same as (a).

2. (a) $1 + 1/x^2$. (b) $2x - 2/x^2$. (c) $-1/x^2$. (d) $1 - 1/x^2$.

3.

	(a) $x = 1$	(b) $x = 3$	(c) $x = -1$	(d) $x = 100$
Eqn. 2 (a)	2	$1\frac{1}{9}$	2	$1\frac{1}{10000}$
Eqn. 2 (b)	0	$5\frac{7}{9}$	−4	$199\frac{4999}{5000}$
Eqn. 2 (c)	−1	$-\frac{1}{9}$	−1	$-\frac{1}{10000}$
Eqn. 2 (d)	0	$\frac{8}{9}$	0	$\frac{9999}{10000}$

4. The value of the derivative is zero at $x = 1$ and at $x = -1$.

EXERCISE 1.9 (page 21)

1. (a) $y = 4x - 4$. (b) $y = -6x - 9$.
2. (a) $y = 4x$. (b) $y = -2x - 3$.
3. (a) $y = 27x - 54$. (b) $y = 27x + 54$.
4. (a) $17x + 4y = 20$. (b) $15x - 4y + 12 = 0$.
5. (a) $y + 1 = 0$. (b) $36x - y = 81$.
6. (a) $8x - 4y = 17$. (b) $4x + 8y = 1$.
7. (a) $8x - y - 9 = 0$. (b) $6x - y - 6 = 0$.
8. (a) $y = 6x + 6$. (b) $1062x - 32y - 513 = 0$.
9. (a) $13x - 3y - 15 = 0$. (b) $777x - 27y + 485 = 0$.
10. $24x - 16y = 73$. **11.** $2x + y = 6/\sqrt{3}$; $2x + y = -6/\sqrt{3}$.
12. $2x - y + 8 = 0$; $54x - 27y - 40 = 0$.
13. $4x - 2y - 1 = 0$; $16x + 32y + 1 = 0$.
14. Points of intersection are $(+1, 0)$ and $(-1, 0)$. Slopes of tangents at $x = 1$ are 2 and −2. Slopes of tangents at $x = -1$ are −2 and 2.
15. Point of intersection is at $x = 1$. Slope of both curves at $x = 1$ is −1.

REVIEW EXERCISE 1 (page 23)

1. (a) 20. (b) 3. (c) −4. (d) 2. (e) 0. (f) 12.
2. (a) $20x - y = 15$. (b) $3x - y = 3$. (c) $4x + y = 0$.
(d) $2x - y = 5$. (e) $y = 0$. (f) $12x - y + 16 = 0$.

3. $2(2x - 1)$.

4. (a) $8x$.   (b) $15x^2$.   (c) $3 - 6x^2$.
    (d) $2 + 4/x^2$.   (e) $6x - 10$.   (f) $3x^2 + 4x + 1$.
    (g) $1 - 5/x^2$.   (h) $\frac{1}{5} + 2/5x^2$.   (i) $3x^2 - 6x$.
    (j) $1 + 3/x^2$.

5. $y + 2x = 0$; $6x - y = 12$; $3x - y + 3 = 0$.

6. $6x - y = 8$.   **7.** $8x - 4y = 1$.   **8.** $2x - y = 3$; $x + y = 6$.

9. $(1, 3)$; $\left(-\frac{5}{3}, \frac{337}{27}\right)$.

10. $\left(2, -\frac{28}{3}\right)$; $\left(-2, \frac{28}{3}\right)$; $\left(1, -\frac{26}{3}\right)$; $\left(-1, \frac{26}{3}\right)$.

Chapter 2

EXERCISE 2.1 (page 26)

1. (a) 52 m.p.h.   (b) 68.6 m.p.h.   (c) 56.1 m.p.h.   (d) 58.4 m.p.h.

2. (a) 3.75 m.p.h.   (b) 0 m.p.h.

3. 500 miles, 62.5 m.p.h.

4. (a) A-B, 300 m.p.h.; B-C, 750 m.p.h.; C-D, 800 m.p.h.; D-E, 720 m.p.h.;
     E-F, 450 m.p.h.   (b) 573 m.p.h.
    (d) Slopes are steeper for intervals where velocity was higher.

EXERCISE 2.2 (page 31)

1. 0-1, 80 ft/sec; 1-2, 48 ft/sec; 2-3, 16 ft/sec;
    3-4, -16 ft/sec; 4-5, -48 ft/sec; 5-6, -80 ft/sec.

2. 1.9-1.95, 34.40 ft/sec;   1.95-1.98, 33.33 ft/sec;   1.98-1.99, 32.00 ft/sec;
    1.99-2.0, 32.00 ft/sec;   2.0-2.01, 32 ft/sec;   2.01-2.02, 32.00 ft/sec;
    2.02-2.05, 30.67 ft/sec;   2.05-2.1, 29.60 ft/sec;   at 2.00, 32 ft/sec.

3. Near $t = 3$: 0 ft/sec, 1 ft/sec, 0 ft/sec, 0 ft/sec, -1 ft/sec, 0 ft/sec.
    Near $t = 5$: -64 ft/sec, -63 ft/sec, -64 ft/sec, -64 ft/sec, -65 ft/sec,
                -64 ft/sec.
    At $t = 3, v = 0$; at $t = 5, v = -64$ ft/sec.

4. Quadratic function; s increases when velocity is positive and decreases when
    velocity is negative; yes, at $t = 3.00$ sec.

5. 8.6 cm/sec, 25.3 cm/sec, 40.0 cm/sec, 52.4 cm/sec, 62.1 cm/sec,
    69.4 cm/sec, 74.8 cm/sec, 78.6 cm/sec, 81.2 cm/sec, 83.0 cm/sec.

6. 66.85 cm/sec, 68.25 cm/sec, 69.50 cm/sec, 70.75 cm/sec, 71.90 cm/sec.
    At $s = 230$ cm, $v = 70$ cm/sec.

7. 85.4 cm/sec, 86.3 cm/sec, 86.6 cm/sec, 86.8 cm/sec, 86.8 cm/sec, 86.8 cm/sec.
    Yes, it approaches an apparently constant value, $\{(t, s) \mid s \simeq 659.7 + 86t\}$.

EXERCISE 2.3 (page 35)

1. $v = 4t - 10$.
    (a) 4 ft, 0 ft, 0 ft, 4 ft, 12 ft.
    (b) -10 ft/sec, -6 ft/sec, -2 ft/sec, 2 ft/sec, 6 ft/sec, 10 ft/sec, 14 ft/sec.
    (c) -8 ft/sec, -4 ft/sec, 0 ft/sec.
    (d) Negative when $t < 2.5$; positive when $t > 2.5$.
    (e) When $t = 2.5$ sec.   (f) $s = -.5$ ft.

2. $v = 2t + 4$

   (a) 11 ft, 18 ft, 27 ft, 38 ft, 51 ft.

   (b) 4 ft/sec, 6 ft/sec, 8 ft/sec, 10 ft/sec, 12 ft/sec, 14 ft/sec, 16 ft/sec.

   (c) 5 ft/sec, 7 ft/sec, 9 ft/sec.

   (d) Positive for all values of $t \geq 0$.

   (e) Never for $t \geq 0$.   (f) No value.

4. (a) $v = 4 - 10t + 6t^2$.   (b) $v = 3t^2 + 4t + 3$.   (c) $v = 27 - 3t^2$.

5. (a) $v = 25/t^2$.   (b) $v = 4t + 4 + 6/t^2$.   (c) $v = 6t^2 - 24$.

   Velocity becomes 0 only in part (c) when $t = 2$.

6. (a) 13 ft/sec.   (b) 13 ft/sec.   (c) 13 ft/sec.

7. (a) 28 ft/sec.   (b) 28.5 ft/sec.   (c) 27.75 ft/sec.

8. In (6), s is quadratic in t; i.e., v is linear in t.

   In (7), s is cubic in t; i.e., v is quadratic in t.

EXERCISE 2.4 (page 39)

1. (a) $10 - 2t, 6, 0$.   (b) $2, 2, 2$.   (c) $1 - 4/t^2, 0, -\frac{7}{9}$.

   (d) $3(t - 1)^2, 12, 48$. (e) $3t^2 - 48, -36, 0$.

2. (a) $v = 2t - 2, a = 2, 2, 2$; negative direction to $t = 1$, then positive.

   (b) $v = 2t - 10, a = 2, -6, 2$; negative direction.

   (c) $v = 8 - 2t - 3t^2, a = -2 - 6t, -8, -14$; positive to $t = 4/3$, then negative.

   (d) $v = 5, a = 0, 5, 0$; positive direction.

   (e) $v = t^2 - 8t - 12, a = 2t - 8, -24, -4$, negative direction.

3. $v = 4 - 14t + 6t^2$; $a = 12t - 14$; $v = 0$ at $t = 1/3, 2$; $a = 0$ at $t = 7/6$; direction changes when $v = 0$.

4. $v = 6 - 2t$; $a = -2$; when $v = 0$, $t = 3$, $a = -2$, $s = 25$; larger than any other distance.

EXERCISE 2.5 (page 41)

1. Min value of $s = 12$; $v = 2t - 6$; $v = 0$ at $t = 3$; $s = 12$.

2. Max value of $s = 31$; $v = 4 - 8t$; $v = 0$ at $t = \frac{1}{2}$; $s = 31$.

3. Min value of $s = 13$; $v = 2t + 1$; $v \neq 0$ for $t \geq 0$.

4. Min value of $s = -3\frac{1}{3}$; $v = 6t + 1$; $v \neq 0$ for $t \geq 0$.

5. Min value of $s = 25$; $v = 24t - 60$; $v = 0$ at $t = \frac{5}{2}$; $s = 25$.

6. Min value of $s = -15$; $v = 12t + 1$; $v \neq 0$ for $t \geq 0$.

7. Min value of $s = 14\frac{11}{20}$; $v = 10t - 3$; $v = 0$ for $t = \frac{3}{10}$; $s = 14\frac{11}{20}$.

8. Min value of $s = 21\frac{3}{4}$; $v = 8t - 6$; $v = 0$ for $t = \frac{3}{4}$; $s = 21\frac{3}{4}$.

9. Max value of $s = 12\frac{3}{16}$; $v = 3 - 24t$; $v = 0$ for $t = \frac{1}{8}$; $s = 12\frac{3}{16}$.

10. Max value of $s = 16$; $v = -8 - 8t$; $v \neq 0$ for $t \geq 0$.

EXERCISE 2.6 (page 42)

1. -150 (min).   **2.** 5 (min).   **3.** 3 (max).   **4.** No solution.

5. 4 (min).   **6.** 18 (min).   **7.** 73 (max).   **8.** No solution.

9. $56\frac{2}{5}$ (min).   **10.** 0 (min).

EXERCISE 2.7   (page 45)

1. $v = 36 - 30t + 6t^2$; $t = 3$, $s = 37$ (min); $t = 2$, $s = 38$ (max).

2. $a = 12t - 30$; min velocity at $t = 2.5$ sec is -1.5 ft/sec; smallest value since v is a quadratic function.

3. $v = 2 - 14t + 12t^2$; $a = 24t - 14$; stationary points at $t = \frac{1}{6}$, $t = 1$; min velocity is $-\frac{25}{12}$ ft/sec.

4. $v = -15 + 8t - t^2$; $a = 8 - 2t$; $(3, 22)$, local min; $(5, 23\frac{1}{3})$, local max; yes, maximum when $t = 4$.

5. $v = t^2 - 29 + 100/t^2$; $t = 2$, $s = -105\frac{1}{3}$ (max); $t = 5$, $s = -123\frac{1}{3}$ (min).

6. $a = 2t - 14 + 72/t^2$; $t = 3$, $t = 6$.

REVIEW EXERCISE 2   (page 47)

1. 15, 18.75, 17.5, 11.25, 13.75, 17.5; 15.625 knots.

2.

	v	a	Time for max or min s	Value (s)	Time for max or min v	Value (v)
(a)	$2t - 7$	2	$3\frac{1}{2}$	$-\frac{1}{4}$ (min)	0	-7 (min)
(b)	$3t^2 - 12t$	$6t - 12$	$0, 4$	6(max), -26(min)	2	-12 (min)
(c)	$3t^2 - 4$	$6t$	$\frac{2}{3}\sqrt{3}$	$12 - \frac{16}{9}\sqrt{3}$ (min)	0	-4 (min)
(d)	$36/t^2 - 4$	$-72/t^3$	3	16 (max)	—	—
(e)	$3t^2 + 24/t^2$	$6t - 48/t^3$	—	—	—	—

3. (a) 626, 662, 674, 662, 626.   (b) 626, 662, 674, 662, 626, 650.
   (c) $600 + 60t - 12t^2$.   (d) 648, 672, 672, 648.
   (e) 627, 663, 675, 663, 627.   (f) Velocity falls continuously. in the interval.

4. (a) $60 - 24t$.   (b) $t = 2\frac{1}{2}$.   (c) v reaches maximum.
   (d) 675.   (e) v reaches a maximum in the interval.

5. (a) $v = 600 + 60t + 12t^2$; $a = 60 + 24t$.
   (b) Not in the domain specified for t.
   (c) Not possible since there is no maximum in the domain of t.

6. (a) $v = 2t - 2 - 8/t^2$.   (b) Minimum at $t = 2$.
   (c) Minimum value of $s = -3$; no maximum.   (d) Yes, at $t = \dfrac{1 + \sqrt{33}}{2}$
   and at $t = 1$.

Chapter 3

EXERCISE 3.1   (page 52)

1. (a) 1 (min).   (b) 5 (max).   (c) 6 (max), 2 (min).
   (d) -6 (max), $-6\frac{4}{27}$ (min).   (e) -5 (min), 27 (max).
   (f) 0 (max).   (g) -15 (min), 17 (max).   (h) No solution.
   (i) -4 (max), 4 (min).   (j) -5 (min), $\frac{17}{3}$ (min), $-\frac{19}{4}$ (max).

3. Max -7, min 1.   **4.** $x = 1$.   **5.** When $x > 0$, $y \geq 4$; when $x < 0$, $y \leq -4$.

EXERCISE 3.2 (page 53)

1. $6'' \times 6''$, 36 sq in.
2. $8'' \times 8''$, 32 in.
3. $4'' \times 4'' \times 4''$, 64 cu in.
4. 6 cm $\times$ 6 cm $\times$ 3 cm, 108 cu cm.
5. $54\sqrt[3]{9}$ sq in., $3\sqrt[3]{3}'' \times 3\sqrt[3]{3}'' \times 3\sqrt[3]{3}''$.
6. $\sqrt[3]{196} \times \sqrt[3]{196} \times \sqrt[3]{\frac{196}{2}}$, $(14 + 28\sqrt[3]{4})\sqrt[3]{14}$ sq in.
7. Square, $25' \times 25'$.
8. 450 sq ft, $15' \times 30'$.
9. $400, $200' \times 200'$
10. $r = 3''$, $h = 6''$, 169.56 cu in.
11. 54 sq in, $h/d = 4/\pi$.
12. $h/d = 6/\pi$; $27\sqrt[3]{12}$ or 61.8 cents.

EXERCISE 3.3 (page 56)

1. 8, 8.
2. 8, 4.
3. 3, 3
4. 8, 7.
5. $b = 8\sqrt{3}$, $d = 8\sqrt{6}$.
6. 10 ft.
7. July 25 or July 26.
8. 660 amps.
9. For a solution in the domain, he sells 230 refrigerators at $220 each, or 220 refrigerators at $230 each.

REVIEW EXERCISE 3 (page 58)

1. (a) -2.25 (min). (b) 12.125 (min). (c) 25 (max), -2 (min).
   (d) $4\sqrt{2}$ (min), $-4\sqrt{2}$ (max). (e) -2 (max), 6 (min).
   (f) $9[\frac{3}{2}\sqrt[3]{18} + 1]$ (min).
2. Yes, at $x = 1$; 0; because $D_x y$ is positive for $x > 1$ and for $x < 1$.
3. 3, 3.
4. 1.
5. 216 sq cm, $6 \times 6 \times 8$.
6. $15\sqrt{2} \times 20\sqrt{2}$, $120\sqrt{2}$ ft.
7. 5 ft.
8. $(5 + 6\sqrt[3]{4})$ dollars.
9. $\frac{7}{4}' \times \frac{7}{2}' \times 2'$.
10. $h : d = 5 : 2$.
11. 1750
12. 502, 500; 5.025¢.
13. February.
15. $50\sqrt{2}$ ft. on front, $100\sqrt{2}$ ft on side.
16. 50 stories, $126 million.

Chapter 4

EXERCISE 4.1 (page 61)

1. 5, 7, 9, 11, 13, 15.
2. 2, 5, 10, 17, 26, 37.
3. 1, 6, 15, 28, 45, 66.
4. $-1, 0, \frac{1}{3}, \frac{1}{2}, \frac{3}{5}, \frac{2}{3}$.
5. $\frac{3}{5}, \frac{2}{5}, \frac{1}{3}, \frac{3}{10}, \frac{7}{25}, \frac{4}{15}$.
6. 3, 7, 15, 31, 63, 127.
7. 1.
8. -18.
9. -1.
10. $1\frac{1}{81}$.
11. $f(n) = 2n$, $n \in N$.
12. $f(n) = 2^{3-n}$, $n \in N$.
13. $f(n) = \sqrt{3} \cdot 7^{(n-1)/2}$, $n \in N$.
14. $f(n) = \log 3^{n-1}$, $n \in N$.
15. $f(n) = (-1)^{n-1}$, $n \in N$.

EXERCISE 4.2 (page 64)

1. 2.
2. -1.
3. 1.
4. $-\frac{1}{2}$.
5. 1.
6. 0.
7. 4.
8. 3.
9. 1.5.
10. 5.5.
16. $n_0 = 401$.
17. $n_0 = 101$.

EXERCISE 4.3 (page 67)

1. $S_n = \frac{1}{30}[1 - (\frac{1}{10})^n]$; $S = \frac{1}{30}$.   **2.** $S_n = -\frac{1}{6}[1 - (-\frac{1}{2})^n]$; $S = -\frac{1}{6}$.

3. $S_n = 1 - (-2)^n$; no infinite sum.   **4.** $S_n = 6[1 - (\frac{1}{2})^n]$; $S = 6$.

5. $\frac{1}{2}$.   **6.** 10.   **7.** 19.   **8.** 13.

EXERCISE 4.4 (page 68)

1. Limit appears to be $\sqrt{2}$.

2. $a_3 = 1.4142$, $b_3 = 1.41422712$; $a_4 = 1.41421356$, $b_4 = 1.41421356$; no difference to eight digits.

3. A typical sequence is $a_1 = 1.8$, $b_1 = 1.66$; $a_2 = 1.73$, $b_2 = 1.7341$; $b_n \simeq 3/a_n$, $a_{n+1} = \frac{1}{2}(a_n + b_n)$.

4. (a) .000000005.   (b) .000000005.

EXERCISE 4.5 (page 70)

1. Polynomial   **2.** Algebraic.   **3.** Rational algebraic.

4. Polynomial.   **5.** Rational algebraic.   **6.** Non-algebraic.

7. Algebraic.   **8.** Algebraic.   **9.** Rational algebraic.

10. Algebraic.   **11.** Non-algebraic.   **12.** Non-algebraic.

13. Algebraic.   **14.** Rational algebraic.   **15.** Non-algebraic.

16. Algebraic.   **17.** Non-algebraic.   **18.** Polynomial.

EXERCISE 4.6 (page 73)

1. -4.   **2.** 6.   **3.** 0.   **4.** -2.   **5.** $1\frac{2}{3}$.

6. 0.   **7.** No limit.   **8.** 0.   **9.** $-\frac{2}{7}$.   **10.** 6.

11. -1.   **12.** 0.   **13.** 2π.   **14.** 6.

REVIEW EXERCISE 4 (page 77)

1. 11.   **2.** $1\frac{24}{25}$.   **3.** $3\frac{249}{250}$.   **4.** 82.   **5.** $\frac{1}{72}$.

6. No limit; 2; 4; no limit; 0.   **7.** 31.   **8.** 10.   **9.** $1\frac{1}{3}$.

10. $b_n \simeq 10/a_n$, $a_{n+1} = \frac{1}{2}(a_n + b_n)$.   **11.** Polynomial.   **12.** Rational algebraic.

13. Non-algebraic.   **14.** Algebraic.   **15.** Rational algebraic.

16. Non-algebraic.   **17.** $\frac{2}{3}$.   **18.** $\frac{1}{2}$.   **19.** -5.   **20.** 12.

Chapter 5

EXERCISE 5.1 (page 82)

1. 5.   **2.** 5.   **3.** $8x$.   **4.** $8x$.   **5.** $14x - 12$.

6. $11 - 4x$.   **7.** $2x - 2$.   **8.** $4x + 1$.   **9.** $3 - 2x$.   **10.** $6x^2 - 7$.

11. $-1 - 4x$.   **12.** $6x^2 + 10x$.   **13.** $6x - 2$.   **14.** $x^2 + 3$.   **15.** $x + 2$.

16. $2x^3 + 1$.   **17.** $3x^2 + x$.   **18.** $3x - 4x^3$.   **19.** $x^2 + 4x$.   **20.** $x^2 - x$.

21. $1 - x^2 + 2x$.   **22.** $x^4 + 9x^2$.   **23.** $2x + 3$.   **24.** $12x + 5$.   **25.** $3(x + 1)^2$.

26. $2(x-1)$.   **27.** $-2(1-x)$.   **28.** $6(1+2x)^2$.   **29.** $4x(x^2-1)$.

30. $-6x(4-x^2)^2$.   **31.** $6x^2(x^3+1)$.   **32.** $-24x^2(1-2x^3)^3$.

33. $-12x(1-3x^2)$.   **34.** $-18x(7-3x^2)^2$.   **35.** $x^{-1/2}-2x^{-1/3}$.

36. $3x^{1/2}+(2x)^{-1/2}$.   **37.** $-x^{-2}+\frac{3}{4}x^{-1/4}$.   **38.** $t^{-2/3}-\frac{5}{2}t^{3/2}$.

39. $6x^2+3-3x$.   **40.** $3x^2+\frac{1}{9}x^{-2/3}$.   **41.** $(2x)^{-1/2}+\frac{2}{3}x^{-2/3}$.

42. $8x^{5/3}-\frac{5}{4}x^{1/4}$.   **43.** $\frac{1}{2}\sqrt{3}\,x^{-1/2}+\frac{1}{6}\sqrt{3}\,x^{-1/2}$.   **44.** $3x^2-2x^{-3}$.

45. $1-\theta^{-2}-\theta^{-1/2}$.   **46.** $6x^{1/2}+2x^2$.   **47.** $2x+4x^{-5}$.

48. $4+15x^{-4}$.   **49.** $-2x^{-2}-3x^{-4}$.   **50.** $a-cx^{-2}$.

EXERCISE 5.2   (page 87)

1. $10(2x+1)^4$.   **2.** $-3(1-x)^2$.   **3.** $-4(3-x)^3$.

4. $7(x+6)^6$.   **5.** $-4x(6-x^2)$.   **6.** $4(x+1)(x^2+2x-1)$.

7. $2(3x^2-2)(x^3-2x)$.   **8.** $12x^2(x^3-1)^3$.   **9.** $-18x^2(4-2x^3)^2$.

10. $-8x^3(2-x^4)$.   **11.** $4(2-3x^2)(2x-x^3)^3$.   **12.** $-(x+1)^{-2}$.

13. $(1-x)^{-2}$.   **14.** $-4(2x+3)^{-3}$.   **15.** $(2x+3)^{-1/2}$.

16. $-\frac{3}{2}(2-3x)^{-1/2}$.   **17.** $-(2x+3)^{-3/2}$.   **18.** $4(3-2x)^{-3}$.

19. $2(3x^2-8x)(x^3-4x^2+5)$.   **20.** $3(3x^2-8x+5)(x^3-4x^2+5x+7)^2$.

21. $10-6t$.   **22.** $-720v^{-2}$.   **23.** $-1080v^{-5/2}$.

24. $-4(x+3)^{-2}$.   **25.** $3+4t$.   **26.** $\frac{3}{2}(3u-4)^{-1/2}$.

27. $-\frac{3}{2}(3u-4)^{-3/2}$.   **28.** $6u-15$.   **29.** $2-4t^{-2}$.

30. $-1.4v^{-2.4}$.   **31.** $x(x^2-1)^{-1/2}$.   **32.** $-x(1-x^2)^{-1/2}$.

33. $-x(25-x^2)^{-1/2}$.   **34.** $x(x^2-4)^{-1/2}$.   **35.** $3x(3x^2+5)^{-1/2}$.

36. $-3x(5-3x^2)^{-1/2}$.   **37.** $x(x^2+9)^{-1/2}$.   **38.** $-\frac{3}{2}x^2(27-x^3)^{-1/2}$.

39. $(x+1)(x^2+2x-3)^{-1/2}$.   **40.** $(3x-2)(3x^2-4x+5)^{-1/2}$.

41. $(2-3x)(5+4x-3x^2)^{-1/2}$.   **42.** $\frac{1}{2}(2x+3)(x^2+3x+5)^{-1/2}$.

43. $-x(x^2+1)^{-3/2}$.   **44.** $x(1-x^2)^{-3/2}$.   **45.** $5(1-x)(5x^2-10x+6)^{-3/2}$.

46. $-\frac{1}{2}(6x+1)(3x^2+x+4)^{-3/2}$.   **47.** $x(x^2+1)^{-1/2}$.

48. $x^2(x^3+8)^{-2/3}$.   **49.** $-x^2(x^3+1)^{-4/3}$.

50. $-\frac{1}{3}(9x^2+2)(3x^2+2x+1)^{-4/3}$.   **51.** $12x^2-6x+6$.

52. $-12x(1+4x^2)^{-5/2}$.   **53.** $2x^4(1-x^5)^{-7/5}$.   **54.** $-3t^2(1-2t^3)^{-1/2}$.

55. $\frac{8}{3}t(1+t^2)^{-1/3}$.   **56.** $20(3-2t)^{-3}$.   **57.** $10(1-t)(3t^2-6t)^{-4/3}$.

58. $4(t-3)(6t-t^2)^{-3/2}$.   **59.** $3t(2-t^3)(5t^2-t^5)^{-4/5}$.

60. $3(2x^2-x+1)(4x^3-3x^2+6x)^{-1/2}$.

EXERCISE 5.3 (page 91)

1. $(2x+4)(x^2-4x+3)+(2x-4)(x^2+4x+3)$.

2. $(4x+1)(x^3+x)+(3x^2+1)(2x^2+x-1)$.

3. $(3x^2+2)(x^2+5x-3)+(2x+5)(x^3+2x-1)$.

4. $-2x(4+6x+x^2)+(6+2x)(3-x^2)$.

5. $(5-6x)(2-3x^2-6x^3)+(-6x-18x^2)(5x-3x^2)$.

6. $(2x+1)(x^2+2)+2x^2(x+1)$.

7. $(x^2+2)(x^3+3)+2x(x+1)(x^3+3)+3x^2(x+1)(x^2+2)$.

8. $4(2x-1)(3x+4)^2+6(2x-1)^2(3x+4)$.

9. $4x(x^2 + 1)(x^3 + 8) + 3x^2(x^2 + 1)^2.$

10. $2(2x + 1)(x^2 + x)(2x + 5)^2 + 4(x^2 + x)^2(2x + 5).$

11. $9(3x + 2)^2(5 - x^2) - 2x(3x + 2)^3.$

12. $-(x^2 + 4)(2 + x)^{-2} + 2x(2 + x)^{-1}.$

13. $-2(x - 1)^{-3}(x + 4) + (x - 1)^{-2}.$

14. $-2(2x - 1)^{-2}(x + 2)^{-2} - 2(x + 2)^{-3}(2x - 1)^{-1}.$

15. $(1 - x^2)^{-1/2}(1 - 2x^2).$ **16.** $(x^2 + 2x)^{-1/2}(2x^2 + 6x + 3).$

17. $(x^2 - 5)^{-1/2}(6x^2 + x - 15).$ **18.** $(1 - 3t^2)^{-1/2}(30t^2 - 9t - 5).$

19. $3(3t^2 - 2t)^{-1/2}(10t^2 - 8t + 1).$

20. $-\frac{1}{2}(5t^2 + 3t + 1)^{-1/2}(20t^2 - 21t - 7).$

21. $\frac{1}{2}(3x + 5)^{-1/2}(15x^2 + 47x + 30).$

22. $-\frac{3}{2}(1 - 3x)^{-1/2}(3x^2 - 5)^{-1/2}(9x^2 - 2x - 5).$

23. $-\frac{1}{2}x(1 - x^2)^{-1/2}(1 + x^3)^{-1/2}(5x^3 - 3x + 2).$

24. $\frac{1}{2}(x^3 - 5)^{-1/2}(x^2 - 3x)^{-1/2}(5x^4 - 12x^3 - 10x + 15).$

25. $(x^2 - 2)^{-1/2}(3x + x^3)^{-2/3}(2x^4 + 2x^2 - 2).$

EXERCISE 5.4 (page 95)

1. $\dfrac{-2}{(5x + 6)^2}.$

2. $\dfrac{13}{(x + 5)^2}.$

3. $\dfrac{1 - 2x - x^2}{(x^2 + 1)^2}.$

4. $\dfrac{2x}{(x^2 + 1)^2}.$

5. $\dfrac{1 - 6x - 8x^2}{(2 + 5x + x^2)^2}.$

6. $\dfrac{30x^2 + 8x - 8}{(2x - x^2)^2}.$

7. $\dfrac{3x^2 + 10x + 3}{(1 - x^2)^2}.$

8. $\dfrac{9x^2 + 6x + 5}{(1 + 3x)^2}.$

9. $\dfrac{5t^2 - 2t + 10}{(5t - 1)^2}.$

10. $\dfrac{3(2t^3 + t^2 - 2)}{(1 + 3t)^2}.$

11. $\dfrac{-3x^4 - 3x^2 - 30x}{(3x^2 + 1)^2}.$

12. $\dfrac{-10 + 30t - 6t^2}{(5 - 3t^2)^2}.$

13. $\dfrac{x^4 - 10x^3 + 2x - 5}{(x^2 - 5x)^2}.$

14. $-(x^2 - 1)^{-3/2}.$

15. $-\frac{1}{2}x^{-3}(x - 1)^{-1/2}(3x - 4).$

16. $-(1 - x^2)^{-3/2}(x^3 - 2x + 1).$

17. $\frac{5}{2}(t^{-4})(5 - t)^{-1/2}(t - 6).$

18. $(x^2 - 6x)^{-3/2}(15 - 2x).$

19. $(1 + 3t^2)^{-1/2}(2t + 3)^{-2}(9t - 2).$

20. $x^{-3}(1 - 5x^2)^{-1/2}(5x^2 - 2).$

REVIEW EXERCISE 5 (page 96)

1. $3x^2 - 6x + \frac{3}{2}x^{-3/2}$ **2.** $1 - \frac{3}{2}x^{-3/2}$ **3.** $-x^{-3/2} + \frac{1}{3}\sqrt{3} + \frac{1}{4}\sqrt{2}\,x^{-1/2}.$

4. $-\frac{2}{3}x^{-4/3} - 9x^{-4}.$ **5.** $\frac{1}{2}(3x^3 + 5x - 4)^{-1/2}(9x^2 + 5).$

6. $\frac{1}{2}(3x + x^{-1})^{-1/2}(3 - x^{-2}).$ **7.** $\frac{3}{2}(3t - 6)^{-1/2} - (6 - 2t)^{-1/2}.$

8. $\frac{1}{2}(x^2 - 3x + 3)^{-1/2}(4x^2 - 11x + 9).$ **9.** $-\frac{1}{2}(1 - 3x - x^2)^{-1/2}(8x^2 + 24x + 5).$

10. $-\frac{2}{3}(x^3 - 2x)^{-2/3}(9x^3 - 3x^2 - 12x + 2).$

11. $-(1 - x^3)^{-2/3}(3x^4 + 2x^3 - 2x - 1).$

12. $-3x(3x^2 + 4)^{-2}(x^3 + 4x + 4).$ **13.** $(x^2 - 7x)^{-2}(x^2 - 4x + 14).$

14. $3(3t + 2)^{-2}(1 + 3t^2)^{-1/2}(2t - 1).$ **15.** $\frac{3}{2}(t - 3)^{-1/2}(2t + 1).$

16. $-\frac{5}{2}(3x + 5)^{-1/2}.$ **17.** $-\frac{1}{4}(1 - 5t)^{-1/2}(65t - 7).$

18. $-\frac{1}{2}(1 + t)^{-3/2}(2t - 1).$ **19.** $x(1 + 2x)^{-3/2}(3x + 2) + \frac{1}{2}(1 + 3x)^{-1/2}(9x + 2).$

20. $-\frac{1}{6}x^{-2}(1 + 3x)^{-3/2}(9x + 2).$

21. $\frac{3}{2}(x+6)^{-3/2}(x+12) + \frac{1}{2}(1+3x)^{-1/2}(9x+2)$.

22. $\frac{2}{3}x(2x^2-7)^{-2/3}(8x^2-21)$.   **23.** $-2(x-6)^{-2} - 3x^{-2}$.

24. $-(x^2+5)^{-3}(9x^2+8x-15)$.   **25.** $2(x^2+4)(3x+2)^{-3}(3x^2+4x-12)$.

26. $-2(2t+1)^{-1/2}(2t-1)^{-3/2}$.

27. $\frac{1}{6}x^{-2}(x+4)^{-3/2}(9x^3+71x^2-12x-32)$.

28. $-\frac{8}{3}x(x^2+2)^{-2/3}(x^2-2)^{-4/3}$.   **29.** $-\frac{5}{3}(4x-7)(2x^2-7x+5)^{-4/3}$.

30. $\frac{1}{2}(2-3t+t^2)^{-1/2}(4t^2+3t-14)$.

Chapter 6

EXERCISE 6.1   (page 100)

1. $D_x y = -1$.

2. $D_x y = \dfrac{2xy}{4y-x^2}$.

3. $D_x y = \dfrac{3y^2+4}{6y(y-x)}$.

4. $D_x y = \dfrac{3y+2x}{3y^2+2y-3x}$.

5. $D_x y = -\dfrac{x(y^2+1)}{y(x^2+3)}$.

6. $D_x y = \dfrac{2(2x^3+y^2)}{3y^2-4xy}$.

7. $D_x y = -x^{-1/2}y^{1/2}$.

8. $D_x y = -\dfrac{x^{-1/2}y^{3/2}+2a}{3x^{1/2}y^{1/2}+2b}$.

9. $D_x y = -x^{-1/3}y^{1/3}$.

10. $D_x y = \dfrac{a^2 y}{a^2 x + 2(x^2+y^2)^{3/2}}$.

11. $D_x y = \dfrac{9x^2-y^2}{2(xy+1)}$.

12. $D_x y = -\dfrac{2y(x+1)}{x^2+2x+2y}$.

13. $D_x y = \dfrac{y}{1-x}$.

14. $D_x y = -\dfrac{y(8x+y+3)}{x(4x+2y+3)}$.

15. $D_x y = \dfrac{-2c^2 x(b^4 x^2 + a^4 y^2)}{a^4 y(2c^2 x^2 + b^4)}$.

16. $D_x y = \dfrac{3(2y-3x)}{2(8y-3x)}$.

17. $D_x y = \dfrac{1-x^{-2}-y^2}{2xy}$.

18. $D_x y = -\dfrac{a^2(y^2+b^2)^{3/2}}{b^2 x^2 (x^2+a^2)^{1/2}}$.

19. $D_x y = -x^2/y^2$.

20. $D_x y = x/y$.

EXERCISE 6.2   (page 102)

1. $3x+4y=25$.   **2.** $16x+15y=100$.   **3.** $2x+y+8=0$.

4. $3x+2y+2=0$.   **5.** $2y=5x+20$.   **6.** $8x+7y+112=0$.

7. $x=3$.   **8.** $x=2$.   **9.** $9y=20x-4$.

10. $4y=x+6$.   **11.** $16y=3x+28$.   **12.** $2y=3-x$.

13. $y=1$.   **14.** $x+\sqrt{2}y=2$.   **15.** $16y=12-x$.

16. $x+2\sqrt{2}y=3$.   **17.** $y=\sqrt{2}(3x-2)$.   **18.** $y=4$.

EXERCISE 6.3   (page 104)

1. $xx_1/a^2 - yy_1/b^2 = 1$.   **2.** $yy_1 = 2a(x+x_1)$.   **3.** $x_1 y + xy_1 = 2k^2$.

4. $axx_1 + h(x_1 y + xy_1) + byy_1 = c$.

5. $axx_1 + h(xy_1 + x_1 y) + byy_1 + gx + fy = -c - gx_1 - fy_1$.

EXERCISE 6.4   (page 113)

	Stationary Points	Domain of x in which function is	
		Increasing	Decreasing
1.	$(-3, -6)$	$x > -3$	$x < -3$
2.	$(2, 9)$	$x < 2$	$x > 2$
3.	$(1, 14), (3, 10)$	$x < 1, x > 3$	$1 < x < 3$
4.	$(0, 0), (-3, -27)$	$x > -3$	$x < -3$
5.	$(1, 2), (-1, -2)$	$x < -1, x > 1, x \neq 0$	$-1 < x < 1, x \neq 0$
6.	None	$x > 1$	$x < 1$
7.	None	—	All x except $x = 1$
8.	None	—	All x except $x = 2$ and $x = -2$
9.	None	$x > 0$	$x < 0$

10. The derivative is not defined when $x = 0$ in (5), $x = 1$ in (7), $x = \pm 2$ in (8), and $x = 0$ in (9).   The graph has a cusp at $(1, 1)$ in (6), and at $(0, 0)$ in (9).

EXERCISE 6.5   (page 115)

1. $(0, 1)$.   **2.** $(\frac{2}{3}, \frac{65}{27})$.   **3.** $(0, 0), (-2, -16)$.   **4.** $(1, -1), (-2, -64)$.
5. None.   **6.** None.   **7.** None.   **8.** $(1, 3)$.
9. $(-1, 1)$ max, $(4, -124)$ min.   **10.** $(-2, -82)$ min, $(-6, -50)$ max.
11. $(2, 0)$ min, $(\frac{5}{2}, \frac{1}{16})$ max, $(3, 0)$ min.
13. $(-2, 12)$ min.   **14.** $(2, -4)$ max, $(0, 0)$ min.

EXERCISE 6.6   (page 118)

1. (a) $x = -1$. (b) $x = \frac{1}{2}$. (c) $x = 0$. (d) $x = 0$. (e) $x = 1$. (f) $x = 2, -2$.
2. (a) $y = 0$. (b) $y = 1$. (c) $y = 2$. (d) $y = 0$. (e) $y = 1$. (f) $y = 1$.

REVIEW EXERCISE 6   (page 120)

1. $\dfrac{3y - 2x}{8y - 3x}$.   **2.** $\dfrac{1 - x}{y - 1}$.   **3.** $x^{-1/2}y^{1/2}$.   **4.** $\dfrac{3(x + y - 1)^2 - 2x}{2y - 3(x + y - 1)^2}$.
5. $5x + 2y = 20$.   **6.** $7x + 4y = 56$.   **7.** $12y = 25x - 25$.
8. $25y + 2x = 14$.   **9.** $x = 2$.   **10.** $2x + y = 2$.
11. $(-2, -24)$ is a minimum point; $(1, 3)$ and $(-1, -13)$ are points of inflection.
12. $(0, 4)$ is a point of inflection.   **13.** Cusp at $(1, 1)$.
14. $(8, \frac{1}{16})$ is a maximum point; $(12, \frac{1}{18})$ is a point of inflection; function is not defined at $x = 0$.
15. $(3, \sqrt{3}/3)$ and $(3, -\sqrt{3}/3)$ are points of inflection.
16. $(3, -27)$ is a minimum point; $(0, 0)$ and $(2, -16)$ are points of inflection.

Chapter 7

EXERCISE 7.1   (page 122)

1. $a = \dfrac{20(1 - t^2)}{(1 + t^2)^2}$; max $v = 10$.   **2.** $v = \dfrac{5}{\sqrt{4 + t}}$; $a = \dfrac{-5}{2(\sqrt{4 + t})^3}$.

3. $a = 20t(1 + t^2)^{-1/2}$.   **4.** $\frac{16}{5}$.   **5.** $(5000)^2 5s/(5 + s)^3$.

7. $v = k/(2t^{1/2})$; $a = -k/(4t^{3/2})$.   **10.** $a = -k/2s^2$; max $s = ks_0/(k - v_0^2 s_0)$
from centre of earth; rocket never stops rising.

EXERCISE 7.2   (page 126)

1. $5/9\pi$ ft/min.   **2.** 30 cu ft/min.   **3.** $1/40\pi$ ft/min; $5/32\pi$ ft/min.
4. $\frac{2}{7}$ ft/min.   **5.** $50\pi/3$ cu ft/min; $20\pi/3$ sq ft/min.
6. $1/8(1 + d)$ ft/min; $\frac{3}{44}$ ft/min.   **7.** $1\frac{1}{2}$ ft/sec.   **8.** $5\frac{1}{3}$ m.p.h.
9. $2250\sqrt{10}$ ft/sec.   **10.** 20 knots.   **11.** 12,000 m.p.h.
12. 318 m.p.h.; 389 m.p.h.   **13.** 2.94 miles; 0 m.p.h.   **14.** 650 m.p.h.;
5.11 minutes before second plane reaches the airport.
15. 628.72 m.p.h.; 0 velocity.

EXERCISE 7.3   (page 130)

1. $\sqrt[3]{5b/2a}$.   **2.** $6\frac{2}{3}$ ft.   **3.** $(\sqrt{5} - 1)/2$.   **4.** $I = \sqrt{P_0}$.
5. $v = \frac{40}{3}$; $P_{max} = \frac{8000}{9}$.   **6.** $1600(5)^{-13/2}$.
7. \$21,600; 2 knots (6 knots relative to water).   **8.** 60 ft from A.

EXERCISE 7.4   (page 134)

1. 18 sq in.   **2.** 5 inches each.   **3.** 52.7 sq. ft.
4. 112 sq ft.   **5.** $4\sqrt{2}$.   **6.** 9.9.
7. $r = 2\sqrt{6}/3$ ft; $h = 4\sqrt{3}/3$ ft; $V_{max} = 32\pi\sqrt{3}/9$ cu ft.
8. $h = \frac{20}{3}$; radius of base $= 10\sqrt{2}/3$.   **9.** 9 nautical miles.
10. From factory 284.5 feet along the bank, and then across to power house.
11. To point on shore 2.268 miles from destination, and then walk.

REVIEW EXERCISE 7   (page 135)

1. $a = \frac{15}{2}t^2(1 + t^3)^{-1/2}$.   **2.** $v = 5000(t + 10)^{-2}$; $a = -10,000(t + 10)^{-3}$.
3. $a = 2s/\sqrt{2s^2 - 200}$.   **4.** $-1/(10\pi)$ ft/min.   **5.** 36 m.p.h.
6. 5.81 m.p.h.   **7.** (a) $a/2$; $ka^2/4$.   (b) $(a - b)/2$; $k(a + b)^2/4$.
8. $r = 6\sqrt{2}$ in; $h = 12$ in.   **9.** 698.5 yd from crossroads.
10. $\sqrt{3}\,x + \sqrt{2}\,y = 2\sqrt{3} + 3\sqrt{2}$.   **11.** $(-1, -5)$.

Chapter 8

EXERCISE 8.1   (page 141)

1. $y = \frac{1}{8}x^8$.   **2.** $y = \frac{1}{6}x^6 + \frac{1}{4}x^4$.   **3.** $s = \frac{1}{5}t^5 + \frac{2}{3}t^3$.   **4.** $v = \frac{1}{4}u^4 - \frac{5}{3}u^3$.
5. $y = \frac{9}{25}x^{5/3}$.   **6.** $y = x^{-2}$.   **7.** $y = \frac{1}{3}x^3$.   **8.** $y = \frac{2}{3}\sqrt{5x^3}$.

9. $y = \frac{1}{6}(2x+1)^3$.

10. $s = \frac{1}{6}(2+4t)^{3/2}$.

11. $F : x \to 2x^3 + 2x^4 + c$.

12. $F : x \to x^{2/3} + c$.

13. $F : x \to \frac{2}{7}x^{7/2} + x + c$.

14. $F : x \to \frac{3}{4}(x+2)^{4/3} + c$.

15. $G : x \to (3-x)^{-1} + c$.

16. $G : t \to \frac{1}{2}t^2 - t^{-1/3} + c$.

17. $y = \frac{2}{3}x^{3/2} + 2x^{1/2} + c$.

18. $y = -(x^2 + \frac{4}{3})x^{-3} + c$.

19. $s = \frac{1}{2}t^2 + \frac{8}{3}t^{3/2} + 4t + c$.

20. $v = \frac{1}{5}(t+1)^5 + c$.

21. $y = \frac{1}{4}x^4 + \frac{9}{2}x^2 + c$.

22. $y = \frac{1}{2}x^6 - 8x^3 + c$.

23. $y = \frac{1}{6}(x^3 + 2)^2 + c$.

24. $y = \frac{1}{3}(x^2 + 1)^{3/2} + c$.

25. $y = -\frac{1}{2}(x^2 + 1)^{-2} + c$.

EXERCISE 8.2   (page 145)

1. $y = \frac{2}{3}x + c$.

2. $y = 2x^2 + 2x + c$.

3. $y = \frac{1}{3}x^3 + c$.

4. $y = \frac{1}{4}(x+2)^4 + c$.

5. $y = \frac{1}{8}x^{-1} + c$.

6. $y = (x+1)^{-2} + c$.

7. $y = \frac{2}{3}x^{3/2} + x + c$.

8. $y = x^{1/2} + c$.

9. $y = -(25 - x^2)^{1/2} + c$.

10. $y = (x^2 - 25)^{1/2} + c$.

11.

	(a)	(b)	(c)
(1)	$y = \frac{2}{3}x$	$y = \frac{2}{3}x + \frac{1}{3}$	$y = \frac{2}{3}x + \frac{5}{3}$
(2)	$y = 2x^2 + 2x$	$y = 2x^2 + 2x - 37$	$y = 2x^2 + 2x + 1$
(3)	$y = \frac{1}{3}x^3$	$y = \frac{1}{3}x^3 - \frac{55}{3}$	$y = \frac{1}{3}x^3 + \frac{4}{3}$
(4)	$y = \frac{1}{4}(x+2)^4 - 4$	$y = \frac{1}{4}(x+2)^4 - 321$	$y = \frac{1}{4}(x+2)^4 + \frac{3}{4}$
(5)	no curve	$y = \frac{1}{8}x^{-1} + \frac{95}{32}$	$y = \frac{1}{8}x^{-1} + \frac{9}{8}$
(6)	$y = (x+1)^{-2} - 1$	$y = (x+1)^{-2} + \frac{74}{25}$	no curve
(7)	$y = \frac{2}{3}x^{3/2} + x$	$y = \frac{2}{3}x^{3/2} + x - \frac{19}{3}$	no curve
(8)	$y = x^{1/2}$	$y = x^{1/2} + 1$	no curve
(9)	$y = -(25 - x^2)^{1/2} + 5$	$y = -(25 - x^2)^{1/2} + 6$	$y = -(25 - x^2)^{1/2} + 1 + 2\sqrt{6}$
(10)	no curve	no curve	no curve

EXERCISE 8.3   (page 148)

1. $s = t^2 + t + 3$.

2. $s = \frac{1}{3}t^3 - t^2 + 3t + \frac{17}{3}$.

3. $s = t + 2t^{-1} + 1$.

4. $s = \frac{1}{3}t^3 - t^{-1} + \frac{5}{3}$.

5. $s = \frac{1}{3}t^3 - 2t^2 - 5t$.

6. $v = 18t^2 + 2t + 3$; $s = 6t^3 + t^2 + 3t$.

7. $v = t^3 - t^2 + 4t + 6$; $s = \frac{1}{4}t^4 - \frac{1}{3}t^3 + 2t^2 + 6t - \frac{47}{12}$.

8. $v = t + t^{-2} + 2$; $s = \frac{1}{2}t^2 + 2t + \frac{9}{2} - t^{-1}$.

9. $v = \frac{1}{3}t^3 - t^2 - 8t + 2$; $s = \frac{1}{12}t^4 - \frac{1}{3}t^3 - 4t^2 + 2t$.

10. $v = 10t - t^2$; $s = 5t^2 - \frac{1}{3}t^3$.

11. $v = 32t$; $s = 16t^2$.

12. 160 ft/sec.

13. $v = 40 - 32t$; $s = 40t - 16t^2$; max height 25 ft; returns to start at $t = 2\frac{1}{2}$ sec.

14. $v = 12t$; $s = 6t^2$.

15. $80\sqrt{10}$ ft/sec.

16. $v = 1000t - 5t^2$; $s = 500t^2 - \frac{5}{3}t^3$.

17. $12\frac{2}{3}$ ft.

18. $v = 2(t+1)^{1/2}$; $s = \frac{4}{3}(t+1)^{3/2} - \frac{4}{3}$; $9\frac{1}{3}$ ft.

19. 24 ft/sec; $90\frac{2}{3}$ ft.

20. 2000 ft/sec; 190,000 ft.

EXERCISE 8.4 (page 152)

2. $2\frac{1}{2}$.   **3.** 8.   **4.** $\frac{1}{2}$.   **5.** 16.   **6.** $13\frac{1}{3}$.   **7.** $13\frac{1}{3}$.
8. $26\frac{2}{3}$.   **9.** $10\frac{2}{3}$.   **10.** $2\frac{2}{3}$.   **11.** $1\frac{1}{6}$.   **12.** 16.   **13.** 2.
14. $5\frac{1}{3}$.   **15.** 218.   **16.** 15.   **17.** $\frac{1}{4}$.   **18.** 8.   **19.** $13\frac{1}{3}$.

EXERCISE 8.5 (page 156)

1. $2\frac{1}{2}$.   **2.** 2.   **3.** 2.   **4.** $6\frac{5}{6}$.   **5.** $9\frac{1}{4}$.   **6.** $7\frac{1}{3}$.   **7.** 2.
8. 3.   **9.** 4.   **10.** $21\frac{1}{3}$.   **11.** 1.   **12.** 8.   **13.** $6\sqrt[3]{4} - 4$.
14. $4\frac{2}{3}$.   **15.** $\frac{3}{4}$.   **16.** $\frac{3}{4}$.   **17.** $2\frac{13}{24}$.   **18.** $\frac{3}{4}$.   **19.** $13\frac{1}{2}$.   **20.** $16\frac{1}{2}$.

REVIEW EXERCISE 8 (page 157)

1. $y = \frac{1}{5}x^5 + c$.   **2.** $y = \frac{1}{3}x^3 - x^2 + c$.   **3.** $y = \frac{1}{3}(x + 1)^3 + c$.
4. $y = \frac{2}{3}x^{3/2} - 2x^{1/2} + c$.   **5.** $y = \frac{2}{3}(x + 2)^{3/2} + c$.   **6.** $y = -\frac{1}{2}(x - 1)^{-2} + c$.
7. $y = \frac{1}{8}(2x + 1)^4 + c$.   **8.** $y = -\frac{1}{3}(2 - x)^3 + c$.   **9.** $y = -\frac{1}{3}(1 - x^2)^{3/2} + c$.
10. $y = \frac{1}{2}(2x^2 + 1)^{1/2} + c$.   **11.** $F : x \to 2x^{1/2} + c$.
12. $F : x \to \frac{2}{5}x^{5/2} + c$.   **13.** $F : x \to c + x - \frac{1}{3}x^3$.
14. $F : x \to c + 2x - \frac{3}{2}x^2 + \frac{1}{3}x^3$.   **15.** $F : x \to \frac{1}{4}(x - 1)^4 + c$.
16. $F : x \to -\frac{1}{6}(1 - 2x)^3 + c$.   **17.** $F : x \to -(x + 2)^{-1} + c$.
18. $F : x \to (1 - x)^{-2} + c$.   **19.** $F : x \to (x^2 + 1)^{1/2} + c$.
20. $F : x \to \frac{1}{2}(1 - x^2)^{-1} + c$.   **21.** 36.   **22.** $64\frac{1}{4}$.   **23.** $\frac{1}{2}$.   **24.** $\frac{4}{9}$.   **25.** $4\sqrt{6}$.
26. $\frac{5}{11}$.   **27.** $17\frac{1}{3}$.   **28.** $71\frac{1}{4}$.   **29.** 19.   **30.** $\frac{4}{5}$.   **31.** $4y = x^4$.
32. $y = -(x + 2)^{-1} + 2$.   **33.** $y = \frac{1}{3}x^3 + x^2 - 3x + \frac{17}{3}$.
34. $y = (x^2 + 1)^{1/2} - \sqrt{5} - 1$.   **35.** $y = \frac{1}{2}x^2 + \frac{1}{2}x^{-2}$.   **36.** $v = 192 - 32t$.

37. $v = 100t + \frac{5}{2}t^2$; $s = 50t^2 + \frac{5}{6}t^3$.   **38.** (a) $640t^2 - \dfrac{64t^3}{3}$.

    (b) $\dfrac{256{,}000}{3}$ ft/sec.   (c) $\dfrac{640t^3}{3} - \dfrac{16t^4}{3}$.   (d) $\dfrac{2{,}560{,}000}{3}$ ft.

Chapter 9

EXERCISE 9.1 (page 161)

1. (a) $A_L = 6$; $A_U = 10$.   (b) $A_L = 7\frac{1}{2}$; $A_U = 8\frac{1}{2}$.   (c) 8.
2. $A_L = 25.78$; $A_U = 35.56$.   (b) $A_L = 32.94$; $A_U = 42.94$.   (c) 39.3.

EXERCISE 9.2 (page 165)

1. $4\frac{1}{2}$.   **2.** -2.   **3.** 64.   **4.** 6.   **5.** $6\frac{2}{3}$.   **6.** $226\frac{2}{15}$.   **7.** 4.   **8.** $2\frac{1}{3}$.
9. 60.   **10.** 0.   **11.** $13\frac{1}{3}$.   **12.** $217\frac{1}{15}$.

EXERCISE 9.3 (page 168)

1. $\frac{1}{6}x^6 + c$.   **2.** $-\frac{1}{3}x^{-3} + c$.   **3.** $\frac{2}{5}x^{5/2} + c$.   **4.** $\frac{2}{3}x^{3/2} + c$.   **5.** $2x^{1/2} + c$.
6. $-\frac{2}{3}x^{-3/2} + c$.   **7.** $x^3 + c$.   **8.** $x^{-4} + c$.   **9.** $x^{5/4} + c$.   **10.** $x^{-3/4} + c$.
11. $x^2 + x^4 + c$.

12. $\dfrac{x^2}{2} + \dfrac{1}{x} + c.$ **13.** $\dfrac{x^3}{3} - 2x^2 + 4x + c.$ **14.** $2x^4 + 12x^3 + 27x^2 + 27x + c.$

15. $-(x-2)^{-1} + c.$ **16.** $t + \frac{4}{3}t^{3/2} + \frac{1}{2}t^2 + c.$ **17.** $\frac{4}{9}(t+1)^{3/2} + c.$

18. $2(t+1)^{1/2} + c.$ **19.** $\frac{4}{3}(2t+2)^{3/2} + c.$ **20.** $-(1-3t)^{1/2} + c.$

21. $\frac{1}{2}(x^2+1)^2 + c.$ **22.** $\frac{1}{2}(x^3-1)^2 + c.$ **23.** $-(x^2+1)^{-1} + c.$

24. $-(x^3-1)^{-1} + c.$ **25.** $(x^2-1)^4 + c.$ **26.** $(x^4-1)^2 + c.$

27. $2(x^2+1)^{1/2} + c.$ **28.** $-(1-x^2)^{3/2} + c.$ **29.** $\frac{1}{3}(x^2-4)^{3/2} + c.$

30. $-\frac{1}{3}(4-x^2)^{3/2} + c.$

EXERCISE 9.4 (page 174)

1. $19\frac{1}{2}.$ **2.** $\frac{11}{6}.$ **3.** $\frac{1}{6}.$ **4.** $20\frac{5}{6}.$ **5.** $\frac{1}{6}.$

6. $10\frac{2}{3}.$ **7.** $\frac{1}{3}(92 - 64\sqrt{2}).$ **8.** $20\frac{5}{6}.$ **9.** $41\frac{2}{3}.$ **10.** $\frac{1}{6}(17\sqrt{17}).$

11. $36.$ **12.** $36.$ **13.** $5\frac{1}{3}.$ **14.** $21\frac{1}{3}.$ **15.** $2\frac{1}{4}.$

EXERCISE 9.5 (page 179)

1. $8\pi.$ **2.** $\frac{1024}{5}\pi.$ **3.** $\frac{128}{7}\pi.$ **4.** $\frac{81}{4}\pi.$ **5.** $\frac{500}{3}\pi.$ **6.** $48\pi.$ **7.** $64\pi.$

8. $\frac{512}{15}\pi.$ **9.** $\dfrac{1024\sqrt{2}}{45}\pi.$ **10.** $\frac{1024}{3}\pi.$ **11.** $30\pi.$ **12.** $\frac{992}{5}\pi.$ **13.** $\frac{32}{3}\pi.$

14. $\frac{6}{5}\pi.$ **15.** $\frac{250}{3}\pi.$ **16.** $\frac{52}{3}\pi.$ **17.** $\frac{50}{3}\pi.$ **18.** $\frac{100}{3}\pi.$ **19.** $\dfrac{4\pi r^3}{3}.$

20. $\dfrac{\pi r^2 h}{3}.$

EXERCISE 9.6 (page 183)

1. $\frac{1024}{5}\pi.$ **2.** $8\pi.$ **3.** $\frac{500}{3}\pi.$ **4.** $64\pi.$ **5.** $16\pi.$ **6.** $\frac{64}{3}\pi.$ **7.** $\frac{16}{3}\pi.$

8. $\dfrac{\pi}{6}.$ **9.** $\frac{2}{15}\pi.$ **10.** $\frac{3}{5}\pi.$ **11.** $\frac{4}{3}\pi.$ **12.** $\frac{8}{3}\pi.$ **13.** $\frac{2048}{15}\pi.$ **14.** $\frac{128}{3}\pi.$

15. $\frac{128}{3}\pi.$

EXERCISE 9.7 (page 189)

1. (a) $68.0.$ (b) $65.78.$ (c) $64.0.$ **2.** (a) $226.0.$ (b) $214.26.$

(c) $205.33.$ **3.** (a) $135.52.$ (b) $112.8.$ (c) $107.9.$ **4.** (a) $246.64.$

(b) $243.87.$ (c) $241.59.$ **5.** (a) $186.0.$ (b) $175.0.$ (c) $166.7.$

6. (a) $158.0.$ (b) $154.67.$ (c) $152.0.$ **7.** (a) $24.64.$ (b) $23.32.$

(c) $22.8.$ **8.** (a) $\pi(1 + \sqrt{2}).$ (b) $\frac{\pi}{3}(4 + 2\sqrt{3}).$ (c) $\frac{\pi}{3}(2 + 4\sqrt{2}).$

9. (a) $3912.79.$ (b) $3390.74.$ (c) $3156.28.$ **10.** (a) $13.51.$ (b) $13.58.$

(c) $13.63.$

REVIEW EXERCISE 9 (page 190)

1. $\frac{1}{5}x^5 + \frac{4}{3}x^3 + 4x + c.$ **2.** $\frac{1}{4}x^4 - x^{-1} + c.$ **3.** $\frac{2}{3}x^{3/2} - 2x^{1/2} + c.$

4. $\frac{1}{3}(x+1)^3 + c.$ **5.** $-\frac{1}{4}(1-x)^4 + c.$ **6.** $(4-x)^{-1} + c.$

7. $\frac{1}{4}(x^2+1)^2 + c.$ **8.** $-\frac{1}{2}(x^2+4)^{-1} + c.$ **9.** $\frac{1}{3}(x^2+16)^{3/2} + c.$

10. $(x-1)^{1/2} + c.$ **11.** $4\frac{1}{2}.$ **12.** $22\frac{1}{2}.$ **13.** $\frac{1}{6}.$ **14.** $\frac{32}{5}(28\sqrt{7} - 11\sqrt{11}).$

15. $1\frac{1}{3}$. **16.** $\frac{206}{15}\pi$. **17.** 8π. **18.** 12π. **19.** 12π. **20.** $\frac{15}{2}\pi$.
21. $\frac{206}{15}\pi$. **22.** (a) 4.76. (b) 4.75. **23.** (a) 761.48. (b) 761.07.
24. (a) .697. (b) .693. **25.** (a) 160.57. (b) 153.82.

Chapter 10

EXERCISE 10.1 (page 193)

1. .2558, .1046, .0525, .0267, .0114.
2. 1.1027, 1.0153, 1.0038, 1.0000, 1.0000.
3. 1. **4.** Limit does not exist. **5.** $\frac{1}{2}$. **6.** 0. **7.** 2. **8.** $\frac{4}{3}$. **9.** 1. **10.** 1.

EXERCISE 10.2 (page 195)

2. $\frac{1}{2}\cos\frac{1}{2}x$. **3.** $5\cos 5\theta$. **4.** $-3\sin 3x$. **5.** $-\frac{1}{4}\sin\frac{1}{4}\theta$.
6. $2\cos(2x+4)$. **7.** $\frac{1}{3}\cos\frac{1}{3}(t+2)$.
8. $-3\sin(3x-2)$. **9.** $-\frac{1}{2}\sin\frac{1}{4}(2t+1)$.
10. $2\cos 2x+\cos x$. **11.** $-3\sin 3x-5\sin 5x$. **12.** $-\csc x\cot x$.
13. $\sec x\tan x$. **14.** $2\sin x\cos x$. **15.** $-2\cos x\sin x$.
16. $3\sin^2 u\cos u$. **17.** $-4\cos^3 v\sin v$. **18.** $6\sin^2 2x\cos 2x$.
19. $-6\cos 3x\sin 3x$. **20.** $2\sec^2 2x$. **21.** $-\csc^2 x$.
22. $2x\cos(x^2)$. **23.** $-3x^2\sin(x^3)$. **24.** $2x\cos(x^2+1)$.
25. $-x^{-2}\cos(x^{-1})$. **26.** $-4t\sin(2t^2+1)$. **27.** $-2(s+1)\sin(s+1)^2$.
28. $(2x+2)\cos(x^2+2x+3)$. **29.** $-(4x-1)\sin(2x^2-x)$.
30. $x\cos x+\sin x$. **31.** $\cos x-x\sin x$.
32. $t^2\cos t+2t\sin t$. **33.** $2\theta\cos\theta-\theta^2\sin\theta$.
34. $\theta\cos(\theta+1)+\sin(\theta+1)$. **35.** $\cos(2s+3)-2s\sin(2s+3)$.
36. $2\sin(x+1)+(2x+1)\cos(x+1)$.
37. $3\sin(2x-1)+2(3x+4)\cos(2x-1)$.
38. $\cos(2x+1)-2(x+3)\sin(2x+1)$.
39. $\cos(3\theta-2)-3(\theta-2)\sin(3\theta-2)$.
40. $2x\sin(x^2+1)+2x(x^2+1)\cos(x^2+1)$.
41. $2(x+1)\sin(x^2+2x)+(x+1)^2(2x+2)\cos(x^2+2x)$.
42. $\sin(1-x)-(x+1)\cos(1-x)$. **43.** $(1-x)\cos(x+1)-\sin(x+1)$.
44. $\cos(2-3x)+3(x+2)\sin(2-3x)$.
45. $\cos(1-2x)+2(x-1)\sin(1-2x)$.
46. $\dfrac{(t+1)\cos t-\sin t}{(t+1)^2}$. **47.** $\dfrac{2(s+3)\cos(2s+1)-\sin(2s+1)}{(s+3)^2}$.
48. $\dfrac{-x\sin(x-3)-\cos(x-3)}{x^2}$.
49. $-2\left[\dfrac{(2x-1)\sin(2x-1)+\cos(2x-1)}{(2x-1)^2}\right]$.
50. $\dfrac{-2\sin\theta\sin 2\theta-\cos\theta\cos 2\theta}{\sin^2\theta}$. **51.** $\dfrac{2\cos x\cos 2x+\sin x\sin 2x}{\cos^2 x}$.

52. $\dfrac{-\sin 2x \sin(x+1) - 2\cos 2x \cos(x+1)}{\sin^2 2x}$.

53. $\dfrac{-\sin t \cos(1-t) - \cos t \sin(1-t)}{\sin^2 t}$.

54. $\frac{1}{2}x^{-1/2}\cos(x^{1/2}+2)$.   **55.** $\frac{1}{2}x^{-3/2}\sin(x^{-1/2}+1)$.

EXERCISE 10.3 (page 199)

1. $75\sqrt{3}$; $-75\sqrt{3}$.   **2.** $\pi/4$.   **3.** $\frac{1}{2}a^2$.   **4.** $\pi/6$.
5. $27\sqrt{3}$.   **6.** $18\sqrt{3}$.   **7.** $\pi/4$.   **9.** $\frac{3}{4}\sqrt{3}\,a$.   **10.** $(a^{2/3}+b^{2/3})^{3/2}$.

EXERCISE 10.4 (page 203)

1. $y = -\frac{1}{3}\cos 3x + c$.   **2.** $y = \frac{1}{4}\sin 4x + c$.   **3.** $y = -3\cos 2x + c$.
4. $y = \sin 5x + c$.   **5.** $y = \sin^2 x + c$.   **6.** $y = \frac{1}{2}\sin 2x + c$.
7. $y = -\frac{1}{3}\cos^3 x + c$.   **8.** $y = \frac{1}{5}\sin^5 x + c$.   **9.** $y = \frac{2}{3}(\sin x)^{3/2} + c$.
10. $y = -\frac{2}{5}(\cos x)^{5/2} + c$. **11.** $-\cos(x+1) + c$.   **12.** $\frac{1}{2}\sin(2x-3) + c$.
13. $2\sin(\frac{1}{2}x+1) + c$.   **14.** $-\frac{3}{2}\cos\frac{1}{3}(2x+1) + c$. **15.** $-\frac{1}{2}\cos(x^2) + c$.
16. $\frac{1}{2}\sin(x^2+2) + c$.   **17.** $\sin(x+1)^2 + c$.   **18.** $-\cos(x^2+3x) + c$.
19. $-\cos(x^2-x+6) + c$.   **20.** $\frac{1}{3}\sin(x^3+1) + c$.   **21.** $y = \frac{1}{3}\sin^3 x + c$.
22. $y = -\frac{1}{3}\cos^3 x + c$.   **23.** $y = (2\cos^2 x)^{-1} + c$.   **24.** $y = -\csc x + c$.
25. $y = \tan x + c$.   **26.** $y = \frac{1}{3}\cos^3 x - \cos x + c$.   **27.** $y = (1+\cos x)^{-1} + c$.
28. $y = (1-\sin x)^{-1} + c$.   **29.** $y = \sin x + c$.   **30.** $y = -\cos x - \frac{1}{2}\cos 2x + c$.

EXERCISE 10.5 (page 205)

1. $v = 5\cos 30t$; $a = -150\sin 30t$.
2. $v = 25.6\pi\cos 512\pi t$; $a = -13{,}107.2\pi^2\sin 512\pi t$.
3. $i = -\frac{1}{10}\sin 10^3 t$.   **4.** $q = 5 \times 10^{-6}(1 - \cos 10^4 t)$.   **5.** $\theta = \frac{1}{10}\sin \pi t$; $\frac{1}{10}$ radian.
6. $a = -3200\pi\sin 10\pi t$; $y = 32(\pi)^{-1}\sin 10\pi t$.   Maximum velocity 320 ft/sec; maximum displacement $32(\pi)^{-1}$ ft.

EXERCISE 10.6 (page 209)

1. 2.   **2.** 2.   **3.** 2π.   **4.** $\sqrt{3} - \dfrac{\pi}{3}$.   **5.** 3.   **6.** 4.   **7.** 8.   **8.** $\sqrt{2}$.

9. $\frac{3}{2}\sqrt{3}$.   **10.** $5\frac{1}{3}$.   **11.** $\dfrac{\pi^2}{8}$.   **12.** 2π.   **13.** 2π.   **14.** $\dfrac{\pi}{2}(3+\pi)$.
15. $\pi\sqrt{3}$.

REVIEW EXERCISE 10 (page 210)

1. 2.   **2.** 0.   **3.** 2.   **4.** 1.   **5.** $4\cos 4x$.
6. $-5\sin 5x$.   **7.** $-.25\sin .25x$.   **8.** $\pi\cos \pi x$.
9. $2\cos 2(x+\pi)$.   **10.** $-\pi\sin \pi(x+2)$.   **11.** $4\sin^3 x \cos x$.
12. $-3\cos^2 x \sin x$.   **13.** $-6\cos 3x \sin 3x$.   **14.** $6\sin^2 2x \cos 2x$.
15. $\cos x \cos 2x - 2\sin x \sin 2x$.   **16.** $3\cos x \cos 3x - \sin x \sin 3x$.
17. $3\sec^2 3x$.   **18.** $-2\csc^2 2x$.   **19.** $2x(\sin 2x + x\cos 2x)$.

20. $x^4(5\cos x - x \sin x)$. **21.** $2x^{-3}\sin x^{-2}$. **22.** $2x\cos(x^2+1)$.

23. $\dfrac{-2(x\sin 2x + \cos 2x)}{x^3}$. **24.** $\dfrac{3(x+1)\cos 3x - \sin 3x}{(x+1)^2}$.

25. $4x\cos(2x^2+1)$. **26.** $-2x\sin(x^2-4)$.

27. $\dfrac{\sin(x+2)\cos x - \sin x \cos(x+2)}{[\sin(x+2)]^2}$.

28. $\dfrac{2\sin(2x-1)\cos(2x+1) - 2\cos(2x-1)\sin(2x+1)}{[\cos(2x-1)]^2}$.

29. $x(x^2+1)^{-1/2}\cos(x^2+1)^{1/2}$. **30.** $-x(x^2-1)^{-1/2}\sin(x^2-1)^{1/2}$.

31. $\theta = \frac{1}{2}\alpha + \frac{1}{4}\pi$. **32.** 72 sq in.

33. $v = 4(120\pi)\cos 120\pi t$; $a = -4(120\pi)^2\sin 120\pi t$.

34. Maximum displacement values are 30 and -10; minimum displacement value is -15.

35. $-2\cos 3x + c$. **36.** $\sin^3 x + c$. **37.** $\frac{1}{2}\sin(x^2) + c$. **38.** $-\frac{1}{3}\cos(x^3+1) + c$.

39. $\frac{1}{6}(1 + 2\sin x)^3 + c$. **40.** $-(1 + \sin x)^{-1} + c$. **41.** $-\frac{1}{2}\cos(x^2 + 4x) + c$.

42. $\sec x + c$. **43.** $-\frac{2}{3}\cos^3 x + c$. **44.** $\sin x - \frac{1}{3}\sin^3 x + c$. **45.** $2\frac{2}{3}$.

46. $10\sqrt{2}$. **47.** 2π. **48.** 2π. **49.** $2\sqrt{3} - \frac{2}{3}\pi$. **50.** 4. **51.** 2π. **52.** π.

53. (a) $\dfrac{\pi}{4}(\sqrt{2}+1)$. (b) $\dfrac{\pi}{6}(2\sqrt{2}+1)$. **54.** (a) $\dfrac{\pi}{18}(9 + 4\sqrt{3})$.

  (b) $\dfrac{\pi}{27}(9 + 8\sqrt{3})$. **55.** (a) $\dfrac{\pi}{12}(3\sqrt{2}+4)$. (b) $\dfrac{2\pi}{9}(2\sqrt{2}+1)$.

Chapter 11

EXERCISE 11.3 (page 220)

1. x^{-1}. **2.** x^{-1}. **3.** $3x^{-1}$. **4.** $-2x^{-1}$. **5.** $2(5 + 2x)^{-1}$.

6. $(x-2)^{-1}$. **7.** $2(2x-3)^{-1}$. **8.** $3(3x-4)^{-1}$.

9. $3x^{-1}$. **10.** $-5x^{-1}$. **11.** $2x(x^2+1)^{-1}$.

12. $3x^2(x^3+8)^{-1}$. **13.** $2x(x^2+2)^{-1}$. **14.** $12x^2(4x^3-3)^{-1}$.

15. $(2x+2)(x^2+2x+3)^{-1}$. **16.** $(2x-6)(x^2-6x+5)^{-1}$.

17. $\frac{1}{2}(x+1)^{-1}$. **18.** $\frac{1}{2}(x-2)^{-1}$. **19.** $x(x^2+1)^{-1}$.

20. $\frac{3}{2}x^2(x^3-8)^{-1}$. **21.** $(x+1)(x^2+2x+3)^{-1}$.

22. $\frac{2}{3}(x-1)(x^2-2x)^{-1}$. **23.** $-\frac{2}{5}x(x^2+1)^{-1}$. **24.** $\frac{4}{3}(2x+3)^{-1}$.

25. $(2x+5)(x^2+5x+6)^{-1}$. **26.** $(4x+1)(2x^2+x-3)^{-1}$.

27. $(x+2)^{-1}(x+3)^{-1}$. **28.** $5(x-1)^{-1}(2x+3)^{-1}$.

29. $(x^2+2x-1)(x^2+1)^{-1}(x+1)^{-1}$. **30.** $(3x^2+2x+1)(x^2+1)^{-1}(x+1)^{-1}$.

31. $1 + \ln x$. **32.** $2(x+1)(2x+1)^{-1} + \ln(2x+1)$.

33. $2x(x+1)(x^2+1)^{-1} + \ln(x^2+1)$. **34.** $2x\ln(1-x^2) - 2x^3(1-x^2)^{-1}$.

35. $(1+x)^{1/2}(x+2)^{-1} + \frac{1}{2}(1+x)^{-1/2}\ln(x+2)$.

36. $(x+1) + 2(x+1)\ln(x+1)$. **37.** $2x(x^2+1)^{-2}[1 - \ln(x^2+1)]$.

38. $(2x+3)^2(x^2+3x)^{-1} + 2\ln(x^2+3x)$. **39.** $4x(x^2-1)^{-1}\ln(x^2-1)$.

40. $6x(x^2+1)^{-1}[\ln(x^2+1)]^2$. **41.** $\cot x$. **42.** $-\tan x$.

43. $2\cot x$. **44.** $2\tan x$. **45.** $\tan x$. **46.** $-\cot x$.

47. $x^{-1}\cos(\ln x)$. **48.** $-2x^{-1}\sin(\ln x^2)$. **49.** $2x^{-1}\sin(\ln x)\cos(\ln x)$.

50. $-3x^{-1}\sin(3\ln x)$.

EXERCISE 11.4 (page 224)

1. $3e^{3x}$.
2. $-2e^{-2x}$.
3. $2e^{2x+3}$.
4. $-3e^{4-3x}$.
5. $-e^{-(x+1)}$.
6. $2e^{2x-4}$.
7. $2xe^{x^2}$.
8. $-2xe^{-x^2}$.
9. $-3x^2e^{-x^3}$.
10. $5x^4e^{x^5}$.
11. $-2xe^{1-x^2}$.
12. $2xe^{1+x^2}$.
13. $4xe^{2x^2+8}$.
14. $6xe^{3x^2-9}$.
15. $2(x+1)e^{x^2+2x+1}$.
16. $2(x+1)e^{(x+1)^2}$.
17. $2(x-1)e^{x^2-2x-3}$.
18. $2(x-3)e^{5-6x+x^2}$.
19. $-3(x+1)^2e^{-(x+1)^3}$.
20. $2(1-x)e^{2x-x^2}$.
21. $-x^{-2}e^{1/x}$.
22. $-(x+1)^{-2}e^{(x+1)^{-1}}$.
23. $-2x(x^2+1)^{-2}e^{(x^2+1)^{-1}}$.
24. $-3x^2(x^3-1)^{-2}e^{(x^3-1)^{-1}}$.
25. $(1+x)e^x$.
26. $(2+x)xe^x$.
27. $2(1+x)xe^{2x}$.
28. $(x+2)e^x$.
29. $(2x^2+4x+3)e^{(x+1)^2}$.
30. $2(x^3-x^2+2x-1)e^{(x-1)^2}$.
31. $2(x-2)e^{x^2-4x+3}$.
32. $-(2x+1)e^{2-x-x^2}$.
33. $(x-1)x^{-2}e^x$.
34. $(x-2)x^{-3}e^x$.
35. $x(x+1)^{-2}e^{x+1}$.
36. $4x(2x+1)^{-2}e^{2x-1}$.
37. $\frac{1}{2}x^{-1/2}e^{x^{1/2}}$.
38. $2\pi xe^{\pi x^2}$.
39. $\pi^{-1}xe^{x^2/2}$.
40. $\frac{1}{3}e^{x-3}$.
41. $(x+2)^{-1}\log_{10}e$.
42. $2(2x-3)^{-1}\log_{10}e$.
43. $2x^{-1}\log_{10}e$.
44. $2x(x^2+1)^{-1}\log_{10}e$.
45. $(x+2)^{-1}\log_3 e$.
46. $2(2x+1)^{-1}\log_5 e$.
47. $(\ln x + x^{-1})e^x$.
48. $2[\ln(2x+1)+(2x+1)^{-1}]e^{2x+1}$.
49. $2x$.
50. 2.
51. $e^x\cos(e^x)$.
52. $-e^x\sin(e^x)$.
53. $-2x\,e^{x^2}\sin(e^{x^2})$.
54. $-2x\,e^{-x^2}\cos(e^{-x^2})$.
55. $e^{\sin x}\cos x$.
56. $e^{-\cos x}\sin x$.
57. 1.
58. $-2x^{-3}$.
59. $2x\,e^{x^2+1}\cos(e^{x^2+1})$.
60. $-2e^{\cos(2x+1)}\sin(2x+1)$.
61. $-2\tan 2x$.
62. $\sec x \csc x$.
63. $x^{-1}(1+x)$.
64. $\dfrac{\cos x - x\sin x}{x\cos x}$.
65. $\dfrac{2\cos x - x\sin x}{x\cos x}$.
66. $\dfrac{\cos 2x - 2\sin 2x}{\cos 2x}$.

EXERCISE 11.5 (page 228)

1. $2b$.
2. (a) $(0,1)$ max; $(\frac{1}{2}\sqrt{2}, e^{-1/2})$ and $(-\frac{1}{2}\sqrt{2}, e^{-1/2})$ points of inflection.
   (b) $(-1, -e^{-1})$ min; $(-2, -2e^{-2})$ point of inflection.
3. (a) Minimum at $(e^{-1}, -e^{-1})$; no point of inflection. (b) Minimum at $(1,1)$; no point of inflection.
4. $D_tT = k(T_1 - T_0)e^{-kt}$.
6. $a = g(e^{kt}-1)$; (a) 0; (b) $g(e^{kt_0}-1)$.

EXERCISE 11.6 (page 231)

1. $y = \frac{1}{2}e^{2x} + c$.
2. $y = -\frac{1}{2}e^{-2x} + c$.
3. $y = \frac{1}{3}e^{3x-2} + c$.
4. $y = \frac{1}{4}e^{4x+5} + c$.
5. $y = -\frac{1}{5}e^{3-5x} + c$.
6. $y = -\frac{1}{2}e^{-3-2x} + c$.
7. $y = \frac{1}{2}e^{x^2} + c$.
8. $y = \frac{1}{3}e^{x^3} + c$.
9. $y = -e^{x^{-1}} + c$.
10. $y = 2e^{x^{1/2}} + c$.
11. $y = 3\ln x + c$.
12. $y = -2\ln x + c$.
13. $y = \ln(x+1) + c$.
14. $y = 2\ln(x+3) + c$.
15. $y = -\ln(1-x) + c$.
16. $y = -\frac{1}{3}\ln(2-3x) + c$.
17. $y = \ln(1+x^2) + c$.
18. $y = \frac{1}{2}\ln(x^2-1) + c$.
19. $y = -\frac{1}{2}\ln(1-x^2) + c$.
20. $y = \frac{1}{3}\ln(x^3-1) + c$.
21. $-\frac{1}{5}e^{-5x} + c$.
22. $\frac{1}{6}e^{6x} + c$.
23. $e^{x+4} + c$.
24. $\frac{1}{2}e^{2x-1} + c$.
25. $-e^{-x+2} + c$.

26. $-e^{-(x+2)} + c.$

27. $-\frac{1}{3}e^{-3x+5} + c.$

28. $\frac{1}{4}e^{4x+1} + c.$

29. $-\frac{1}{2}e^{-x^2} + c.$

30. $-\frac{1}{2}e^{-(x+1)^2} + c.$

31. $-\frac{1}{3}e^{-x^3} + c.$

32. $\frac{1}{4}e^{x^4+1} + c.$

33. $-\ln(2 - x) + c.$

34. $\frac{1}{2}\ln(2x + 3) + c.$

35. $\frac{1}{2}\ln(x^2 - 4) + c.$

36. $\frac{3}{2}\ln(x^2 + 9) + c.$

37. $\ln(x^3 + 8) + c.$

38. $\ln(x^4 + 1) + c.$

39. $\frac{1}{2}\ln(x^2 + 6x - 7) + c.$ **40.** $\ln(x - 2) + c.$

EXERCISE 11.7 (page 235)

1. $10(e - e^{-1}).$

2. $(30/\ln 2) - 8.$

3. $\ln 10.$

4. $\ln 4 - \frac{3}{4}.$

5. $\ln 2 - \frac{1}{2}.$

6. $e^2 - 3.$

7. $(24/\ln 5) - (3/\ln 2).$

8. $6 - 2\ln 4.$

9. $7.5 - 4\ln 4.$

10. $12.48 - 2\ln 5.$ **11.** $50\pi(e^{10} - 1).$ **12.** $10\pi(1 - e^{-25}).$ **13.** $\frac{\pi}{4}(15 - 16\ln 2).$

14. $9\pi.$ **15.** $\pi(15 - 4\ln 2).$

EXERCISE 11.8 (page 237)

1. (a) .014.

(b) .023.

(c) .035.

2. $6.3\%.$

3. $p = ke^{-h/k}.$

4. $281°C.$

6. 4.51, 6.99, and 9.50 grams per litre.

REVIEW EXERCISE 11 (page 239)

1. $3(3x - 4)^{-1}.$ **2.** $2x(x^2 + 4)^{-1}.$ **3.** $-\frac{1}{2}(1 - x)^{-1}.$ **4.** $-x(9 - x^2)^{-1}.$

5. $1 + \ln(x + 2).$ **6.** $2 + \ln x^2.$ **7.** $\sec x \csc x.$ **8.** $2\cot 2x.$

9. $x^{-1}\sec^2(\ln x).$ **10.** $-3x^{-1}\sin(\ln x^3).$ **11.** $4e^{4x}.$

12. $2e^{2x+3}.$ **13.** $2xe^{x^2+4}.$ **14.** $2(x + 1)e^{(x+1)^2}.$

15. $e^{\sin x}\cos x.$ **16.** $2x.$ **17.** $(1 + x)e^{x+2}.$ **18.** $(1 - 2x^{-1})x^{-2}e^x.$

19. $(\sin 2x + 2\cos 2x)e^x.$ **20.** $x^{-1}\sin x + (\ln x)(\cos x).$ **21.** $y = \frac{1}{3}e^{3x} + c.$

22. $y = \frac{1}{2}e^{2x+1} + c.$ **23.** $y = \frac{1}{2}e^{(x^2+1)} + c.$ **24.** $y = -\frac{1}{2}e^{x^{-2}} + c.$

25. $y = 4\ln x + c.$ **26.** $y = 2\ln(x + 2) + c.$ **27.** $y = \frac{1}{2}\ln(x^2 - 1) + c.$

28. $y = \frac{1}{2}\ln(x^2 + 2x + 3) + c.$ **29.** $y = e^{\sin x} + c.$

30. $y = \ln\sin x + c.$ **31.** $-\frac{1}{4}e^{-4x} + c.$ **32.** $-e^{3-x} + c.$ **33.** $\frac{1}{3}e^{x^3} + c.$

34. $-e^{(x+1)^{-1}} + c.$ **35.** $-3\ln x + c.$ **36.** $\ln(x + 4) + c.$

37. $-\frac{1}{2}\ln(1 - x^2) + c.$ **38.** $\frac{1}{3}\ln(x^3 + 3x) + c.$ **39.** $-e^{\cos x} + c.$

40. $10(e - e^{-1}).$ **41.** $17.5 - \ln 6.$ **42.** $12.48 - 2\ln 5.$ **43.** $D_{tr} = .231r.$

44. 27, 61, 114. **45.** $4\pi(1 - e^{-10}).$ **46.** $2\pi(1 - e^{-4}).$

47. $\frac{\pi}{32}(495 + 128\ln 2).$ **48.** (a) 435.42. (b) 404.42. **49.** (a) 2.02.

(b) 1.96.

Chapter 12

EXERCISE 12.1 (page 243)

2. (a) $(4, 360°), (-4, 180°).$

(b) $(0, 390°), (0, -330°).$

(c) $(5, 435°), (-5, 255°).$

(d) $(-5, 450°), (5, 270°).$

(e) $(-3, -60°)$, $(3, 120°)$.   (f) $\left(-10\sqrt{2}, \frac{3\pi}{4}\right)$, $\left(10\sqrt{2}, \frac{7\pi}{4}\right)$.

(g) $(-12\sqrt{3}, 240°)$, $(12\sqrt{3}, 60°)$.   (h) $(-3, 30°)$, $(3, 210°)$.

(i) $(3, 210°)$, $(-3, 30°)$.

9. Two. The pole has an infinite number.

11. (a) Circle, centre the pole, radius 4.   (b) Circle, centre the pole, radius a.

13. (a) Line through pole, making angle of 60° with polar axis.

(b) Line through pole, making angle θ_1 with polar axis.

14. Circle, centre $(1, 0°)$, radius 1.   15. Circle, centre $(1, 90°)$, radius 1.

16. Circle, centre $(\frac{3}{2}, 90°)$, radius $\frac{3}{2}$.   17. $163° \, 4'$.

18. Straight line through $(2, 0°)$ perpendicular to polar axis.

EXERCISE 12.2 (page 247)

1. (a) $(4, 0)$.   (b) $(0, -3)$.   (c) $(1, 1)$.   (d) $(0, 6)$.

    (e) $(2\sqrt{3}, 2)$.   (f) $(-1, \sqrt{3})$.   (g) $(-\frac{5}{2}, \frac{5}{2}\sqrt{3})$.   (h) $(2\sqrt{2}, -2\sqrt{2})$.

    (i) $(3, 0)$.   (j) $(0, 0)$.   (k) $(-\frac{3}{2}\sqrt{2}, \frac{3}{2}\sqrt{2})$.   (l) $(0, 4)$.

2. (a) $(5, 0°)$.   (b) $(2\sqrt{2}, 45°)$.   (c) $(6, 90°)$.   (d) $(4\sqrt{2}, 225°)$.

    (e) $(3, 180°)$.   (f) $(5, 270°)$.   (g) $(0, 0°)$.   (h) $(8, 300°)$.

    (i) $(8, 150°)$.   (j) $(5, 53° \, 8')$.   (k) $(13, 112° \, 37')$.   (l) $(5, 216° \, 52')$.

3. (a) $r \cos \theta = 4$.   (b) $r \sin \theta = -3$.   (c) $r = 5$.

    (d) $\tan \theta = \frac{3}{5}$.   (e) $r(3 \cos \theta - 4 \sin \theta) + 6 = 0$.   (f) $r^2 \sin 2\theta = 8$.

    (g) $r \sin^2\theta = 4 \cos \theta$.   (h) $r = 2 \sin \theta$.   (i) $r = 2 \cos \theta + 6 \sin \theta$.

    (j) $r^2 \cos 2\theta = 9$.   (k) $r^2(5 \cos^2\theta - 4) = 4$.   (l) $r^2 \doteq \cos 2\theta$.

4. (a) $x^2 + y^2 = 36$.   (b) $y = \frac{1}{\sqrt{3}}x$.   (c) $x^2 + y^2 = 3x$.

    (d) $y = 6$.   (e) $x^2 + y^2 = 4x$.   (f) $x^2 + y^2 = 2y$.

    (g) $xy = 1$.   (h) $x^2 - y^2 = 3$.   (i) $x(x^2 + y^2) = 2y$.

    (j) $x^2 + y^2 = 3y$.   (k) $(x^2 + y^2)^{3/2} = 2xy$.   (l) $y^2(x^2 + y^2) = a^2x^2$.

5. (a) Parabola.   (b) Ellipse.   (c) Hyperbola.

EXERCISE 12.3 (page 251)

2. (a) $\theta = 45°, 135°$.   (b) $\theta = 30°, 90°, 150°$.   (c) $\theta = 90°$.

    (d) $\theta = 180°$.   (e) $\theta = 60°$.   (f) $\theta = 45°$.

    (g) None.   (h) $\theta = 0°$.   (i) $\theta = 120°$.

3. (a) Symmetric with respect to polar axis, pole, and $\theta = \dfrac{\pi}{2}$.

    (b) Symmetric w.r.t. polar axis.   (c) Same as (a).

    (d) Same as (a).   (e) Symmetric w.r.t. pole.

    (f) Same as (a).   (g) Symmetric w.r.t. polar axis.

    (h) Same as (a).   (i) Symmetric w.r.t. polar axis.

    (j) Symmetric w.r.t. polar axis.   (k) Symmetric w.r.t. $\theta = \dfrac{\pi}{2}$.

    (l) Symmetric w.r.t. pole.   (m) Same as (a).

    (n) No symmetry w.r.t. pole, polar axis, $\theta = 0°$, or $\theta = \dfrac{\pi}{2}$.

(o) Symmetric w.r.t. polar axis.   (p) Symmetric w.r.t. $\theta = \dfrac{\pi}{2}$.

(q) Symmetric w.r.t. polar axis.   (r) Symmetric w.r.t. $\theta = \dfrac{\pi}{2}$.

4. (a) $180° < \theta < 360°$.   (b) $45° < \theta < 135°$, $225° < \theta < 315°$.
  (c) $120° < \theta < 240°$.   (d) $90° \le \theta \le 270°$.
  (e) $90° \le \theta < 180°$, $270° \le \theta < 360°$.   (f) None.
  (g) $\theta = 270°$.   (h) $90° \le \theta \le 270°$.   (i) $180° < \theta < 360°$.

5. (a) Pole.   (b) $(1, 0°)$, $(-1, 0°)$.
  (c) $(-1 + \sqrt{3}, 0°)$, $(-1 - \sqrt{3}, 0°)$.   (d) $(2, 0°)$, $(-2, 0°)$.
  (e) Pole.   (f) Pole.   (g) $(\sqrt{2}, 0°)$, $(-\sqrt{2}, 0°)$.
  (h) Pole.   (i) Pole.

6. (a) $(\tfrac{3}{2}, 60°)$, $(\tfrac{3}{2}, 300°)$.   (b) $(\sqrt{2}, 45°)$, $(0, 0°)$.
  (c) $(2, 30°)$, $(2, 150°)$, $(0, 0°)$.

EXERCISE 12.5 (page 263)

1. θ.   2. $\dfrac{\pi}{2} + \theta$.   3. θ.   4. $\dfrac{\pi}{2} - \theta$.   5. $\pi - \theta$.   6. $\tfrac{1}{2}(\pi + \theta)$.

7. $\cot^{-1}\!\left(\dfrac{-\sin\theta}{2 + \cos\theta}\right)$.   8. $\cot^{-1}\!\left(\dfrac{-2\sin\theta}{1 + 2\cos\theta}\right)$.   9. $\tfrac{1}{2}(\pi - \theta)$.

10. $\cot^{-1}\!\left(\dfrac{2\sin\theta}{1 + 2\cos\theta}\right)$.   11. $\cot^{-1}(\tfrac{1}{2}\cot\theta)$.   12. $\dfrac{\pi}{2} + 2\theta$.

13. $\cot^{-1}(\csc 2\theta)$.   14. $\dfrac{\pi}{2} - \theta$.   15. (a) 1. $\left(1, \dfrac{\pi}{2}\right)$.   2. $(3, 0)$.

3. $\left(-4, \dfrac{\pi}{2}\right)$.   4. $(-1, \pi)$.   5. $\left(1, \dfrac{\pi}{2}\right)$.   6. $(8, 0)$.   7. $(3, 0)$, $(1, \pi)$.

8. $(3, 0)$, $(-1, \pi)$.   9. $(1, 0)$.   10. $(\tfrac{2}{3}, 0)$, $(-2, \pi)$.   11. $\left(\pm 2, \dfrac{\pi}{2}\right)$.

12. $(\pm 1, 0)$.   13. no points.   14. $(4, 0)$.   (b) 1. $\left(\dfrac{1}{\sqrt{2}}, \dfrac{\pi}{4}\right)$.   2. $(3, 0)$.

3. $\left(-2\sqrt{2}, \dfrac{\pi}{4}\right)$.   4. all points of function.   5. no points.   6. $(8, 0)$.

7. $(1, \pi)$, $(3, 0)$.   8. $(\tfrac{1}{2}, \pm 105°)$, $(3, 0)$.   9. $(1, 0)$.   10. no points.

11. $(\pm 1.5, 35°)$, $(\pm 1.5, 145°)$.   12. $(\pm 1, 0)$.   13. $\left(\pm 1, \dfrac{\pi}{4}\right)$.

14. no points.   (c) 1. $(0, 0)$, $\left(1, \dfrac{\pi}{2}\right)$.   2. $\left(\dfrac{3}{\sqrt{2}}, \pm\dfrac{\pi}{4}\right)$.   3. $(0, 0)$,

$\left(-4, \dfrac{\pi}{2}\right)$.   4. no points.   5. all points of function.   6. $\left(6, \pm\dfrac{\pi}{3}\right)$.

7. $\left(\dfrac{3 + \sqrt{3}}{2}, \pm 68.5°\right)$.   8. $\left(\dfrac{3 + \sqrt{33}}{4}, \pm 54°\right)$, $\left(\dfrac{3 - \sqrt{33}}{4}, \pm 147°\right)$.

9. no points.   10. no points.   11. $\left(\pm 2, \dfrac{\pi}{2}\right)$.   12. $\left(\pm\dfrac{1}{\sqrt{2}}, \pm\dfrac{\pi}{6}\right)$.

13. no points.   14. no points.

EXERCISE 12.6 (page 267)

1. $\frac{\pi}{4}$. 2. $\frac{9\pi}{4}$. 3. 4π. 4. $\frac{\pi}{8}; \frac{\pi}{8}; \frac{\pi}{8}; \frac{\pi}{8}$. 5. $\frac{3\pi}{2}$. 6. 24π. 7. $\frac{9\pi}{2}$.

8. $2\pi + \frac{3\sqrt{3}}{2}; \pi - \frac{3\sqrt{3}}{2}$. 9. $4; 4$ 10. $\frac{\pi}{8}; \frac{\pi}{8}$.

REVIEW EXERCISE 12 (page 268)

2. (a) About polar axis. (b) About pole. (c) About $\theta = \frac{\pi}{2}$.
   (d) About pole.
3. (a) $(\frac{3}{2}\sqrt{2}, \frac{3}{2}\sqrt{2})$. (b) $(\sqrt{3}, 1)$. (c) $(-5, 0)$. (d) $(0, 3)$.
4. (a) $(6, 90°)$. (b) $(-2, 0°)$. (c) $(4, 120°)$. (d) $(8, 210°)$.
5. (a) $r = 2 \cos \theta$. (b) $\tan \theta = \frac{2}{5}$. (c) $r \sin^2\theta + 9 \cos \theta = 0$.
6. (a) $y = 2$. (b) $(x^2 + y^2)^2 = 2xy$. (c) $y^2(x^2 + y^2) = 4x^2$.
7. (a) Circle, radius, 2, centre $(2, 90°)$. (b) Circle, radius 4, centre at pole.
   (c) Circle, radius 2, centre $(2, 180°)$. (d) Line $y = 4$.
   (e) Line $x = -5$. (f) Line $x = 2$.
9. True if $f(2\theta_1 - \theta) = f(\theta)$.
10. $\frac{\pi}{2}$; does not exist; $\frac{\pi}{2}$. 11. $\frac{\pi}{4}; \frac{\pi}{2}; \frac{3\pi}{4}$; does not exist.

12. does not exist; $26°$; does not exist. 13. $\frac{\pi}{2}; \frac{\pi}{4}$; does not exist.

14. does not exist; $\frac{\pi}{4}$; does not exist. 15. does not exist; $\frac{\pi}{4}; \frac{\pi}{2}$.
16. 4π. 17. 3π. 18. 11π. 19. 2. 20. $\pi + 3\sqrt{3}$.

Chapter 13

EXERCISE 13.1 (page 272)

1. (a) $6, -\sqrt{2}$. (b) $\frac{1}{2}, \frac{1}{2}$. (c) $-\pi, 6$. (d) $2x, 3y$.
   (e) $4, 3$. (f) $0, -5$. (g) $\frac{1}{2}, -\sqrt{2}$. (h) $5\sqrt{2} + 3, 0$.
2. (a) $3 - 2i$. (b) $0 + 6i$. (c) $2 + (3 + \sqrt{2})i$. (d) $x + yi$.
3. (a) $(5, -\frac{3}{2})$. (b) $(-\sqrt{2}, 3)$. (c) $(\frac{2}{3}, -\pi)$. (d) (p, q).
5. (a) $2\sqrt{13}$. (b) $\sqrt{13}$. (c) $\frac{1}{2}\sqrt{10}$. (d) $2\sqrt{5}$.
   (e) 3. (f) 3. (g) 2. (h) $\sqrt{\pi^2 + 16}$.
7. (a) 5. (b) $\sqrt{29}$. (c) 5. (d) $2\sqrt{10}$. (e) 4. (f) 3.
   (g) $\sqrt{11}$. (h) 5.
8. $0 + 0i$. 9. The imaginary axis. 10. The real axis.
11. (a) Line $x = y$. (b) Line $x + y = 0$.

EXERCISE 13.2 (page 275)

1. (a) $x = \frac{2}{3}, y = \frac{2}{3}$. (b) $x = -\pi, y = \frac{1}{3}\sqrt{2}$. (c) $x = -\frac{1}{2}, y = \frac{11}{2}$.
   (d) $x = 3, y = -3$. (e) $x = 0, y = -3$. (f) $x = -2, y = 1$.
   (g) $x = \frac{7}{5}, y = \frac{8}{5}$. (h) $x = -\frac{10}{9}, y = -\frac{13}{9}$.
2. (a) $11 + 5i$. (b) $4 + i$. (c) $-2 + i$. (d) $12 + 0i$. (e) $2 - \frac{1}{2}i$.

(f) $0 + 2\pi i$. (g) $(3 + \sqrt{2}) + 3i$. (h) $(6\sqrt{2} - 3) + (1 + \sqrt{2})i$.
(i) $(\pi + \sqrt{3}) + (2 + \sqrt{2})i$.

3. (a) $-5 + 2i$. (b) $3\sqrt{2} - \frac{1}{2}i$. (c) $\frac{1}{2} - \frac{\sqrt{3}}{2}i$.

4. (a) $10 + 0i$. (b) $5 + 3i$. (c) $-1 + 2i$. (d) $\frac{5}{2} - i$. (e) $\frac{5}{2} + \frac{7}{2}i$.
   (f) $12 + 0i$. (g) $-4\sqrt{2} + 4i$. (h) $(3\sqrt{2} - \pi) + (4 - \sqrt{2})i$.
   (i) $\left(\dfrac{1}{\sqrt{3}} - 2\right) + (1 + \sqrt{2})i$.

8. (a) $-6 - 2i$. (b) $6 - \frac{5}{2}i$. (c) $(\sqrt{2} - 4) + (1 - \sqrt{2})i$.
   (d) $6 + (\sqrt{2} - 6)i$.

EXERCISE 13.3 (page 278)

1. (a) -1. (b) i. (c) 1. (d) $-i$. (e) $-i$.
   (f) 6. (g) 2. (h) -24. (i) 1. (j) -24.
2. (a) $22 + 29i$. (b) $0 + 30i$. (c) $\frac{27}{4} - \frac{7}{2}i$.
   (d) $52 + 0i$. (e) $\frac{1}{4} - \frac{17}{4}i$. (f) $(-\pi^2 - 16) + 0i$.
   (g) $(3\sqrt{2} - 2) + (3 + 2\sqrt{2})i$. (h) $-19\sqrt{2} + 9i$.
   (i) $14 + 5i\sqrt{2}$. (j) $36 + 9i\sqrt{2}$.
7. $uv = 0 + 5i$, $u^2 + v^2 = 0 - 8i$, $u^3 - v^3 = -9 - 9i$.
8. -8. 9. No. 10. No.
12.

$\times$	1	i	-1	$-i$
1	1	i	-1	$-i$
i	i	-1	$-i$	1
-1	-1	$-i$	1	i
$-i$	$-i$	1	i	-1

16. (a) $1 + 0i$. (b) $-7 + 24i$. (c) $-\sqrt{2} - i\sqrt{2}$. (d) $69 - 13i$.

EXERCISE 13.4 (page 283)

1. (a) $4 + 3i$. (b) $-5 + 4i$. (c) $4 - 0i$. (d) $-3 + 3i$.
   (e) $0 + 5i$. (f) $8 - 5i$.
2. (a) 8 and $-6i$. (b) -10 and $-8i$. (c) 8 and 0.
   (d) -6 and $-6i$. (e) 0 and $-10i$. (f) 16 and $10i$.
3. Complex numbers $a + 0i$.
4. (a) 37. (b) 20. (c) $\frac{1}{2}$. (d) 16. (e) 7. (f) 52. (g) $\frac{1}{4}$. (h) 1.
7. (a) $4 + 4i$. (b) $-5 + 15i$. (c) $8 + 2i$.
8. (a) $4 + 7i$. (b) $-12 - 28i$. (c) $-15 + 23i$.

EXERCISE 13.5 (page 285)

1. (a) $\frac{34}{53} + \frac{13}{53}i$. (b) $-\frac{6}{5} - \frac{9}{10}i$. (c) $-\frac{4}{5} - \frac{1}{10}i$.
   (d) $\frac{27}{25} - \frac{14}{25}i$. (e) $\frac{5}{13} - \frac{12}{13}i$. (f) $-\frac{11}{29} - \frac{13}{29}i$.
   (g) $\dfrac{\pi^2 - 16}{\pi^2 + 16} + \dfrac{8\pi}{\pi^2 + 16}i$. (h) $\dfrac{2 + 3\sqrt{2}}{13} + \dfrac{3 - 2\sqrt{2}}{13}i$. (i) $-\frac{17}{11}\sqrt{2} - \frac{15}{11}i$.
2. (a) $-3i$ and $\frac{1}{3}i$. (b) $\frac{1}{5} + \frac{2}{5}i$ and $1 - 2i$.
   (c) $\dfrac{4 + \sqrt{6}}{19} + \dfrac{4\sqrt{2} - \sqrt{3}}{19}i$ and $\dfrac{4 + \sqrt{6}}{3} + \dfrac{\sqrt{3} - 4\sqrt{2}}{3}i$.

3. (a) $\frac{4}{17} - \frac{1}{17}i$.   (b) $\frac{3}{13} + \frac{2}{13}i$.   (c) $\frac{2}{15} - \frac{1}{15}i$.   (d) $-\frac{3}{20} - \frac{1}{20}i$.

(e) $1 + i$.   (f) $\frac{\sqrt{3}}{4} - \frac{1}{4}i$.   (g) $\frac{1}{3} + \frac{1}{6}i\sqrt{2}$.   (h) $\frac{\sqrt{3}}{5} - \frac{i\sqrt{2}}{5}$.

4. $\frac{a}{a^2 + b^2} - \frac{b}{a^2 + b^2}i$.

5. (a) $\frac{1}{2} - \frac{5}{2}i$.   (b) $\frac{-19}{13} + \frac{4}{13}i$.   (c) $-\frac{9}{40} + \frac{17}{40}i$.   (d) $\frac{8}{25} + \frac{6}{25}i$.

EXERCISE 13.6 (page 288)

1. (a) $0 + 5i$.   (b) $4 - 11i$.   (c) $0 + 10i$.
(d) $0 + 36i$.   (e) $-9 + 0i$.   (f) $0 + 60i$.
(g) $-2\sqrt{2} + 0i$.   (h) $-13\sqrt{5} + 0i$.   (i) $-14\sqrt{3} + 0i$.

2. (a) $\frac{1 \pm \sqrt{47}i}{12}$.   (b) $\frac{\sqrt{2}}{6} \pm i\frac{\sqrt{10}}{6}$.   (c) $\frac{5\sqrt{2}}{4} \pm i\frac{\sqrt{46}}{4}$.   (d) $\frac{\sqrt{3}}{6} \pm \frac{i\sqrt{5}}{2}$.

(e) $0 + \left(\frac{1 \pm \sqrt{17}}{2}\right)i$.   (f) $\pm\frac{\sqrt{2}}{3} - \frac{i}{3}$.

(g) $0 + i(-3 \pm 2\sqrt{3})$.   (h) $\pm\frac{\sqrt{23}}{4} + \frac{i}{4}$.

4. (a) $-\frac{5}{2} \pm \frac{\sqrt{7}}{2}i$.   (b) $1 \pm \frac{i\sqrt{2}}{2}$.   (c) $\frac{5}{12} \pm \frac{i\sqrt{23}}{12}$.   (d) $-\frac{1}{6} \pm \frac{i\sqrt{23}}{6}$.

7. $1 + i$ and $2 - i$.

10. (a) $x^2 - 4x + 5 = 0$.   (b) $x^2 + 6x + 13 = 0$.   (c) $x^2 + 1 = 0$.
(d) $x^2 + (2\sqrt{2})x + 11 = 0$.   (e) $x^2 - 12x + 39 = 0$.   (f) $x^2 - x + \frac{3}{4} = 0$.

EXERCISE 13.7 (page 293)

1. (a) $4 + 0i$.   (b) $-10 + 0i$.   (c) $0 + 3i$.   (d) $0 - 5i$.
(e) $1 + 0i$.   (f) $-3 + 0i$.   (g) $0 + 5i$.   (h) $\sqrt{3} + i$.
(i) $-\frac{3}{2}\sqrt{2} + (\frac{3}{2}\sqrt{2})i$.   (j) $\frac{5}{2} + i\left(\frac{5\sqrt{3}}{2}\right)$.   (k) $7 + 0i$.
(l) $2 - 2i\sqrt{3}$.   (m) $-\frac{\sqrt{2}}{2} - \frac{\sqrt{2}}{2}i$.   (n) $-\frac{3}{2} - \frac{3i\sqrt{3}}{2}$.
(o) $-\sqrt{3} - i$.   (p) $\frac{3}{2}\sqrt{3} + \frac{3}{2}i$.   (q) -1.
(r) $-\frac{3}{2}\sqrt{3} + \frac{3}{2}i$.   (s) $-3\sqrt{3} - 3i$.

2. (a) $4 \operatorname{cis} 0°$.   (b) $3 \operatorname{cis} \frac{\pi}{2}$.   (c) $2 \operatorname{cis} \pi$.   (d) $\operatorname{cis} 270°$.
(e) $2 \operatorname{cis} 60°$.   (f) $2 \operatorname{cis} 300°$.   (g) $2 \operatorname{cis} 120°$.   (h) $2 \operatorname{cis} 240°$.
(i) $6\sqrt{2} \operatorname{cis} 45°$.   (j) $4 \operatorname{cis} 150°$.   (k) $5 \operatorname{cis} 270°$.   (l) $12 \operatorname{cis} 240°$.
(m) $6 \operatorname{cis} 120°$.   (n) $4\sqrt{2} \operatorname{cis} 225°$.   (o) $10 \operatorname{cis} 0°$.   (p) $\operatorname{cis} 120°$.
(q) $\sqrt{2} \operatorname{cis} \pi$.   (r) $2 \operatorname{cis} 330°$.

3. (a) $4 \operatorname{cis} 2k\pi, k \in I$.   (b) $2 \operatorname{cis} (2k + 1)\pi, k \in I$.
(c) $\operatorname{cis}(\frac{1}{2} + 2k)\pi, k \in I$.   (d) $6 \operatorname{cis} (\frac{3}{2} + 2k)\pi, k \in I$.
(e) $2 \operatorname{cis} (\frac{5}{6} + 2k)\pi, k \in I$.   (f) $6 \operatorname{cis} (\frac{7}{4} + 2k)\pi$.

4. (a) $1.532 + 1.2856i$.   (b) $-.5208 + 2.9544i$.   (c) $-.9397 - .3420i$.
(d) $-2.9544 - .5208i$.   (e) $.1744 - 1.9924i$.   (f) $3.9976 + .1396i$.

5. (a) $2k\pi, k \in I.$ (b) $(2k+1)\pi, k \in I.$ (c) $(2k+\frac{1}{2})\pi, k \in I.$
(d) $(2k+\frac{3}{2})\pi, k \in I.$

8. (a) $6.$ (b) $6 \text{ cis } \dfrac{3\pi}{2}.$ (c) $6 \text{ cis } \pi.$ (d) $6 \text{ cis } \dfrac{\pi}{2}.$

(e) $\sqrt{2} \text{ cis } \dfrac{7\pi}{4}.$ (f) $3\sqrt{2} \text{ cis } \dfrac{\pi}{4}.$ (g) $2 \text{ cis } \dfrac{\pi}{6}.$ (h) $2 \text{ cis } \dfrac{\pi}{3}.$

EXERCISE 13.8 (page 295)

1. (a) $3\sqrt{2} + 3i\sqrt{2}.$ (b) $0 + 8i.$ (c) $0 - 4i.$
(d) $-1 + 0i.$ (e) $\sqrt{2} - i\sqrt{2}.$ (f) $\dfrac{2}{3}\sqrt{2} + \dfrac{2i\sqrt{2}}{3}.$

(g) $0 + \frac{1}{2}i.$ (h) $\dfrac{1}{2} - \dfrac{\sqrt{3}}{2}i.$ (i) $-6 + 6i\sqrt{3}.$
(j) $-\frac{2}{5} + 0i.$ (k) $-6\sqrt{2} + 6i\sqrt{2}.$ (l) $-5\sqrt{2} - 5i\sqrt{2}.$

3. (a) $\dfrac{9}{2} + \dfrac{9i\sqrt{3}}{2}.$ (b) $0 + 2i.$ (c) $-\dfrac{9}{2} + \dfrac{9i\sqrt{3}}{2}.$

5. (a) $\frac{1}{2} \text{ cis } 300°.$ (b) $2 \text{ cis } 30°.$ (c) $\dfrac{\sqrt{2}}{2} \text{ cis } 225°.$

6. (a) $2 + 2i\sqrt{3}.$ (b) $-4 + 0i.$

EXERCISE 13.9 (page 298)

1. (a) $\dfrac{1}{2} + \dfrac{\sqrt{3}}{2}i.$ (b) $1 + 0i.$ (c) $-1 + 0i.$

(d) $\dfrac{1}{2} - \dfrac{\sqrt{3}}{2}i.$ (e) $0 + 4i.$ (f) $-\dfrac{81}{2} + \dfrac{81i\sqrt{3}}{2}.$

(g) $\frac{1}{8} + 0i.$ (h) $\dfrac{\sqrt{3}}{8} - \dfrac{1}{8}i.$ (i) $243 + 0i.$
(j) $-\frac{1}{9} + 0i.$ (k) $16 - 16i.$ (l) $16\sqrt{3} + 16i.$
(m) $0 + 512i.$ (n) $0 - i.$ (o) $\frac{1}{16} + 0i.$
(p) $-1 + 0i.$ (q) $-64\sqrt{3} - 64i.$ (r) $65,536 + 0i.$

2. (a) $64 + 0i.$ (b) $\dfrac{1}{2048} - \dfrac{\sqrt{3}}{2048}i.$ (c) $0 - \dfrac{1}{2}i.$ (d) $-32,768 + 0i.$

3. (a) $\cos 2\theta = \cos^2 \theta - \sin^2 \theta,$ (b) $\cos 4\theta = \cos^4 \theta - 6 \cos^2 \theta \sin^2 \theta + \sin^4 \theta,$
$\sin 2\theta = 2 \sin \theta \cos \theta.$ $\sin 4\theta = 4 \sin \theta \cos \theta (\cos^2 \theta - \sin^2 \theta).$
(c) $\cos 5\theta = \cos \theta (\cos^4 \theta - 10 \cos^2 \theta \sin^2 \theta + 5 \sin^4 \theta),$
$\sin 5\theta = \sin \theta (5 \cos^4 \theta - 10 \cos^2 \theta \sin^2 \theta + \sin^4 \theta).$
(d) $\cos 6\theta = \cos^6 \theta - 15 \cos^4 \theta \sin^2 \theta + 15 \cos^2 \theta \sin^4 \theta - \sin^6 \theta,$
$\sin 6\theta = 6 \cos^5 \theta \sin \theta - 20 \cos^3 \theta \sin^3 \theta + 6 \cos \theta \sin^5 \theta.$

EXERCISE 13.10 (page 301)

1. (a) $\pm\left(\dfrac{3\sqrt{2}}{2} + \dfrac{3\sqrt{2}}{2}i\right).$ (b) $\pm(\sqrt{2} - i\sqrt{2}).$ (c) $\pm(2 + 2i\sqrt{3}).$

(d) $1 + i\sqrt{3}, 1 - i\sqrt{3}, -2 + 0i.$ (e) $3 + 0i, -\dfrac{3}{2} + \dfrac{3\sqrt{3}}{2}i, -\dfrac{3}{2} - \dfrac{3\sqrt{3}}{2}i.$

(f) $0 + 2i, \sqrt{3} - i, -\sqrt{3} - i.$
(g) $\sqrt[3]{9} \text{ cis } (30 + 60k)°, k = 0, 1, 2, 3, 4, 5.$

(h) 2 cis $(30 + 72k)°$, $k = 0, 1, 2, 3, 4$.
(i)   cis $60k°$, $k = 0, 1, 2, 3, 4, 5$.   (j) $2 + 2i, -2 + 2i, -2 - 2i, 2 - 2i$.
(k) $\frac{1}{2} + \frac{\sqrt{3}}{2}i, -1 + 0i, \frac{1}{2} - \frac{\sqrt{3}}{2}i$.

(l) $\sqrt{3} + i, -1 + i\sqrt{3}, -\sqrt{3} - i, 1 - i\sqrt{3}$.
(m) cis $(15 + 60k)°$, $k = 0, 1, 2, 3, 4, 5$.
(n) $\sqrt{2}$ cis $(27 + 72k)°$, $k, = 0, 1, 2, 3, 4$.

(o) $\pm\left(\frac{\sqrt{6}}{2} - \frac{i\sqrt{2}}{2}\right)$.

(p) cis $(15 + 45k)°$, $k = 0, 1, 2, 3, 4, 5, 6, 7$.

2. (a) $4 + 0i, -2 + 2i\sqrt{3}, -2 - 2i\sqrt{3}$.   (b) $\pm(2\sqrt{2} + 2i\sqrt{2})$.

(c) $\pm\left(\frac{3\sqrt{2}}{2} + \frac{3\sqrt{2}}{2}i\right), \pm\left(\frac{-3\sqrt{2}}{2} + \frac{3\sqrt{2}}{2}i\right)$.

(d) 2 cis $72k°$, $k = 0, 1, 2, 3, 4$.   (e)   cis $(36 + 72k)°$, $k = 0, 1, 2, 3, 4$.

(f) $\pm\left(\frac{\sqrt{2}}{2} + \frac{\sqrt{6}}{2}i\right)$.   (g) $\sqrt[4]{8}$ cis $(60 + 90k)°$, $k = 0, 1, 2, 3$.

(h) $\sqrt[6]{5}$ cis $\left(\frac{\theta}{3} + 120k\right)°$, $k = 0, 1, 2$, where $\theta = \tan^{-1}\frac{1}{2}, 0° < \theta < 90°$.

3. (a) $\pm(2 + i)$.   (b) $\pm(3 - 2i)$.   **4.** $4.175 + 1.397i, .825 - .3968i$.

REVIEW EXERCISE 13 (page 303)

1. (a) 3 and 5.   (b) 4 and -1.   (c) $-\frac{1}{2}$ and 2.   (d) 5 and 0.
2. (a) $\sqrt{34}$.   (b) $\sqrt{17}$.   (c) $\frac{1}{2}\sqrt{17}$.   (d) 5.
     (a) $-1 + 3i, \sqrt{10}$. (b) $-1 + 3i, \sqrt{10}$. (c) $7 - 7i, 7\sqrt{2}$. (d) $-7 + 7i, 7\sqrt{2}$
4. (a) $-5 - 2i$. (b) $-5 - 2i$. (c) $-3 - 4i$.   **5.** (a) $-5 + 9i$. (b) $1 - i$.
7. (a) $-17 - i$.   (b) $-17 - i$.   (c) $65 + 55i$.   (d) $65 + 55i$.
     (e) $-31 - 24i$.   (f) $-31 - 24i$.   (g) $1 - 18i$.   (h) $1 - 18i$.
8. (a) 10.   (b) -6. (c) -8.   (d) 29.   (e) 10.   (f) 25.   (g) $2 - 3i$.
     (h) $2 - 3i$.   (i) $-17 + i$.   (j) $-17 + i$.   (k) $65 - 55i$.   (l) $65 - 55i$.
9. (a) $-\frac{13}{10} - \frac{11}{10}i$.   (b) $\frac{9}{25} - \frac{13}{25}i$.   (c) $-\frac{26}{29} - \frac{7}{29}i$.
     (d) 1.   (e) $\frac{5}{29} - \frac{2}{29}i$.   (f) $-\frac{3}{10} - \frac{1}{10}i$.
     (g) $-\frac{4}{25} + \frac{3}{25}i$.   (h) $\frac{13}{1450} - \frac{11}{1450}i$.
10. (a) $\frac{14}{25} + \frac{23}{25}i$.   (b) $-\frac{18}{13} - \frac{12}{13}i$.

11. (a) 4.   (b) $-\frac{3\sqrt{2}}{2} - \frac{3i\sqrt{2}}{2}$.   (c) $-\sqrt{3} - i$.   (d) 4.

12. (a) 6 cis $0°$.   (b) cis $240°$.   (c) 6 cis $150°$.   (d) 2 cis $30°$.
13. (a) $0 + 15i$.   (b) $\sqrt{2} + i\sqrt{2}$.   (c) $2 + 2i\sqrt{3}$.   (d) $0 + 3i\sqrt{3}$.
     (e) $\frac{\sqrt{3}}{4} - \frac{1}{4}i$.   (f) $\frac{3\sqrt{2}}{8} - \frac{3i\sqrt{2}}{8}$.

14. (a) $16 - 16i$.   (b) $-128 - 128i\sqrt{3}$.
15. (a) $\frac{3}{2}\sqrt{3} + \frac{3}{2}i, -\frac{3}{2}\sqrt{3} + \frac{3}{2}i, 0 - 3i$.
     (b) $\sqrt[5]{16}$ cis $(-12 + 72k)°$, $k = 0, 1, 2, 3, 4$.
16. (a) 3 cis $(67\frac{1}{2} + 90k)°$, $k = 0, 1, 2, 3$.
     (b) $\sqrt[4]{8}$ cis $(-15 + 90k)°$, $k = 0, 1, 2, 3$.

INDEX